Harem Slave

One Thousand Nine Hundred and Four Days of Hell
on the Persian Gulf

A Novel

By
Nancy Hartwell Enonchong
© 2013

"Sudden thought. A guy could kidnap a number of good-looking women, put them on a ship bound for who knows where, and sell them to some sultan. You could get away with it!"

- Serial killer Kemper, as quoted in *Newsweek* -

When everything else fails, try love.

This book is dedicated to Marisa, Nenzima,
and all the other girls
who are sucked into this terrifying vortex
and do not survive.

PART ONE
KIDNAPPED

July-August 2005
(Jumada Al-Thany – Rajab 1425)

Even before the pale glimmer in the back of her mind warned her that consciousness was drawing near, Tammy knew something was terribly wrong. She was fearful of waking up, uneasy about leaving the safety of oblivion. The world had a sinister feel to it. A sinister smell.

She drifted reluctantly toward wakefulness. The nauseating odor of hot diesel fuel. Muffled voices, strange and ominous. The world heaved and swayed. She was dizzy. Falling. She reached out to steady herself.

Oh God, she thought, what's the matter? Why can't I move my arms? Cautiously, furtively, she opened her eyes.

"No-Tits is coming to!" a voice beside her trumpeted in accented French. "We can party now."

"Calm down, calm down, will you, Kamal? Is that all you ever think about?"

She was lying naked on the rusty metal floor of a boat cabin, tied hand and foot. She stared, disbelieving the scene around her. Three men, two in caftans and one in khaki, were standing amid a dozen or so other bound and naked women sprawled unconscious on the rough cabin floor. She shivered. Felt a surge of nausea.

"She's throwing up!" Kamal said excitedly.

Vomit dribbled onto the floor, around and under her. She wanted to lift her hand to wipe it away. She couldn't. She wanted to get out of the way of the putrid mess. She couldn't. Nor could she escape the lecherous gaze of the three men.

1

You're completely helpless, little demons in her brain screamed. *These are evil men, and they can't wait to hurt you.* A deep elemental fear rose bitter in her throat.

"No tits at all, but just look at that ass," Kamal said. "The men at the club will be standing in line." He grabbed a handful of flesh and kneaded it roughly. The skin he touched burned as if it had been brushed with acid.

"We've got some expensive pieces in this shipment and you're not to mess with them, especially the Swede and the two little ones. Off limits. You hear me, Kamal? I say, off limits."

"Don't worry, Fuad, I'll be careful. Besides, if there's an accident, your brother can always turn them back into virgins."

"You bastard! Don't even think about it!"

"Look, she's wide awake now, Fuad, just look. I'll start breaking her in." It was the man in khaki. Tammy looked closer. A customs officer!

"No, Jean-Paul, that piece is mine. Pick out another one."

"Ah, this job does have great benefits," Kamal said, surveying the scene on the floor and smacking his lips. "Look at the tits on this piece over here. Why don't we keep her around and put her through with the next shipment?"

"Not this time. She's a special order, and the old man's fuse is already short because he's waited so long. He seems to think you can pull Swedish pieces with a front porch like that out of stock as readily as fucking Ethiopians or Vietnamese."

"Can't wait 'til Big-Tits wakes up," Kamal said, eyeing a stun-ningly beautiful platinum blonde.

rewarded by approving glances. She chatted easily with them almost as if she'd shopped in French all her life.

By the time she'd scratched out every item on the list but the turnips and the veal kidneys – she'd postpone those for as long as pos-sible – more than an hour had gone by. She snacked on some cherries, bought a magazine, and stopped at a sidewalk café for another huge bowl of café au lait. She sauntered over to a row of shops on the edge of the Arab Quarter. Twenty past eleven. Forty minutes to kill.

"Bonjour, mademoiselle," said a caftaned shopkeeper. "I have more slippers inside, many more beautiful things." He held out his hand and showed her his establishment.

She made a quick survey. No basement; the shop was no bigger than her bedroom in Bethesda. Embroidered caftans were hanging from the ceiling, backless slippers stacked on the floor, brassware heaped on the counters.

"Gifts for your family in Denmark?" The vendor was tall and thin, with jack-o'-lantern teeth.

"No, for my family in America." He was the third person that morning who'd thought she was Scandinavian. She was surprised. Her grandfather was born near Rotterdam, and she'd always thought she looked typically Dutch.

"Ah, American." A calculating look.

Oh brother, she thought, I bet now he's busy doubling all his prices in my honor.

"Here is beautiful bell from my own village. You know Algeria?"

He sized her up as the bell tinkled in his hand. What did he think, that she was going to walk out with half his stock? "No," she replied, "but I lived in Morocco when I was little." She wasn't crazy about the bell; besides, her father had one almost like it.

"Here. I have caftans from Morocco. This one, pure silk. *Magni-fique*."

It was dazzling, a pale blue-and-aqua swirled design lavishly embroidered with silver. The front was rowed with tiny hand-crocheted silver buttons.

"It is beautiful with your eyes, your hair," he went on. "Beautiful."

It was also very expensive. "It's nice." She resolutely put it aside. The money she had with her was for Marc's cycling outfit.

"Here is beautiful serving tray for monsieur. You say, 'My dear, here is my heart,' and no man can resist you." He struck such a dram-atic pose she had to laugh. "Monsieur is with you?"

"No, he's back in Washington."

"What? A beautiful lady like you? Alone? So far? *Mais non,* I do not understand this American way."

"I'm not alone," she hastened to tell him, remembering Pierre's caution. "A friend will be back to pick me up in five minutes." She wasn't worried, but there was no point in inviting trouble.

"Beautiful caftan, mademoiselle, so beautiful. Just try on?" That jack-o'-lantern smile again. That capitalistic sparkle in his eye.

"Oh, no thank you, I really shouldn't."

"You are in hurry? No time? Just try."

Eleven-thirty five. There was still time. "I just…"

"If you no like, no problem. Or come tomorrow, I keep for you. Just try."

She did some quick arithmetic and was more befuddled than ever. "That's absolutely nuts. Then it ought to be 1383. I can't–"

"We use a lunar calendar that's ten or eleven days shorter."

"Oh." She groaned. "Nessim, you naughty boy, you still haven't told me what day it is."

He laughed again. "All right, all right, it's the 24th of July."

"Frankly, I don't understand why you don't just use the same calendar as everybody else. Look, while you're here, can we please try to call Bethesda again?"

"Of course." Nessim brought the phone in and plugged it into the wall jack. He'd barely picked up the receiver when he was summoned urgently away. "I'll be right back," he assured her. "It's real compli-cated, so I'll make the call for you."

Tammy waited for a moment, then sprang to life. Complicated? What did he take her for, a total ninny? She'd watched, so she knew the access code for international calls, and although the so-called "Arabic numerals" bore only occasional resemblances to what she was used to, she closed her eyes and dialed from finger-memory. The phone rang.

"Hello, Wellie?"

"Who's this?" he said absently. "Really awesome. Turn it up, Zyko, this song really rocks."

"Wellie, I can hardly hear you. This is Tam. Let me speak to Mom or Dad. I'm calling from overseas on somebody else's phone, so make it snappy."

"Not home. No, it's not Pelican, it's only my sister."

"Where are they?"

"Pelican and Julep? That's just it, they were supposed to be here *hours* ago. Oh, awesome, play it again, really awesome."

"Wellie, listen! I was kidnapped. I'm okay, but I'm in a hospital in an emirate on the Persian Gulf. I'll give you the number. Ask Mom and Dad to call me, okay?"

"Sure. Dad's over there looking for you. Hey, Zyko, get me a pencil. Hold on, Tam."

"Listen, potato-brain, hurry *up!*"

"Don't short your circuits, mudface. All right, go ahead."

She read it off to him and made him repeat it. She hung up less than ten seconds before Nessim opened the door.

"Sorry to keep you waiting, Taamm. Don't worry, this time we'll get through." He put the receiver to her ear. The phone rang and rang. There was no answer.

"But–" Something told her not to elaborate.

How odd, she thought, how very odd.

The sixth trip around the block in noon traffic, Pierre's Gallic willingness to forgive a woman for being late had worn perilously thin. For the love of God, Tam, how long does it take you to buy a couple stupid souvenirs?

Twelve-thirty. Not at all like her to be so late. She was, after all, an American, and they were almost as chronometered as the Swiss. A little naïve, and cotton-candy idealistic, but it certainly wasn't like her to keep someone waiting so long.

Pierre swallowed. Naïve. No, no. That made it seem as if…no. He tried to push aside troubling thoughts. Maybe it wouldn't hurt, though, to have a look around.

"Ah, oui," the toothless tomato-lady said, "beautiful girl, so friendly, such an adorable accent." She threw Pierre a knowing wink. "She went to the café. Over there."

The café. Of course. Knowing Tam, she'd probably made friends with half the customers. Somebody'd offered to buy her a cup of coffee, and…

"Je regrette, monsieur," I'm sorry, sir, said the headwaiter. "She left here oh, probably eleven o'clock. She said she wanted to buy some presents in the Arab shops." He chuckled. "I told her to be careful, because they might want to steal a pretty thing like her for their harems." His laughter stopped abruptly when he saw the stricken look on Pierre's face.

Pierre sighed. She was sure to be nearby, he told himself, maybe just got turned around on the way back to the pharmacy. Quarter of one. Clotilde must be getting worried. He dialed. *"Chou-chou?"* he said.
"Oh, *chéri,* how'd everything go?" Her voice was warm and welcome.

"Look, I've been delayed a little bit."

"Your voice sounds funny. What's the matter?"

No use getting her upset. "Oh, nothing, we'll be back soon. Just wanted you to know that we'll be a little late."

He checked the pharmacy again. Then he drove slowly around, searching with growing desperation for any sign of a blonde ponytail.

One-fifteen. He rested his perspiring forehead on the steering wheel. Better call the police, he decided, just as a precaution. He tried to ignore the tiny voice within him that said it was already too late.

Merde, he thought, what a day. How will I ever break the news to Clotilde that the bank has turned me down? And how will I ever explain to John and Catherine that Tam has disappeared?

"Here's where they found the market basket," Pierre said with a trembling voice.

John put his hand on his Pierre's shoulder. "Listen, we've been friends for fifteen years. This isn't your fault, we don't blame you. Things happen. Everything will turn out all right."

"It's not all right. I can't sleep. I can't–"

"We'll find her. I have some pretty decent contacts, and so do you. I assume the shops around here have been searched?"

"Of course. Like the three monkeys, hear nothing, see nothing, say nothing."

They walked together down the sidewalk. With every step, John wondered, is this where my Tammy-girl was snatched away from me? Is this where she cried for help and no one came? He had to keep himself together, especially in front of Pierre. John saw his daughter everywhere, and nowhere. What was happening to her? Was he a failure as a father, as a protector? He cut the thought short. Instead of beating up on himself, he had to concentrate on getting her home. His eye caught a display of brass bells.

"Oh, look, Pierre, this bell is like the one I got when we were in Algiers, remember?"

"Bonjour, messieurs," said the shopkeeper, smiling brightly. "I have many more beautiful things inside. You like bell? From my own village, this bell."

"Oh, so you're from Algeria? I have one like it, actually." John's eyes swept the tiny establishment. Dingy. Cramped. Creepy. And the guy needed a dentist in the worst possible way.

"Yes, from Algeria. Look, monsieur, beautiful tray."

"No, thanks," John said, as they continued down the street. He turned to Pierre. "The door at the back of that place gave me the spooks. Who knows where it leads?"

"Perhaps," said Pierre thickly, "that is the door to hell."

Again and again, Tammy started letters to Marc and tore them up. This was just not what you could talk about in an email. Sometimes she made light of things; other times, she sensed she'd said too much. She could never seem to find the right balance of respect for his feelings and her own. How could she explain to him how filthy she felt, as if she could take twenty thousand showers and still not feel clean? It hadn't been her fault, but that didn't keep her from feeling guilty, and if she had such mixed emotions, how could she expect him to do otherwise?

She thought it would help to file a report with the police. Dr. Has-san hardly shared her enthusiasm, saying that under Islamic law rape was extremely difficult to prove, and that she would probably be disappointed. Nevertheless, since she insisted, he arranged for a police sergeant to interview her. She was annoyed at having to be veiled for the visit. Maybe it was one of the reasons the session went straight downhill.

The sergeant was a world-class nincompoop. Not only was he not the least bit scandalized about her abduction, he kept implying that it was her fault. He kept harping on how she'd entered the country illegally, wanted to know how long she'd been a prostitute, preached that in this part of the world where morality still had some value, prostitution was a serious crime, on and on. There she was, lying face down in a hospital room with rope burns on her wrists, her back a mass of bruises, and thirteen stitches up her rear, and Sgt. Nabil kept referring to her "alleged" abduction. She had to hold onto the bed linens with both hands to keep from jumping up and smacking him. He didn't bat an eye when she told him about Marisa; he said any slut willing to parade around in skimpy swimsuits in public had no business coming to a proper Muslim country in the first place.

"I'm sorry," Dr. Hassan said after the idiot left, "but unfortunately that's about what I expected."

"What year did you say this was?" she asked, ripping off the veil.

"Fourteen twenty-five."

"Sounds just about right," she fumed.

"Do you know how beautiful your eyes are when you get angry?" he asked with a slanting smile. "They're ten times bluer than usual."

She groaned. "Sometimes I think you're as much of a Neanderthal as that lame excuse for a sergeant. I'm trying to talk about something serious and you want to talk about my eyes." The stricken look on his face filled her with remorse. "I'm sorry, Doctor, I really am. You've been just wonderful and I shouldn't lump you in the same category with that jerk."

"Thank you," he said mildly. "Now let me check your stitches."

As her health improved it got harder and harder for her to stay cooped up in the hospital room, but she wasn't allowed to venture into the hallway where – horrors! – a *man*

"Thank you so much for everything," she said, overcoming the urge to hug him. *"Shukran shukran shukran shukran,"* she said, hoping that by sheer volume she could make up for her almost-non-existent Arabic vocabulary. "When I get home I'll send you something so you can remember the girl from *Amrikiya."*

"Allah maa kum," may God be with you, he replied.

Suddenly overcome by gratitude for those who had offered a hand of kindness to a suffering person, she went quickly outside.

She inspected the contents of her beige snakeskin handbag. Ticket? Check. New passport? Check. The 100 euros Dr. Hassan had insisted on giving her? Check. His card, so she could write and let him know how she was doing? Yes. Everything was just perfect, except for the fact that she had to cover up her beige pleated Gucci with the stupid black cloak.

Enveloped as she was in the ankle-length black *abaaya,* a hair wrap, and a long black veil, just in the fifty feet or so between the air-conditioned clinic and the white stretch limo, she thought she'd posi-tively suffocate. She felt bizarre, too, as if she weren't actually a person at all, but just an oversize Idaho potato wrapped up in a black bag.

She'd resisted the veil. "If Arab women let men oppress them, it's their business," she said, "but I'm not covering up my face."

He gasped. "It's not oppression at all," he explained, "just a little different sense of decency. No self-respecting Arab woman would expose her face to strange men any more than you'd walk topless down the Champs Elysées. My wife, for instance, who studied in Paris, wouldn't have things any other way. She likes having men deal with her on the basis of her intelligence rather than on her looks."

Her dad had always insisted that they respect other cultures, so she finally broke down and let him put the darn thing on her. What a pain! Even her own mother wouldn't have known her. Brother, she thought, am I glad I don't have to fool with this stuff all the time.

The two suitcases went into the trunk. Dr. Hassan had said that it would be preferable, since she didn't speak the language, to let the driver handle the airport formalities. It annoyed her – didn't these men think women were capable of *anything?* – but she capitulated and let the driver take the ticket and passport. She eased into the white leather seat. She sighed contentedly, and to her amusement, the veil puffed out. She experimented blowing it out and sucking it in. Fascinating.

She groaned when she noticed that the limo windows were heavily curtained, reminding her of a hearse. Dr. Hassan had told her that the Arabic word for "chaste" or "clean" also meant "well guarded," but they took things to ridiculous lengths. Oh well, just this once was no big deal. Besides, she was feeling downright woozy. "Yes, Jensen, another glass of champagne, thank you dahling. Oh, dear me, an emer-gency! I've nicked a nail! Fifi, quick, a manicure, dahling." The veil obligingly went puff-puff-puff. How could Arab women talk to each other and manage to keep a straight face?

The driver cast questioning looks at her as she chattered away to herself. Okay, so she was feeling silly, but didn't she deserve a little fun? What really mattered was that she was on her way *home*.

She felt like she'd had about three "ti many martoonis" by the time they arrived at a huge gated compound where Dr. Hassan had men-tioned that they would drop something off. She hadn't expected to get out of the car, but after the driver spoke briefly with one of the sen-tinels, he drove through the gate and grandly opened the door.

"Oum Mohammed, Sheikh Khalid's wife, invites you to have a refreshing glass of lemonade with her."

"But we need to get to the airport."

"We have time. It would be extremely rude to refuse, and ten or fifteen minutes won't really matter. Don't spend all afternoon, though, or you'll miss your plane."

"Fat chance of that!" Maybe some lemonade would perk her up a little. She finally located the assorted parts of the black lump and managed to get them all out into the staggering heat. She almost swooned.

Ferocious-looking guards draped with bandoliers of ammunition relaxed on a wide arched portico, behind them to the left a beautiful white marble building, to the right a vine-covered wrought iron gate. One of them nodded politely and unlocked it, and Tammy was admitted into a small courtyard where she was immediately greeted by two smil-ing women wearing long dresses but – much to her indignation – no cloaks or veils. Then she remembered. Behind a locked gate. Behind a high wall. What Dr. Hassan would call "protected."

"Ahlan wa-sahlan," Welcome welcome, the taller and very preg-nant one said, a large-boned woman of maybe 35 with a plain face and pretty eyes. *"Ismii Zeynab. Zeynab,"* she repeated with a smile. My name is Zeynab.

They seemed to be expecting her.

"Ismii Haifa," My name is Haifa, the other one said. She was much younger, quite pretty, Asian, and only half as pregnant. *"Alham-dulilah alla salama."* She knew Alhamdulillah meant thank God, because Dr. Hassan made sure she said it after every meal.

"Ismii Tam," she replied, recklessly using up a huge percentage of the Arabic that Nurse Nessim had taught her. She said it a little more breathily than she had to, to make the veil puff out. It did. She giggled. Haifa and Zeynab seemed puzzled. Then she giggled again because they hadn't. They exchanged nervous glances, like, are Americans always this harebrained?

"Taamm." They pronounced her name like Dr. Hassan did, stretching it out like salt-water taffy. He said it meant "complete," but for all she knew it meant "complete idiot." The trouble was, she was never entirely sure she could believe him, because he was always skating on the border between chivalry and mischief and wasn't above saying something flattering even if it weren't entirely true.

The courtyard was set with potted geraniums and lemon trees. A grape arbor provided a little thin shade, cutting the 120-degree heat to a mere 115 or so. Off to the back was an odd wooden building with a pair of huge doors that looked like they belonged on a medieval castle. She giggled. Zeynab let them through with a six-inch key. She and Haifa helped Tammy out of the cloak and veil and exclaimed admiringly over her wilted Gucci. Her wrappings took their place, next to many others, on hooks by the door. They were as alike as quarters. How would she know the right one to take when she left? She giggled again. What difference could it possibly make?

It was only marginally cooler inside the house. That lemonade, perchance? Dr. Hassan had said that Sheikh Khalid was a fabulously wealthy commodities trader. Maybe so, but his house was a shambles. From the entryway of chipped patterned tiles, they climbed a rickety stairway that led to a shabby living room with lattice-covered windows and built-in couches. Two middle-aged women were doing needlework and a curly-haired girl was teaching a teddy bear how to read. Oh good, Tammy thought, now for that lemonade. She stopped, too dizzy to con-tinue, and steadied herself. She made circles in the air with her finger, and they seemed to understand. They helped her up and continued around a couple of odd corners, up two or three more small flights of swayback wooden stairs, flattening themselves against a wall while squealing twin boys raced by. I'll be darned, she thought, if this is where the women and children live, it must be the harem. I'm actually visiting a sheikh's harem. Wait until Elaine hears about this!

It wasn't at all like Hollywood had led her to expect. A touching crayon drawing of a purple horse? What, no belly dancers, no be-jeweled women in harem pants lounging seductively on fringed sofas? Where were the naked-chested eunuchs in draped pants and gold earrings? Even an ironing board? Her father would be pleased with all the stereotypes this short visit had exploded.

Next stop on the tour was a small dim room furnished only with a window-seat. Tammy looked politely out the window, trying to see what the world looked like through a carved lattice screen. She turned around just in time to see the door close. That's odd, she thought, where'd everybody go?

A heavy bolt slid solidly into place.

PART TWO
SHEIKH KHALID

August – September 2005
(Rajab – Shaban 1425)

Everything suddenly made horrifying sense: what the driver was supposed to deliver to Sheikh Khalid was *her.* How, how had she missed all the signposts? The way Dr. Hassan always deftly changed the subject when she pressed him for details about her rescue. The fact that nobody called, only sent flowers, which could have come from the corner florist. Marc's using the name "Tam." The odd coincidence about the telephone. The "anti jet-lag shot" that was probably a strong sedative. She was furious at herself for being so gullible, but no amount of self-reproach was going to unlock that door.

No, it couldn't be, she fought back, Dr. Hassan bought me the ticket; I had it in my own hand. Why would he buy it if he wanted me to stay here?

Why not? Those pesky little demons retorted, *especially if it made you believe what you desperately wanted to believe?*

And replacing the passport? All the trouble he'd gone to for that?

It was probably a forgery, and besides, a passport and ticket don't do you a particle of good if the driver takes them away. Face it, Tam, you've been bamboozled. Dr. Hassan has you right where he wants you.

"Oh, that's a bunch of nonsense!" she said aloud, but she threw up all over the rug anyway.

I know, she told herself, gagging on the sour stench that over-whelmed the stuffy little room. I've just stumbled into

fill the tank, way up by the ceiling, from a bucket that was extremely hard to maneuver over her head. She balanced on two raised footrests and squatted, hoping like crazy she wouldn't slip. Finally she pulled a chain connected to the flush tank.

At that precise moment a loud clap of thunder rattled the house. Thunder? No, jet planes and anti-aircraft fire! The Marines! She dived under the towel-table, heart pounding fiercely.

Zeynab didn't seem too worried. She was leaning against the wall, breathless with laughter. Okay, sister, Tammy wanted to tell her, we're talking Shores of Tripoli and A Few Good Men. She cocked her ear for the final barrage. What she heard instead were thunderous bangs and clangs and gurgles and splutters that sounded like a thousand sledge hammers attacking the pipes. Zeynab, still leaning against the wall, pointed weakly to the toilet.

What? All that? No way.

Tammy sheepishly crawled back out. Nothing like impressing everybody with her suave sophistication, right? Brother, she wondered, with plumbing as noisy as that how'd you ever go to the bathroom without everybody knowing? She soon found out: you didn't. You never did *anything* in that place without everybody knowing.

Her fourth afternoon in the harem, a fuzzy-edged Haifa opened the door and beckoned. Her mouth went dry and her palms began to sweat. Leave her safe cocoon? Oh, no, she thought, here it comes. She stum-bled along, shimmers of terror shooting through her.

In a downstairs salon food was laid out on mats. The elegant old woman with the incandescent eyes said something friendly, and grace-ful long fingers indicated where she should sit. Tammy sat, transfixed with fear, conscious of appraising stares, getting an occasional spoonful of yogurt past her mouth, until one by one the others murmured *"Alhamdulillah,"* Thank God, and left.

Haifa accompanied her back upstairs. Tammy stopped to study the photograph of Sheikh Khalid. He was a striking aristocratic man of 65 or 70, in long white robes and a white headdress held by black ropes. She'd almost decided he was handsome when she noticed the arrogant tilt to his chin, the bloodless lips, the cunning eyes. She felt a sudden chill. Brother, she thought, that expression belongs on a crocodile.

Haifa had a full mouth that smiled at the slightest provocation and big black eyes that radiated friendliness. She patted Tammy's hand and took her back to her room. Don't worry, she seemed to say, we know it's hard at first, but we're nice people and we'll help you. Sheikh Khalid is patient. Oum Mohammed is gracious. And I am prepared to be your friend.

Tammy smiled wanly at her. Haifa's concern was touching, and it certainly helped take a small edge off the pain, but a generous heart couldn't erase reality. She sighed as she stretched out on the worn blue velvet window-seat. What was worse, she wondered, being behind a bolted door? Or the frightening world on the other side?

After a week, Zeynab stopped giving Tammy pills during the day, and would give her only one at night. Soon there were none at all. "Please, Zeynab, I need them. If I let myself think about what's happening I'll go insane," she begged, but Zeynab smiled apologetically and shook her head. Face all those people twice a day with her mind unobscured? It was as if the protective peel had been removed from her brain, exposing it raw and tremulous, pleading for reality to come and swallow it.

And so it did. Where before there had been disbelief now there was outrage. Where there had been numbness there was now frus-tration, where there had been uncertainty there was now crippling fear. "Why me?" she demanded of the wooden walls of her room, stained dark from generations of despondency. "Just what are you going to do with me?" she challenged the picture in the entryway, pulling herself tall with indignation. "Don't you know that this is 2005 and there are laws against these things?" The man with the crocodile eyes smiled smugly past his aquiline nose. *What do you think I intend to do with you?* she could almost hear him cackle.

Now that her brain was in working order again she decided she simply had to escape, and the overwhelming odds against success didn't slow her down a bit. She was hemmed in by people all day and locked up at night, not to mention the high walls and the guards outside. Zeynab or Haifa even escorted her to and from the bathroom.

Tammy sensed that Oum Mohammed's x-ray eyes could see right through that door. Her serenity was unnerving. Long aristocratic fingers wielded knitting needles like a maestro's baton and dispensed money, permission, keys, instructions. One well-aimed glance from her small black eyes could stop a missile. Once she caught Tammy picking her nose, and that Look made her feel like she'd been trampled on. Oum Mohammed never raised her voice, but heaven help you if she took her glasses off and set her knitting down. Even the twins – the most undisciplined brats Tammy had ever seen – were so unnerved by her eyes that a steady gaze would fling them screaming into their mother's arms.

Often, Oum Mohammed would ask the latest addition to the harem to hold the yarn for her while she wound it; at such times Tammy would just sit on the threadbare blue-and-red rug and look around. The once-elegant living room with its latticed windows and frayed velvet curtains was much like Oum Mohammed herself, who forty years be-fore must have been a much sought-after beauty. Her skin was flawless, almost waxen. It was only her eyes that betrayed her advancing years. They glittered with too much knowledge, too much experience, too much self-control; they consumed everything around them, digested, analyzed. They weren't really the eyes of an old woman, but they couldn't have belonged to anyone young.

Oum Mohammed's eyes settled disapprovingly on the glamorous Leyla, smiling indulgently as her twins climbed on the curtains and poured date molasses on the rug. Leyla gulped, dissolved, and took her two-year-olds elsewhere.

Must you insist on being such a peasant? The eyes reprimanded Oum Hussein, Sheikh Khalid's other wife, a plump, overly loud, un-kempt but good-natured woman of perhaps 50 who spent all day embroidering. Oum Hussein shrugged confidentially in Tammy's direction, as if they were both privates in the army of a troublesome general. She's always uptight, that's her job, hon, Oum Hussein seemed to say.

Other times, Oum Mohammed took aim at Tammy's unspoken terror. I know why my husband has brought you here, those eyes told her. Despite what my own wishes might be I accept graciously what-ever life requires of me and so, my dear, must you.

Which only served as a reminder to Tammy that she had to get out of that place before…before it was too late. That old man? She just couldn't. She wouldn't. She had to find a way *out*.

Oum Mohammed ignored her martyred pout and spoke to her. Maybe she was recounting her childhood; maybe she was explaining the sexual fantasies of her husband. Even if she'd spoken fluent Arabic, she doubted that very much would have soaked in. One thing she understood: the undercurrent of finality. This is where you are. This is what you are going to do.

She studied her room, looking for some flaw. It was roughly seven by eight, drunkenly skewed to one side. There was one big window, covered with a lattice box, which, while it served the purpose of calming Arab paranoia about keeping women hidden, also cut sunlight into flower-shaped pieces and siphoned off half the air. The built-in settee covered with a worn cut-velvet throw and a couple faded blue cushions ran from one end to the other of the window wall. The bare overhead bulb had burned out. The ceiling fan, a quarter-inch thick with dust, didn't even wheeze. At high noon the room was dim, stuffy, and thoroughly depressing; in the dark it was filled with the ghosts of other fears, other miseries.

Could she unscrew the door hinges and slip out? Too rusty. Besides, she'd never get past the courtyard. Pry some loose boards out and let herself down? She couldn't pull them away with her bare hands, and pounding would attract too much attention. Tammy looked out the shrouded third-story window, trying to identify a way to climb down. The view was hardly an inspiration: an outdoor laundry with big old-fashioned tubs, a clothesline, even a wringer! Beyond was a high wall, and beyond that, scrub desert. Not a tree, not a house, not a sign of civilization. Where, crossed her mind, would she run *to?*

Well, she thought, I'll just find some other way to get out of this fire-trap. She made a mental blueprint of the building, a complicated warren of oddly arranged rooms. Adjoining areas rarely had the same floor level; either she stepped up or stepped down, but she always had to keep one eye on where she put her feet. Going anywhere was a major operation. Down two stairs and up three, double back, go around, climb over, duck under. She wanted to weep in frustration. How was she ever going to escape from the blasted place if it took GPS just to get down-stairs?

Almost for lack of anything else to do, she continued to scheme. Locks? Guards? Nosy women? She was going to get *out.* She con-sidered bribing the guards and stealing a car. She thought about jumping Oum Mohammed and grabbing her keys.

Then she had a stroke of genius: she'd simply get a taxi. She still had the 100 euros that Dr. Hassan had given her; she could get to the airport or the Embassy and have a ticket sent in. Her big problem was how to make a quick getaway in high-heeled shoes. Another one of Dr. Hassan's diabolical plans, damn him! But high heels were still better than being barefoot when her big chance arose.

Every day when Haifa would get her, Tammy would clomp down-stairs to the salon for lunch, which was usually served at about five-thirty, according to the grandfather clock. Like so many other things in the harem, she was convinced it simply didn't work. When the men had eaten their fill in the big marble house next door, the leftovers were sent to the harem. Sometimes the women got platters of couscous, gristle, and carrot; sometimes it was nothing but fishbones and rice.

Tammy was scandalized. What kind of selfish bastard would make his own wife eat leftovers? The more she thought about it, the madder she got. The day that lunch consisted of nothing but bread soaked in meat juice, when the men had clearly polished off an entire lamb roast, she exploded. "How do you put up with this nonsense?" she demanded of Oum Mohammed, who for once seemed thoroughly perplexed.

Haifa looked at her funny and knitted her brow. *Now* what was the matter?

The women had as much breakfast as they wanted, though, be-cause Haifa fixed it. Behind the harem was a half-outdoor kitchen that looked ancient enough to have witnessed visits from the Prophet himself. Zeynab and Tammy would bring wood for the fire, while Haifa filled teakettles from the water filter. Inside, in a beautiful salon with blue-patterned tiled walls and floors, they set plates of fruit and bread on mats on the rug, and then retraced their convoluted steps up to the living room.

When breakfast was over, except for Zeynab and Haifa, they'd all troop to the second-floor salon, where a groaning air conditioner made a little difference in spite of all the cracks and gaps in the walls. Except for its rundown condition, it was a pleasant room, downright sunny by Arab standards with windows on three sides – albeit covered with wooden screens. Wall lamps were often unnecessary – fortunately, since only two of the six worked. Built-in settees lined the walls; mismatched threadbare oriental rugs covered the floor.

Right after midday, all the residents of the harem assembled for the *dhuhr*, or noon prayers. Tammy was enchanted. It was a moving scene, the women and children standing and kneeling in unison. She hated to admit that she liked anything at all about Sheikh Khalid's harem, but seeing that family pray together never failed to stir her. It reminded her of church services with her own family, and she was stricken with aching loneliness.

Tammy hated the place because it interfered with her life, but it would have interfered with her decorator mother's respiration. She could just picture her, frantically ripping the screens off the windows, suggesting a "cheerful" color scheme, wondering how fast she could get the contractors to shore up the sagging beams. Her heart lurched. Mom. What was she thinking? Did she still have shreds of hope? Or had one of Dad's friends at the State Department sat her down and gently explained that girls who vanish never reappear?

Soft laughter brought her back to the harem. Rokhiya – Moham-med's very pregnant wife and Oum Mohammed's daughter-in-law – was off in one corner tutoring the three older children. Leyla, also pregnant, sat on cushions on the floor, sighed languorously, shot mur-derous looks in Tammy's direction, and drove Haifa to distraction on silly errands. Oum Hussein was on a window-seat embroidering, and Oum Mohammed took her place on another and knitted. Tammy wondered what she was working on. A muffler, perhaps, for the Planet Earth? Or merely sweaters for every member of the human race?

Tammy had to admit that Leyla was beautiful, with huge long-lashed eyes and luxuriant wavy black hair, and thought that maybe the reason she resented Tammy so much was because she threatened her title as the prettiest woman in the harem. Leyla was resolutely shallow, just the kind of woman Tammy had been brought up to hold in polite contempt. She whined. She toyed with her make-up. She filed her nails. She read her fashion magazines and photo-romans. She played with her jewelry. And she thought her demolition-derby twins were adorable no matter what.

Tammy noticed one thing: Leyla was too high-class, too aristocratic, to actually take care of her twins, but Haifa wasn't allowed to discipline them. Result: two wild animals.

Tammy was so bored she was beside herself. She couldn't participate in conversations, there was no radio or TV, and only a few Arabic-language magazines. Once, when Oum Mohammed had to go to the men's house to respond to a buzzer from her husband, Tammy was overjoyed to find a stray copy of English-language *Vogue.* Of course, it was Leyla's, and when she caught Tammy leafing through it, she almost bit her head off.

Tammy had been in the harem ten days, when one morning, Oum Mohammed settled down to do some accounts, and Tammy was sent downstairs to help Haifa scrub the parlor. She took off her shoes, careful to hide the folded bill far in the toe.

The physical exertion felt wonderful. It had been over a month since Fuad, and her back was still covered in hard knots, but she didn't mind playing Cinderella, lifting the heavy buckets for Haifa and taking satisfaction in the gleam of the beautiful tiles.

"Ya Haifa!" (Yoo-hoo, Haifa), whined Leyla from upstairs.

Haifa sighed, dried her hands, and trudged dutifully off.

Alone! Downstairs! Heart pounding, Tammy grabbed a cloak and veil and threw them on as she raced across the courtyard. The gate was unlocked, and she strode through. Look self-assured, she told herself, as if you sneaked out of harems every day.

Damn. A guard had noticed her. Smiling, but coming her way. *"Sabah al-khayr, ya aanisah."* Good morning, miss.

She nodded politely. Best thing, bluff it. Act normal. Momentary panic. She knew how to say please – different if you were addressing a man or a woman – but what was the Arabic word for taxi? She closed her eyes. What had they been called in Morocco? *"Taksi, min fadlik,"* she said, holding up her bill.

"Taksi, ya aanisah?"

It worked! He'd understood her! Uh-oh. Calm down, she told herself, all he probably wanted to know was where to. She was ready with the word for airport. *"Al-mataar."*

The guard smiled again. *"Hal anti Taamm?"* Are you Tam?

Damn. Even a veil couldn't conceal blue eyes. There was only one thing to do. She put the bill firmly in his hand.

He shook his head and gave it back to her. *"Laa, laa, ya aanisah."* No no, miss. And he led her politely back to the gate.

Haifa was in the courtyard, hand clutching her heart. When she saw Tammy she let loose a barrage of emotional Arabic.

Haifa hung their cloaks and veils back on the hook, shaking her head. She beckoned, and Tammy followed her meekly to a wooden chest in the corner of the salon. Haifa opened it and withdrew a small whip.

"American?" Haifa suddenly asked.

"Yes. From right outside Washington." Tammy was confused.

"Your little tirade the other day about the food…"

"Positively outrageous. Leftovers!"

"Get used to it. Listen, my real name is Carlita and I'm from the Philippines. Everybody thinks you're Swedish, so don't let on. Don't *ever* speak English to me in front of anybody."

"But–"

"I've been here for nine years. I know. You scared me half to death. Don't ever do that again, or they'll whip us both."

Tammy flinched. "How on earth did you end up here?"

"A recruiter came to Los Baños and said wealthy Arab households were looking for housekeepers. Top salary, great benefits, free trans-portation. A bunch of us signed on, because we couldn't find jobs at home, and it sounded just wonderful. Our families threw us send-off parties because of all the money we'd be sending home."

She bit her lip, refilled a bucket, and continued as they both worked on the floor. "When I got here, the first thing they did was gang rape me. They kept me in a room like a jail cell in the basement of the big house. I don't even know how many men came to that cell. Finally they locked the door and about a week later, when I had more or less recovered, they brought me to the harem. Oum Mohammed imme-diately took my passport and locked it up in the safe. Then they gave me a mountain of ironing to do. And an Indonesian maid named Fatima was responsible for keeping an eye on me."

"Like you have to watch me," Tammy added, catching on.

"Exactly. You're lucky; you belong to the Sheikh, nobody else can touch you. But I belong to the house, which means I'm fair game. Men in the compound can send for me whenever they like, and between the guards and the drivers and the houseboys and the stable boys and the gardeners and the cooks and the stewards, the ironing piled up, especially the first month or so when every man here had to check me out. But Oum Mohammed was furious about the ironing, so she had me beaten. Bad. I was in bed for almost a week. Hello? Didn't she realize how busy I was? After two months I got up the nerve to ask for my paycheck, and the reaction was, *pay* you? We *bought* you! That's when it hit me that I was a slave. In 1996! So I tried to run away. Got caught, of course, and they beat the soles of my feet. I couldn't walk for weeks, had to crawl everywhere. You just try crawling up and down these stairs. Leyla laughed at me. I even had to crawl over to the big house when somebody would send for me. You're really lucky it was Suley-man who caught you; if it'd been somebody else, they'd have done the same thing to you. Plus they'd have whipped me because I was supposed to watch you."

Tammy blanched. Whipped? Did she say *whipped?* She went pale. Then she remembered the whip that Haifa had shown her.

Haifa touched her stomach. "This is my fifth child. As soon as the baby's born they'll take it. They tell me it'll be adopted into a good home, but Suleyman says it'll be sold to a pedophile."

She was crying now. "I thought this was such a wonderful oppor-tunity, but it's nothing but hell. If it weren't for Suleyman, I'd have gone insane. This is his child. Everybody else leaves me alone now out of respect for him. He even asked permission to marry me, but Sheikh Khalid refused. After all, then he'd have to go to the trouble of buying another slave. He's trying to find a way for us to run away together, but it's so hard. He recently met a guy who wants to help us, but we have to be really careful."

"Can I go with you?"

Haifa smiled. "Sure, but we haven't figured out how. These people think that because they have money, they can get away with anything. And the trouble is, it's usually true. Nine years I've been trapped here in this hell-hole. Nine years."

Damn. Suleyman was a guard, and even he hadn't been able to find a hole in the system.

Tammy made a mental inventory of the harem. "Have I met Fatima?"

"Umm, no, umm, she died in childbirth. It was a breech delivery and the midwife couldn't help her. And they couldn't call in a male doctor because he'd have to see her female parts, and that's against Sheikh Khalid's rules. One thing I've learned is, there's no such thing here as male and female human beings. Two different species: men, with lots of privileges, and women, who are like pet dogs. Useful body parts, and sometimes amusing, but utterly expendable, especially if you're not part of the nobility. *Everything* depends on gender. Have you noticed? If Leyla's sitting somewhere and her brats want that place, she has to defer to them, because they're male. Their own mother! Of course they're spoiled, they're *boys*." She almost spat the words out.

"Tell me about Sheikh Khalid."

"You're lucky, Tam, the sheikh isn't a pervert, like a lot of them. He has a big appetite – the last new girl he had he kept for four days – but at least he won't brutalize you. That's an old picture, by the way, he's 81."

"81? Did you say 81? Oh, brother. So, what happened to her?"

48

"She smothered her baby and was sold to an S&M club. No matter how bad you think things are, there's always somewhere worse, and they make sure you know that."

"Sorry, but what's S&M?"

"Oh lord, you really are new here. Sadism and masochism."

Tammy felt weak. "I think I'm going to throw up."

"Get used to it. There's a huge, huge underground network of men's clubs that cater to every fetish, every fantasy, every sort of per-version, and surprise surprise, you've been sucked into that vortex. They even have what they call a snuff club, where they get their jollies by torturing people. You're basically a piece of meat, and nobody cares what happens to you. If you don't follow orders, they'll sell you somewhere worse. And if you don't follow orders there, you might as well stop eating. They have high-class clubs that don't allow violence, but in most of them, anything goes. At the Ranch they brand the women and keep them in stables. At the Frontier, in cages. There's one place – I can't remember the name – they fuse the soles of your feet together. At least here we're well fed, and Oum Mohammed only has us beaten every now and then. Suleyman tells me that in some places, the servants are raped practically every day and beaten all the time just to keep them under control."

You won't ever be able to get away, her demons sniped. But she told herself resolutely that one way or another, she'd get her life back.

She'd have only one attempt. If it failed…it just couldn't. She had to pull it off, and soon. Meanwhile, she had to lie low and pretend she'd given up hope.

"You're right," Suleyman told Haifa, "we almost gave up. But I met a guy named Chopsticks who wants to help us, and he promised he would, as long as we help smuggle out the new girl. He said we should wait until the last possible minute to tell her, though, so she won't accidentally tip anybody off. He got very excited when I told him about the new wing they're going to build onto the men's house; he said it'll provide a good amount of confusion as well as construction vehicles coming in and out. I have his phone number and I'll give him a call as soon as the work starts." He gave Haifa a soft kiss. "My dear little Haifa, we're only a few weeks away from being together."

"We've located Bulbul," Abubakr announced to a very keyed-up John, "sector 11C. She's in the home" – he almost said harem, which he knew wouldn't be what a father wanted to hear – "of a wealthy trader. Security is tight. The good news is, they're planning an addition to the house and before long a lot of construction vehicles will be coming and going. Be patient. We're working hard to figure things out."

"I'm keeping my fingers crossed," said John.

Abubakr decided to omit telling John about the clinic. Fake phone number, fake address, even a fake country. The Emirate of Surgery? Come on, now. It was a critical link in a major syndicate, providing castrations, revirginizations, devocalizations, strategic amputations, sex change operations, and multiple other sordid services. Dr. Hassan was a much-feared kingpin, a particularly heinous "specialty livestock" bro-ker to princes, brothels, and private collectors. It sickened him to think that Bulbul had fallen into his clutches.

The guard had told them that she seemed to be in good condition, though, and while Sheikh Khalid didn't have the reputation of being kinky, he did admit to having a thing for voluptuous Swedes. Now, Abubakr had seen pictures of Bulbul. While she was a very, very pretty girl, voluptuous wasn't what would spring to mind.

50

Construction should start soon. Then they could strategize on how to get her out.

Tammy got little sleep, worrying that Sheikh Khalid would send for her, trying to come up with other plans to escape, thinking about that terrifying whip downstairs. After her third almost sleepless night she caught a look at herself in Leyla's mirror. She looked thirty, not eighteen, with ugly bruise-colored circles under her eyes, stringy unkempt hair, and so many pimples she looked like she had chicken pox. This is horrible, she thought, I can't let this *happen*.

The grand scale was still beyond her comprehension; the bite-size problems were what galled her. Control her temper while the bratty twins threw marbles at her. Not scream when for the umpteenth time Oum Mohammed made her hold her yarn. No lipstick. No chocolate bars. No phone chats with Elaine. No Redskins games with Marc. No silly jokes from Dad. No chocolate brownies. The wrong brand of shampoo. No Diet Cokes. No mall. No pop rock stations – indeed, no radio or TV at all; Sheikh Khalid did not approve of them. No onion rings. No tee-shirts and jeans. Her vomit-splattered Gucci had vanished into the laundry and had never reappeared; she had to wear a faded blue-flowered ankle-length hand-me-down that was too tight through the shoulders and clung to her sweaty body like wet leaves. Every morning when she put it on she thought of her bulging closet back in Bethesda, and she'd want to cry.

It was another bad day when she discovered that the suitcases of clothes she thought belonged to her turned out to be for Leyla. Dr. Hassan had lied to her again! Leyla made a point to prance around in "her" outfits, while Tammy was consumed by humiliation. It was faint consolation that Leyla's pregnancy made it impossible for her to wear some of the clothes right away, and ruined the effect with the others.

Oum Mohammed was showing more and more suspicion about Tammy's insistence on clomping around in her high-heeled shoes. Tammy noticed, but without them, she knew she'd never even get across the broiling stones in the courtyard. On the thirteenth day she was in the living room holding Oum Mohammed's yarn when the mistress of the harem motioned for her to take them off. Tammy pretended that she didn't understand. Zeynab reached over, grabbed them, and handed them to Oum Mohammed. The money, of course, fell out. Oum Mohammed turned the bill over in her hand, put it in her pocket, and bore a hole right through Tammy with a reprimanding glare.

There, just like that, went Escape Plans A to Z.

The last screw that held her composure together came loose. Part of her stepped back horror-stricken, while the rest of her jumped up and ran out of the room. "I hate you I hate you I hate you I hate you!" she screamed, not caring who heard or who understood. "A plague on you, every last damned one of you!"

The twins followed her, giggling and pointing. "You snotty brats, leave me the hell alone!" She slammed the door. It wouldn't stay shut. Oh damn, she thought, can't I even have a shred of privacy without being locked in? The twins were still heckling her. "I said, get the hell away from me!" They may not have understood the words but they sure understood the music, because their eyes opened wide and they took off down the hall like their spoiled little rears were on fire.

You see? carped the demons. *You'll never find a way to escape now that you're barefoot and penniless. Soon you'll be pregnant like everyone else.*

She cried for an hour. Everyone left her alone, and eventually there was nothing to do but calm down. Hope? Just a flickering candle in a hurricane.

Next day she ventured back into the living room, where a smirking Leyla was wearing one of the designer outfits. Really rubbing it in. Then, Leyla "accidentally" spilled a whole glassful of grape juice down the front of Tammy's only dress.

She leapt to her feet, ready for war. At five-eight Tammy towered over Leyla by several inches, even though she was now barefoot and Leyla was in high heels. Oum Mohammed dropped a stitch. Oum Hussein pricked her finger. Even the twins stopped and gawked. Tam-my was spun far beyond fury into a windless plain where nothing existed except Leyla and her. She was cold. Calm. At her most dan-gerous. "Don't. You. Dare."

Nervous silence. Leyla flounced out. The twins resumed demol-ishing their toy truck. Oum Mohammed briefly shut her eyes and took a deep breath. Rokhiya almost smiled.

Next day everybody trooped downstairs and started putting on their cloaks and veils, even, to Tammy's astonishment, Rokhiya's elder daughter Amina, who was only about ten. An outing! But Oum Mohammed said something to Zeynab and Haifa, whose faces fell, and they put their veils and Tammy's back on the hooks. They were disappointed; Tammy was shattered. She'd been there fifteen days and, except for her one brief foray, not once had she been able to set foot outside those high walls. She was tired of looking at the world through latticed windows. She wanted to feel the sun on her face. She sat glumly on a window-seat in a small third-story salon overlooking the garden, where Sheikh Khalid and two other men sipped coffee and traded laughs, as if life were perfectly normal.

She wasn't paying much attention to the men until she heard a familiar chuckle. She froze. Next to Sheikh Khalid was a strikingly handsome man with a silvery laugh. He was broad-shouldered, with a streak of white cutting through his thick black hair like a blaze of platinum set in onyx. She sucked in her breath. If she'd wound up in *his* harem, she

53

might not have so much of a problem. The third man was partially obscured by a bush, but he laughed again, and this time there was no mistaking Dr. Hassan. No! With tears stinging her eyes she turned away from the window. He'd laughed loud on purpose, she figured, just so she could hear him from her dismal prison.

Not long after everybody else got back, hair smelling of smoky incense, she was surprised to be summoned before Oum Mohammed, who handed her a folded sheet of paper. A note? For her? She felt a sudden rush of hope.

> My golden treasure,
> I want to thank you for being so cooperative.
> My brother Fuad, my cousin "Sgt." Nabil and
> I hope that Sheikh Khalid finds you pleasing
> and that over the years you will bear him
> many handsome sons.
>
> Yours always,
> Dr. Hassan

The bastard! Did he have to be so cruel? She ripped the note into tiny confetti, stomped on the pieces, and flushed them down the toilet.

As heartless as the note was, however, it marked a turning point. She was determined to show the man with the mask of a matinee idol and the soul of Judas that she could handle whatever he threw her way. Maybe she wouldn't have picked this place to live, but as Haifa had reminded her, it could certainly be a lot worse, and she'd show him she could do perfectly well wherever he dumped her.

She'd finally concluded that her chances of escape were virtually nil, and for the first time actually opened a mental file on how she'd adapt to the harem. She remembered her English teacher's favorite comeback when someone would say, "I think I'm doing all right under the circumstances." She'd slide her glasses down to the end of her nose and challenge, "And just what are you doing *under there?*"

She still had Dr. Hassan's card, and she pulled it out from its hiding place behind the cushions of the settee and memorized his ad-dress. One day, she thought, she was going to turn him in, and she wanted to be ready. That tiny act improved her morale immeasurably.

"Ya Taamm!"

Oum Mohammed. Tammy pasted a brave smile on her face and decided grandly that no matter what, she'd hold her head up high. The paragon of long-suffering nobility. Distant. Dignified. Majestic. Cinderella had ended up with a prince, right? She caught a glimpse of her faded dress and bare feet, and gulped.

The dratted yarn again. This time, though, instead of glowering in resentment, she pinned a noble smile on her face. Oum Mohammed looked searchingly at her, as if trying to figure out her angle, but she seemed relieved, and she caught the lady smiling at her softly a few times. She's not a bad person at all, Tammy told herself. A young woman is brought into the harem, destined for her husband's bed, and she manages to be nice? It was hard not to respect her tolerant heart.

The next days showed improvements on all fronts. She still felt foreign, stupid, scared, and utterly out of place, but less like an alien who'd been parachuted in from outer space.

Learning to survive in her new surroundings was one thing; becoming blasé was something else. It shook her to the core when she noticed that she'd forgotten to be offended at eating leftovers. On the other hand, she figured it was wasted effort to get upset about some-thing she was powerless to change.

Sometimes, in fact, even leftovers weren't hard to take. There was one dish, tabbouleh, the men didn't seem to care for too much, a heavenly salad of chopped parsley and bulgur wheat and lemon juice, so there was always plenty.

"Laziz?" Oum Mohammed inquired, smacking her lips.

"Laziz!" You bet it was yummy.

"Laziz jiddan?" She held her arms wide.

"Laziz jiddan!" Really yummy.

From that day on, she always made sure Tammy had an extra helping.

Almost in spite of herself, Tammy was growing to like her. Oum Mohammed often went to extra effort to be kind. If she'd been one ounce less of a lady Tammy honestly did not know how she could have managed.

One morning, Oum Mohammed sent for Haifa and Tammy and gave them Tammy's housekeeping assignments. Laundry, carrying in heavy cans of water, vacuuming, working through a huge pile of mend-ing...

Haifa motioned for her to come to the courtyard with her. "Let me show you how to use the washing machine."

It was probably from the 1950's and even had a wringer. Tammy had to laugh. If they could afford to buy a fleet of Maseratis and a stableful of thoroughbreds, they could afford a modern washing machine. But why waste money when a mere *woman* would use it?

She soon got the hang of the washer and actually enjoyed being outside hanging the clothes in the bright sunlight. The ironing board, however, was in a windowless corner of the basement. Wait a minute. Iron? Did anybody ever iron *anything* anymore?

"What are you going to do now that you're not stuck with the laundry?" she inquired of Haifa.

"I'm still the personal maid for Rokhiya and Leyla, and now they want me to clean out the storage room that looks like it hasn't been reorganized since about 1600. And oh, by the way, your buzz is two short, one long, and two short. When you hear it, you drop everything, and report immediately to Oum Mohammed."

"So, you don't have to watch me all the time now."

"You're barefoot now, and settling in."

On the twenty-second day, soon after lunch, Tammy was working on her fourth load of laundry when the buzzer sounded. One long; that meant it was from Sheikh Khalid. Two short, one long, and two short. She hesitated, then it hit her. This was it.

She turned off the iron and went upstairs. Oum Mohammed took off her glasses. *"Ya Taamm."*

She'd spent three weeks dreading this moment. It was like Grandma Caldwell. Everyone knew she was going to die and did their best to prepare, but when it happened they were destroyed anyway. Do the wash, okay, but let that old geezer put his paws all over her?

There went her lunch, all over the carpet.

Oh Grandma, she thought, suddenly remembering her warning, why didn't I pay attention to you? You were right about Jean-Paul; he strangled his new girlfriend only a few months after you told me to break up with him. But I thought, what could possibly be dangerous about a vacation in France? You went to all that trouble to come to me, and I should've listened. I really, really should have listened.

Oum Mohammed summoned Zeynab to clean up the mess. Then she squeezed Tam's hand. Her look said, you'll live, so there's no need to be such a baby.

Tam thought she'd be immediately escorted to the big house, but no, the entire afternoon was spent getting her ready. Carefully bathed and depilated, creamed and oiled to the point she could have slid all the way across the courtyard, nails manicured, hair shampooed and brushed until it glistened. Then her eyes were made up with kohl, and henna paste was applied to her hands and feet, staining them brick red. Haifa turned out to be quite the artist and drew trailing vines up her legs and around her middle. The hard part was lying stock-still for nearly an hour while the paste dried.

Then Oum Mohammed picked out her dress: a long navy caftan practically covered in silver embroidery. It was splendid, and set off her blue eyes and pale ash-blonde hair to perfection. Her complexion resembled a bad embalming job; she needn't have worried, though, since she later learned that Arabs consider pasty skin particularly attractive.

She stared at her reflection as if it were a stranger's. Three months from graduation? Less than five months since the prom? It couldn't possibly be the same person. Zeynab thoughtfully slipped her a tranquilizer. Tammy wished it'd been a dozen.

Everybody started rooting around for just the right jewelry. Leyla was really in her element on this score and to Tammy's amazement, was suddenly helpful and friendly. She had never been so covered with silver. Chains dripping with turquoise beads for her forehead. Lavish chandelier earrings, necklaces, bracelets. She thought there wasn't room for another single bead, but Leyla rustled around and pulled out some jingly things to put around her ankles. She'd take a step, ka-chink. It was like playing with the veil in the limo; it felt so strange she didn't know whether to laugh or cry.

Zeynab spritzed her with perfume, and suddenly the whole room smelled of roses and lemon and jasmine. Oum Mohammed adjusted one of the necklaces, stepped back, and nodded.

Sweet little Najab, who'd been darting in and out excitedly and who'd insisted on "helping" with Tammy's hair, tipped her curly head to one side and gave her the one

Arabic compliment she could under-stand. *"Laziz jiddan,"* she proclaimed, and everybody, including Tam-my, burst out laughing.

At length another buzzer sounded. Zeynab squirted her with more perfume. Veil in place, Haifa and Zeynab escorted her to the harem gate, where Suleyman and another guard took over.

The back hallway of the men's house was magnificent. The ceiling was domed, supported by graceful scalloped arches. It looked like a combination mosque and museum, with bands of tiled calligraphy circling the walls. Thick rugs of rich colors and impossibly intricate patterns. The air conditioning worked. So did the lights. Of course, this was where the *men* lived. The guards whisked her through palatial travertine hallways hung with heavy tapestries and abstract paintings. At length they motioned her through a padded brocade door.

She swallowed. This was it. Survival, survival, she reminded herself. Be sweet to him, and you'll be okay.

Sheikh Khalid was waiting for her, propped up on pillows on a pale blue silk-draped bed, smiling like a five-year-old ready to unwrap a Christmas present. The room was so garish it was almost laughable. Approximately the size of Lafayette Square, it contained four or five living areas, an oasis of palm trees, and even a ten-foot waterfall. An arched bridge was covered with blue-flowering trellises.

A tuxedoed butler guided her toward the sheikh.

"Kom," Sheikh Khalid said, still smiling, holding out his hand. Wearing a royal blue silk robe, he rose from the bed, sat on an ornate couch, and patted the seat next to him. He said something to the butler, who removed her veil and served them spiced coffee called *gawaha* in little gold-rimmed porcelain cups. Tammy focused on the big-beaked coffee pot that reminded her of a toucan. *"Skal!"* he said,

quite unex-pectedly. Then a thin wrinkled hand reached under the dress and fondled her thigh.

She flinched, but only a little. Smile. Be nice. Control yourself.

"Giuseppe?" he said. She thought that meant that the butler would leave, but no, he started removing the jewelry, then the dress. Giuseppe looked at her and turned a funny shade of gray, while the sheikh rattled on in a language that Tammy didn't understand.

"Det ar battre," he said, when everything was gone except for her anklets. She shivered from confusion, fright, and from the extremely cold air conditioning. She'd almost thought he was speaking German, but as he chattered away, she concluded it wasn't German at all. And she realized he was expecting answers. *Ja, mein herr* seemed to satisfy him a couple of times, but she knew she couldn't keep up the charade for very long. Swedish! Of course!

Then two things happened simultaneously: he figured out that she didn't understand a thing he was saying, and he took a good look at her.

He jumped to his feet, screaming. He shook her until her teeth rat-tled. Then he took her little cup and hurled it against a palm tree. It shattered, sending tiny gold-flecked remains raining down like sparkling fireworks. Sheikh Khalid slumped into a chair, holding his head in his hands, suddenly looking very old indeed. She almost felt sorry for him. Almost.

"Hal anti min sued?" She panicked. Oh! Sweden! The question sounded like a death knell. Are you from Sweden?

"Laa, ya sayid. Anaa min Amrikiya." No sir, I'm from America."

Then the light dawned: he was the old man with the special order, and he thought she was Marisa! Had Dr.

Hassan really thought they could get away with passing her off as the voluptuous Swede? *Her?*

He closed his eyes in anguish. Then, having reached a decision, he called for Giuseppe, muttering under his breath. She caught *toubib* – doctor. Oh brother, she thought, I sure am glad I'm not the one who tried to pull a dirty trick on someone like Sheikh Khalid. She wished she could tell him she'd be glad to offer her assistance if he ever decided to commit murder.

Giuseppe appeared. The sheikh said something, and the butler grabbed her arm and bundled her out the door.

Damn, she thought, he's *fired* me. I don't even have the proper qualifications to be a harem slave. How far downhill can I go?

He took her to the basement to a small windowless room furnished with a bare metal cot and a toilet. The jail cell. He took off her foot-jinglies, slammed the metal door, and turned the key.

She lay awake most of the night, wondering what men did in S&M and fetish clubs, what happened in snuff clubs. Her dad was fond of saying, *Cheer up, baby, things could always get worse. So I cheered up, and sure enough, they got worse.* Haifa's terrifying words came back to her. "There's always somewhere worse, and they make sure you know that." She eventually sobbed herself to sleep.

PART THREE
SHEIKH SAUD

September 2005 – August 2006
Shaban 1425 – Shaban 1426

Next morning three guards unlocked the door, pointed at her chest, and howled with laughter. They were sweaty, smelly, and thoroughly disgusting. They didn't care that she was weeping with humiliation while two held her down and the third gnawed on her nipples, banging her with the bandolier of ammunition that he hadn't even bothered to remove. When he finally grunted with satisfaction another took his turn, and then the third, the roughest and most revolting of the three. Oh God, she thought, is my life going to be one rape right after another? What did I ever do to deserve this?

They found an old smelly dress, veil and *abaaya* for her, and stuffed her into a Rolls Royce, completely oblivious to staggering con-tradictions. After twenty or thirty minutes it stopped in an enormous underground garage. Guards practically carried her inside, where she was handed over to a white-robed man who wore his obvious importance as easily as his lizard shoes.

"You must be exhausted after such a long trip," he said in beautiful Oxford-accented English. "Come, my dear, sit down and refresh yourself. My name is Mr. Abdul and I'm here to ensure your comfort."

"Nice to meet you, sir," she said with a quivering voice. Reminded her a lot – a lot! – of a certain sleazy doctor.

"There, there, we'll wash the road dust off you and put a good hot meal in you, my dear, so just relax. You'll have plenty of time to adjust before you assume your new responsibilities. Sheikh Ahmed believes in keeping his

63

domestics well fed, well exercised, and scrupulously clean." Mr. Abdul smiled affably and nodded in the direction of a gilt-framed portrait of an elderly man.

Sheikh Ahmed? More of a Methuselah than Sheikh Khalid! And "well exercised." She burst into tears.

Mr. Abdul was taken aback. "What's the matter, my dear?"

"There's been a very bad mistake. You see, I'm not supposed to be here," she blubbered, "My classes at Georgetown have already started. I'm a college student, not a – a – maid."

Mr. Abdul handed her a tissue. "There, there, you'll get used to it soon enough. And please, when we call you a domestic, don't think you'll be washing dishes and scrubbing floors. Oh no, my dear, not at all."

She had very strong suspicions about what she'd be doing. "Listen, I'm not the kind of person you want for this job. I speak three languages. I'm going to be a diplomat like my dad. I was on the honor roll. I–"

"That's very nice, my dear," he said dismissively, settling back into his navy leather chair. "You seem to misunderstand. We won't hold any of that against you. You are a beautiful young woman, created by God not to fill your head with useless facts but to fill a lucky man's life with joy. Look around. I would be very surprised indeed if you ever lived in such luxury. If you let yourself, you will like it here. Now dry your tears and smile. How do you think you can please a man if you look so gloomy?"

"I don't *want* to please men," she insisted, aware of the petulance creeping into her voice, "all I want to do is go *home*."

Mr. Abdul stroked his graying goatee. The warmth in his voice had vanished. "You will fulfill your intended purpose. Have you yet converted to Islam?"

"No, I–"

"You will kindly address me as sir. Well, I am privileged therefore to welcome you into the faith. Your new name is Farida, and I will arrange for you to be properly instructed. Do you have any allergies or medical issues?"

"No. Sir."

"Excellent. We will however give you a thorough physical; we have to be very careful about non-Muslim women, you know, since their low standards of morals leave them highly susceptible to nasty diseases."

She was boiling. Not only had he insulted her intelligence, now he was insulting her morals.

"I will also schedule you for classes in the Arabic language, aero-bics, and sessions with our staff psychiatrist, Dr. Ibrahim. Now," he continued, blithely unconcerned that with every sentence he was spinning her farther into space, "let me explain exactly what you'll be doing. Almighty God has generously blessed Sheikh Ahmed with four devoted sons. The second of these is Saud, who is recently widowed. You will grow fond of him, I'm sure. He's rather handsome, by the way. However, I need to caution you. We have had problems with this position. You must therefore do everything in your power to please him; if you fail, there will be serious consequences. Now, my dear, let me get an escort to take you over to Mr. Mohammed in Personnel."

The brocade-hung hallway tipped and swayed as she stumbled along. She tried convincing herself that a handsome young sheikh was preferable to an old one, but didn't make much headway.

She sat on a bench in the disorderly Personnel Office and waited. The clock on the wall said it was nearly four; the hands moved, but it couldn't have been past ten in the morning. She gave up trying to make sense of it. Everything else seemed to be in a time-warp too. The phone rang and rang; no one was there to answer. She fidgeted. After thirty minutes, she figured Mr. Abdul should know that Mr. Mohammed still hadn't appeared.

His jaw dropped. *"Ya Allah!* What are you doing here, Farida? I told you to wait for Mr. Mohammed."

"Nobody's there, so…"

"If I tell you to wait, you wait."

"But I thought—"

"I gave you an order, and you are expected to obey it without question. Moreover, you are not to be wandering around the halls unescorted." He sighed. "This time, you will stay put until Mr. Moham-med arrives and gives you further instructions. Is that understood?"

"Yes sir."

She took her place on the bench again. Thirty, forty-five minutes, still nobody. Hmm, she thought, maybe they could use a little help with their filing. Feeling deliciously wicked, she picked up a stack of folders. A few papers from this one went into that one, and a few from over here somehow found their way over there. And, oh dear, a whole pile of files accidentally slid off the table, and when she picked them back up, by sheer coincidence, some of their contents got into the wrong folders too. She rearranged another stack of files, and another, and another. Finally, after more than two hours, she heard the door handle turn. The picture of innocence, she managed to get the files on her lap back onto the heap on the table just in time.

In breezed a lanky man with a huge moustache, whistling cheer-fully, with a golf bag slung over his shoulder. He picked up the card on his desk and read it over. *"Ahlan wa-sahlan ya Farida,"* he greeted, Welcome, Farida. He clapped his hands together like a second-grade teacher calling the class to order. "Sorry. No Engliss."

"Sorry," she returned, "No Arabic."

It took an excruciatingly long time, but eventually, Mr. Moham-med handed her a schedule card. "Wass. Eat. Okay?"

"Okay," she said.

He sounded a buzzer and a few moments later a bald pear-shaped man wearing a white tee shirt and khaki shorts appeared. Mr. Moham-med picked his golf bag back up, handed the man a card, and whistled his way back out the door.

"Hi, dearie," greeted the pear, "See you're American. I'm Dutch. Grew up in Canada. Farida, huh? Must be Sheikh Saud's new gal. Poor kid, he's no treat. What's your real name?"

"Tammy. And I'm Dutch-American."

"They call me Heineken, but my real name's Per." She couldn't help but giggle. "You get into trouble here if you use your real name; Rule Seventeen in the book there. Let's see. First we take you to Hygiene where you get cleaned up, after that, time for lunch. You'll be able to meet some of the folks. Ready?"

"Are you kidding?"

"You'll do fine. You can get away with a lot here if you smile. Let's go, dearie."

The first week in the House was crammed full of check-ups, orientation classes, counseling sessions, crash courses in Arabic cul-ture, and waiting for Mr. Mohammed. During that week she was supposed to learn all 44 pages of the rules and "adjust" to the new surroundings. The rules were incredible. They regulated standing, speaking, sleeping; forbade crying, complaining, criticism; they required cheerfulness and cooperation, diligence and devotion.

"These rules are horrible," she told another domestic, a stunning redhead from Savannah named Amberine. "This place is nothing but a high-class concentration camp."

The redhead blanched. "You just did a very dangerous thing. For-tunately, I won't tell on you, but the other domestics here are very likely to. You've got to remember that."

Tammy'd halfway thought the Rule Book was to keep rule-happy gnomes placated; she never dreamed that people actually followed it.

The medical results came back clear, which meant that as soon as Orientation Week was over she'd be promoted from the dormitory room she'd been sharing with five other girls to a Duty Room right in Sheikh Saud's apartment.

Despite Mr. Abdul's breezy assurances, it would've taken a total character implant to "adjust," but right on schedule during the morning of the eighth day, she was scrubbed inside and out until she squeaked and dressed in the long white uniform with a maroon border that identi-fied her as Sheikh Saud's "personal attendant."

At a quarter of eight – soon after lunch – Heineken picked her up from the dining room and grinned. "So! Big day today. Get to meet your new boss."

"Oh, shut up," she snapped.

"Last gal hated his guts. Said she'd rather pet a grizzly–"

"Please."

"Just trying to help." He searched her face. "You all right, dearie? Looks like you just jumped into a pail of whitewash."

"I'm not cut out to be some stupid sheikh's toy. I want to go *home*."

"Don't cry now, you can do it. It'll get easier. After the first time it'll be a piece of cake."

She struggled to compose herself.

"There, that's better."

"You mean, getting raped the second time is easier than the first? That's not true, Heineken. In some ways, it's even worse. I've been raped, I know."

"So have I," he said quietly. "They don't think of it that way and you know it. It's your job. Now go do it, and do it right."

"You told me yourself the man is impossible."

"So, just makes it more challenging."

"Is he ugly?"

Heineken shrugged. "He's okay when he covers up his horns and puts down his pitchfork."

"Heineken!"

"Tsk, tsk, Rule Eleven. No shouting, now." He winked. He was trying, God bless him.

"Why is he so difficult?"

"He's a grouch. Took the death of his wife real hard and hasn't been the same since."

Ornate hallways, soft swishes of bare feet on the thick rug. With every step they drew nearer. The elevator opened on the second floor, Heineken ran a security card through a sensor, and they went through another door. She gasped. Carnelian and alabaster walls. Silk rugs. Crystal chandeliers. Jasmine-scented air. Huge vases overflowing with tropical flowers. And that was just the hallway.

"See? What did I tell you? These chaps know how to live. Guess if you have all that money you can have whatever you want."

"Even beer imported from Holland and blondes from America," she reminded him blackly.

"Better get you to your boss before we both get in trouble, dearie. You see that door over there?"

She'd been gaping at it. Intricately carved ivory that seemed to cover a city block.

"That's the back door of his apartment. It opens onto a short hallway. Your Duty Room is the door on the right; his bedroom door is on the left."

She steadied herself.

"Remember Rule Six. When Sheikh Saud sounds the buzzer, you have ten seconds to open the door. Okay, ready?"

"Not in the least."

"Chin up, dearie, smile. Don't let him intimidate you. He's just a guy, okay? Just...a...guy." He rang the chime.

Blood roared in her ears.

A butler raked her with his eyes, coughed disdainfully, and motioned her inside. The huge door closed softly, like the lid of a padded coffin. He opened the door on the left and ushered her in.

"So, you're the garbage my doting father has dumped on me now." Sheikh Saud rattled a map in disgust and sighed as if he were the object of great persecution. "And why do they always inflict me with attendants named Farida? Is that the only fool name anybody can think up around here?"

He wasn't by any means gorgeous, but he wasn't as bad she'd feared, and he sounded almost as American as she did. He was only a couple inches taller than her, of average build, mid-forties, with a very black moustache and small goatee, a dot of a beard right under his lower lip, and bushy black brows that met over his nose. Unibrow, she said to herself with twisted delight, I'll call the idiot Unibrow.

He was sitting in a sunken living area on a burgundy leather sofa stamped with gold designs and framed with gold wooden filigree. The couch was littered with maps and charts, and others were spread out on the rug. To the far end of the long room was a king-size bed; in the middle was a large mahogany desk. Everything was in tones of burgundy and gold, right down to the border on her uniform.

Redskins colors! She caught herself from laughing just in time.

"Well, let's get this over with. Come here," he snapped.

Nothing like a sex-crazed sheikh who'd give his soul for a night with a teenage blonde, she thought. Right foot, move. Left foot, move. Somehow she got within five feet of him.

He said something to the butler, who unzipped her uniform and let it slide to the floor.

Sheikh Saud gasped. He leapt from the couch and circled her, mouth agape. "Flat as a parking lot, and skinny as a meat skewer. What has happened to our standards? I don't like the way you look, I don't like the way you act, and I wish to have nothing further to do with you."

Her mouth opened, but she clamped it shut in the nick of time. Rule Two.

71

He turned like a panther ready to attack. "I know what you wanted to say, and believe me, I don't want you here either. I can't keep my father from picking out toys for me, but he can't force me to play with them. I'm stuck with whatever he throws at me until I can get rid of it. Then what does he do? Goes straight out and buys me another one. You stay as far away from me as you possibly can, do you hear me?"

He was sharper – and more dangerous – than she'd thought. "Yes sir," she replied. Meekly and respectfully. Rule Four.

"Spare me, another groveler! I've wasted enough time on you. There is your room." He arrogantly pointed with his goatee towards a full-length glass door. "You are dismissed."

Not daring to reach down for the uniform, she stepped out of it, and with head held high – not groveling, right? – strode the few yards to the door. It clicked decisively behind her.

To her immense relief the room was nothing like the jail cell she'd pictured. Painted a pleasant pink, it contained a narrow bed, a leather hassock, a small table and chair, a thermal pitcher of ice water and a glass, a toilet and wash basin, the Rule Book (sigh) and an Arabic/ English Koran. The overhead light was on, way too bright. She looked around for a switch. Then she started looking for a pillow, with no luck either. By that time she'd run out of things to do, so she lay down.

A buzzer sounded. For a moment she couldn't figure out what was going on. Oh God, ten seconds! By the time she got her wits organized it had stopped, and the door wouldn't open.

Oh brother, there went Rule Six.

She tried to see how angry Sheikh Saud was, but to her consterna-tion, she couldn't even see her own face. One-way glass! Of course.

She watched at the door for a few minutes, but nothing happened, so she lay back down. No sooner had her back touched the bed than the buzzer rang again. He'd *waited.* He was *watching,* the bastard. She tried to cool her blood, and this time, she made it on time.

"Sir." She tried to sound respectful, but instead it came out sarcastic.

He raised one side of his long brow. "This is the last time I will summon you twice without issuing demerits." He paused to let the warning sink in. "I don't appreciate garbage leaving trash on my floor." The uniform came flying through the air and hit her full in the face. "You are dismissed. And oh, for your information, I control the light in your room. Just the way I press this button and control you."

She made it back inside the room without losing her cool. But she'd barely had time to sigh in relief when the stupid buzzer rang again. It was going to be a long day.

"I've changed my mind. You will stay in here."

"Yes sir." For someone who wanted nothing to do with her, he sure was going about it funny.
"Put that uniform back on. I simply want you where I can keep an eye on you. You will not open your mouth."

"Yes sir."

"Sit cross-legged over there on the rug."

"Yes sir."

Unibrow studiously ignored her. He made phone calls, fiddled with his computer, measured lines on the charts, argued vehemently with someone on the telephone, referred to big books. She took in the raw silk-hung walls and hand-carved furniture. She memorized the elaborate design of the rug. She admired the workmanship in the silk curtains that graced the double-high windows. She rubbed her nose.

"Stop that! Keep your filthy hands folded."

She sighed – skirting on the edges of Rule Five – and folded her hands. She was itching to tell the lout to make a trip through Hygiene sometime. She wasn't just clean, she was *sanitized*. Amstel had given her such a vigorous scrubbing she'd wanted to remind him that she wasn't made of stainless steel. Filthy, indeed.

Hours passed. To think she could've been eating pizza on M Street. Cramming for exams. Giggling with girlfriends.

She thought back to a conversation earlier in the day with Amber-ine, Sheikh Farook's attendant. He was Sheikh Ahmed's oldest son, quite popular among the domestics for his modern ideas and easygoing personality. He reportedly even made periodic visits to the servants' quarters for no other reason than to see how everyone was doing.

"How do you get along with him?" Tammy had asked her.

"We love each other very much," she replied. "It's a funny way to meet, but it's as good as any, I suppose. You never know what life will throw your way."

Tammy was flabbergasted. "You *love* him?"

"I've been here twelve years. I was only fifteen when I was given to him. He's gorgeous, and loads of fun, and smart and sexy and – well, why not?"

She hadn't been prepared for this at all. "But, you were *forced.*"

Amberine shrugged. "Yes, the first couple times, I was scared to death. Absolutely scared to death. But he was nice. He was gentle. He made me laugh. He helped me through it."

"But your education. And your–"

"Education? When I ran away from home I was a fourteen-year-old ninth-grade dropout. Now I have a master's in economics that I got by e-learning and I've done all the course-work for a doctorate. Sheikh Ahmed won't let me out to take the exams and defend my dissertation on monetary policy, or I'd have my Ph.D. by now. I've received far more education this way than if I'd stayed home. And Farook has en-couraged me every step of the way."

Tammy was dumbfounded. "But what earthly good does an education do you here?"

"For the time being, I have to be contented with helping Farook with his research and writing, but after we're married I'll be able to do a lot more."

"Married?"

"As soon as Sheikh Ahmed gives his permission."

"I thought Sheikha Ayissa was Sheikh Farook's wife."

Amberine's smile was as dazzling as it was gentle. "She is. You may have noticed by now that this isn't the USA. I'll be his second wife."

Talk about making lemonade when life hands you a lemon. No, make that a lemon daiquiri!

"Oh, yes, every bit of that's true," Heineken had confirmed later, "but did she happen to mention how long it's been since they've been asking permission?"

"No," she said, suddenly developing dark doubts.

"Eight years. And did she happen to mention what Sheikha Ayissa thinks about this idea?"

"No."

"Didn't think so. She's probably the only person in the whole House who can outscream Sheikh Ahmed. And even if he allows the marriage, which he thinks is outrageous because aristocrats only marry other aristocrats – usually close cousins, in fact – life for Amberine won't be smooth sailing. Farook would have to keep his two ladies far away from each other. Different zip codes. Preferably, different solar systems. And, dearie, did Amberine tell you that Sheikh Ahmed has threatened to sell her to the most brutal brothel on the Gulf if Sheikh Farook raises the question of marriage one more time? She's twenty-seven, you know, way too old by House standards to be a personal attendant. Cut-off age is usually twenty-five. That's no joke, either. Sheikh Mohammed's assistant didn't take her aerobics class seriously and was sold off a couple months ago, and she was only twenty-three."

Tammy stayed quietly in her corner, head swimming, trying to absorb everything. Finally, Heineken came to take her down to dinner. What a relief to see a friendly face! Sheikh Saud eyed her menacingly but let her go without a word.

"How was he?"

"He fell head over heels in love in love with me and made passionate love to me for hours and hours."

"Yeah, right." Heineken threw back his head and laughed. "I saw how he'd planted you on his rug."

"Well?" Hamida asked eagerly in the dining room. She was a platinum blonde from Germany, in a wheelchair until the soles of her feet recovered. She'd been found unescorted in an off-limits part of the House, which was automatically considered attempted escape. She barely tolerated Sheik Aziz, who had a voracious sexual appetite. Everyone looked eagerly Tammy's way.

"He has the body of Adonis and the disposition of St. Francis of Assisi," she announced.

"Rule Nineteen!" they chorused, then giggled knowingly.

After supper, Heineken took her back to the apartment. This time Sheikh Saud left her alone in her room, but with a security camera focused right at her and with the one-way mirror, she knew that every move she made was being watched.

Not that there was anything interesting to see. There was nothing to read except the Koran and the Rule Book, no radio, no TV, no pictures, no windows. She lay on the bed, her biggest ambition to keep from crying. Rule Fourteen.

That morning she'd asked Heineken how he managed to stay sane.

"Been here almost nine years, for one thing. It's amazing what you can get used to. I was real rebellious. Tried running away, got whipped. Tried organizing strikes, got whipped. Hauled off and punched Mr. Mohammed, got whipped. Takes some of the oomph out of you after a while. Main thing is, I'm still alive. Tell myself one of these days I'm going to buy myself a little cabin in the Rockies. Have a couple German Shepherds, a nice flower garden, maybe even a nice gal. That's all that keeps me going."

She vowed to do like Heineken and hang onto hope, but it was harder than she thought. When she followed the rules she was ashamed of herself for capitulating, but the few times she'd allowed herself the luxury of expressing an opinion or making a suggestion, she was slapped and called a troublemaker. Now that Orientation was over, they'd start handing out demerits, which translated into loss of privileges and even, as they referred to paddlings or floggings, "enhanced motivational training."

The buzzer sounded; she swallowed hard and responded on time. *"Labaika, ya sayidi,"* she said politely. Here I am, sir. She'd learned the phrase in Arabic just that morning.

77

"No point trying to butter me up by speaking Arabic to me," he snapped. "I have a Ph.D. from Texas and speak English better than you do. Now. I can't stand the sight of you and want you to get the hell out of my life. There's only one thing to do, however, and that's to keep my father guessing. You will therefore sleep tonight under my bed. And if one of his spies questions you, you will reply honestly that you spent the entire night beneath me. Then perhaps they will leave me the hell alone. Do you hear me?"

"Yes sir." She inched her way under the bed. The clearance was too low for her to turn over or lie on her side, but she didn't care. Soon she heard him snoring like a diesel truck, and she too drifted off to sleep.

The next morning after breakfast, instead of taking her to Religion, Heineken said she had an appointment with Mr. Abdul. She knew his office was on the first floor, and the staff dining room was on the first floor, so she was baffled when they got to an elevator and Heineken pushed the Down button.

He laughed when he saw the puzzled look on her face. "Faster than going all the way around."

"Around what? Where I come from they've invented something called a straight line."

"Listen, dearie, you and I and the other three dozen domestics in the House aren't supposed to exist. Not talking about the valets and stable-boys and the gardeners and the guards and the maids and the stewards and the chefs, mind you, just folks like you and me. It could cause trouble if somebody saw us who wasn't supposed to. So they built the House with separate service hallways and whenever they have to cross a real hall where real people can go we have to go to the sub-basement. Got it?"

She groaned. "How'd they get you, Heineken? I mean, what did you do before?"

"Me?" He shot her a strange look. "I try not to think about it." He swallowed. "My father was with Shell not far from here. I was a real cute teenager, with curly blond hair, although you'd never know that now. Can't stand having my head shaved like this, can't stand it. Mom didn't want to live here year-round, but we'd come for summer vacations. Well, one of Dad's colleagues, a guy named Ahab, had a thing about blond boys, but Dad didn't know. Ahab convinced my father to let him take me falconing. Part of my 'cultural enrichment,' see. He'd arranged for thugs on horseback to abduct me and take me back to his place, where he tied me up and raped me four or five times a day. After a few weeks he started bringing his friends over so they could play with me too. Once he took me to an orgy where I was gang raped. On the way back I decided to make a run for it. Got caught, of course. Ahab blew up. Sent me to a clinic where they cut my nuts off and cut my cord so I can't have an erection. From there I was sold here. I will never, ever be able to make love to a pretty woman my entire life. That's what they stole from me." He shrugged in bitter resignation. "Better places, worse places. At least here, we're fed every day."

"A clinic?" She had a funny feeling.

"Yeah, one of the best doggone surgeons anywhere, but crooked, slippery as snot on a doorknob. Do anything. Abortions, castrations, revirginizations, devocalizations, the works. Everybody hates him. But he knows everybody's dirty secrets and blackmails anybody who tries to shut him down."

She hardly needed to check. "Dr. Hassan?"

"You already run into him?"

"One of these days I'm going to kill the SOB."

"You and me and dozens of others have the same idea. They know how we feel about them, so they take precautions. They don't even let you have pencils or long fingernails. Forget that idea, dearie. Concen-trate on staying alive."

79

They arrived at Mr. Abdul's office. "Be careful. In this country everybody's related, or they went to school together, or their aunt married their cousin-in-law's nephew. You can't trust anyone. And Mr. Abdul in particular seems to be related to half the population. He's the one who really runs this place, so stay on his good side, whatever you do." Heineken placed her in the custody of the pleasant full-bearded secretary Abu Khalid, who told her a dozen times in charmingly labored English that Mr. Abdul would be right with her. She missed Arabic. She missed Aerobics. And she even missed Religion. Mr. Abdullah was a sweet sincere man, but an hour-long class conducted in Arabic, in a monotone, on a boring subject, just wasn't her idea of fun.

Although his class did provoke a few jokes. What? Make a pilgrimage to Mecca? When did they say the bus left? Mr. Abdullah told them with a straight face that they could aspire to make the trip "some day." When he started preaching to them about *zakat,* or giving alms, she wondered how he was going to get around the fact that none of his students had any money. He solemnly distributed coins, and then immediately took up a collection, in order to inculcate "good habits" in them. He recycled the same coins week after week; they saw them so often they could recognize each one, a certain nick there, a flattened place here.

Arabic class, on the other hand, was really fun. Mr. Ali, the in-structor, had a great sense of humor and excellent mastery of six or seven languages. Tammy found the language fascinating and made rapid progress. Masculine and feminine variations of the word "you"? Okay, if you say so. "Sun" and "moon" letters? Okay. Start books at the back and read right to left until you get to the front? Not just pre-fixes and suffixes but infixes? Verbs that fell into four well organized categories? She just ate it up, even though the vocabulary wasn't the least like Spanish or French, and the grammar was sometimes down-right diabolical. She loved the beautiful calligraphy and was thrilled when Mr. Ali complimented her on her excellent handwriting.

He told them about Grimm's Law of Consonant Displacement, which bored the other students to tears but which Tammy found absolutely riveting. The Brothers Grimm were not only literary his-torians, but also linguistic scholars. They documented how consonants change in predictable patterns, like R's and L's, B's and P's, F's and P's, V's and F's. "Anybody ever wonder why the Amstel River is in Amster-dam? Or why in English you say title and in French *titre?* Or why in Spanish you say *papel* and *azul* and in English paper and azure? Does anybody know where tulips come from? Yes, Kronenbourg, Turkey, you're correct. They call them turbans, because the flowers are shaped like little turbans. In Dutch this word became what, does anyone know? Yes, Farida, correct, *tulpen.* See? the R changed to an L and the B changed to a P, but it's essentially still the same word. In Arabic we say burghul; in English you say bulgur. The R and the L both changed places.

"My favorite example of Grimm's Law concerns the Alcazar, the Moorish fortress in Spain. It's actually the Arabic word *al-qasr,* but they added an extra A to make it more pronounceable in Spanish. Now, if you change the R at the end of *qasr* to an L, what do you have? Yes indeed, Farida, you have caught on, you have the word qasl, or castle. And of course, it means fortress or castle. Every word has a story behind it; it didn't just fall out of the sky."

That day Tammy went up to him after class and asked him more about Grimm's Law. He said he'd written a treatise on it and offered to show it to her, but then remembered that it wasn't on the list of approved reading. "Sorry about that. I'll try to get special permission if you'd like."

"Thank you, sir! I'd like that very much."

Mr. Ali was nice enough to apologize for giving the students bro-ken stubs of chalk and kindergarten-style chalkboards to write with; he was daring enough to vary the lessons from the Rule Book and the Koran. And he kept everyone in stitches with the rules he made up to illustrate grammatical principles. "House Rule Six Thousand Seven Hundred and Eighty-Eight: domestics will refrain from tormenting underpaid teachers of Arabic," or "comely female domestics will fling themselves passionately at all House teachers of Arabic." He was terribly fond of Mardya, the French girl assigned to the Employees' Lounge. It was against all the rules, but he'd sneak out with her sometimes during class, leaving the students all by themselves, and return a half-hour or so later looking very relaxed. The students so appreciated the rare chance to goof off that nobody squealed on him.

"I'm so sorry," he told her after class one day, "Mr. Abdul sees no reason why you should read my article on Grimm's Law, but if you want to come to my office for a few minutes, we can talk about it."

The "talk" involved removing her uniform and submitting to a quickie on his couch. "Don't worry," he said, "Since I used a condom, Hygiene will never know. And unless you want me to tell Mr. Abdul what a constant disciplinary problem you are, you won't mention it either."

She was his star student and he hadn't reprimanded her a single time. It was blatant blackmail, but he was who he was, and she was who she was, so he could get away with it.

And still she waited for Mr. Abdul. Partway through the time she was supposed to be in Adjustment, he finally appeared. "Ah, my apologies. This has been an unusually difficult morning. Tell me, my dear, did you sleep well?"

She gave him an honest answer. "No, sir." Heineken would later explain to her that the "difficult morning" was the disappearance and presumed escape of Brunehaut, a Belgian-born eunuch.

Mr. Abdul beamed and motioned for her to sit on one of the ivory-and-navy striped silk chairs. Even her mother would have approved of the decor. It radiated quiet authority, with off-white raw silk walls, an ivory-bordered navy rug, an ornate French-style desk. A peaceful abstract in blues and grays covered much of one wall. His desk was heaped high with files.

"So, if I understand correctly, Sheikh Saud summoned you?"

Unibrow knew what he was talking about; Mr. Abdul proceeded to question her closely. He sat back at last in his leather chair, pensive. "We have a problem," he said, which from her standpoint qualified as a monumental understatement. "You have substantiated his own account, even to the fact that you mightily displease him. On the other hand, his father has grown weary of sending him the finest attendants to be found and having them systematically rejected. He has decided to identify precisely what Sheikh Saud's objections are to you and then work to resolve the issues. Sheikh Saud claims that you were totally unresponsive and showed no enthusiasm whatsoever. Is that true?"

Oh, shrewd shrewd! Unibrow had massaged the truth into a tightrope across which Tammy now had to pass. She despised him, but in a grotesque way was anxious to help him subvert authority. "Yes sir."

"I must remind you that we expect our attendants to be cheerful and cooperative. Sheikh Saud has been in a deep depression ever since he buried his wife and you have been brought here to help him enjoy life again. We have very little patience with reluctance. Is that understood?"

The phone rang. "Still nothing? Shit. And the silver Harley too. Have you interrogated all the drivers? Yes, I've been looking for that but for some reason the files are a mess. It's almost as if someone…" A light bulb went off. "I'll call you back." He turned to her. "You'd better hope that my instincts are off, but I don't think they are." He dialed. "Run the feed from the security cameras in Mr. Mohammed's office from the morning of the 22nd and tell me if you see anything unusual. Ah. I thought so." He rose, visibly trying to control his mounting rage. "On your knees."

His slap knocked her to the ground. He motioned her to kneel again. A second knocked her over the other way. He let her just lie there. "You take us for idiots? Let me ask you something. Have you ever been flogged?"

She was shaking. "No sir."

"Would you like to find out what it feels like?

"No sir."

"If you continue like this, I can almost guarantee that you will. Rule Twenty-Nine says any act of sabotage may result in up to what, Farida?"

"Forty lashes, sir."

"Now, I was about ready to warn you about your disrespectful tongue when I discovered that you're also a determined troublemaker. You've barely set foot in this House and you're already demonstrating the worst possible attitudes. I will notify Sheikh Saud when Sheikh Ahmed and I have reached a decision about how to correct your conduct. You are dismissed."

Sheikh Saud was appalled. "Four security cameras pointed right at you and you thought you wouldn't be caught? How idiotic can you get? You're lucky that your owner is reluctant to have a *jaria* flogged, because the ugly scars mar her appearance and reduce her resale value. Not every owner would be so humane. And they also took into consideration that you hadn't yet gone through Orientation. Nevertheless, you knew perfectly well that you were misbehaving. First, you will be paddled 50 strokes every week for six weeks. Second, you are to be confined to this room or your duty room for the next six weeks except for the times you are taken to Training for correction. Third, you are on the strictest probation during this six-week period and if you commit any other serious infractions you will receive eighty lashes with a barbed whip – that's eight zero – and immediately be sold somewhere not so concerned about domestics' welfare. Is that clear?"

"Yes sir." *Barbed whip?* She suddenly went weak.

"We're not talking about high school detention here, Farida, we're talking real whips, and an expert flogging-master. Now, this is coming from me. I'm sending you to your room right now with no lunch and no dinner. By the way, I'm being nice. For the first two or three days you won't be able to stand up or go to the toilet, and nobody's going to come clean you up, if you catch my drift. You are dismissed."

It wasn't Heineken who escorted her to Training and rolled her back upstairs on a gurney afterwards; it was a sour-faced armed guard. Food was served through a pass-through that she'd never noticed before, a bowl of yogurt for breakfast, plain rice and lukewarm water for lunch, and scorched vegetables for dinner. Then it was the month-long daylight fast of Ramadan, so no breakfast, no lunch, and those god-awful burned vegetables for dinner. The pass-through was on the opposite wall from the bed, and for the first two days, as Unibrow had said, she couldn't walk over to get it, so the food remained untouched. Sheikh Saud largely ignored her, which was just as well, since she spent three or four days after the paddlings lying on her stomach, recovering from one just in time to be subjected to the next. The only breaks were weekly visits to Hygiene and one week when it was her "female time," when she was back in the dormitory.

She had a lot of time to think about the chilling detour her life had taken. She prayed with all her heart for strength and guidance. Three things kept coming up: the story of the second mile, her mother's frequent admonition, When everything else fails, try love; and Heineken's reminder that Sheikh Saud was just a guy.

At last it was over, and she was back in Mr. Abdul's office being lectured on the virtues of devotion and submissiveness. "Sheikh Saud complains that you are sullen and distant. You're supposed to bring him joy, help him relax, and you're not making the least effort. Warm some fragrant oil and massage his feet and shoulders. Lift the tea to his lips yourself. Caress him. And when he takes you to his bed, be warm and welcoming. Give yourself to him, don't just lie there like a board with a hole in it. He has also complained about your appearance. We are considering implants but Sheikh Ahmed has not yet decided one way or the other. We will, however, adjust your diet so that you gain at least five kilos, as Sheikh Saud has requested."

"Yes sir."

"Now. To assist you with your motivation, you must prove beyond any doubt that you have pleased his son. If you have not become pregnant by the end of the month of Rabi al-thani – that gives you more than eight months – you will be sold elsewhere. I am sure you will do whatever is appropriate. Your predecessor, by the way, is currently starring in dirty movies. You are dismissed."

"Would they really be rotten enough to make me do porno films?" she inquired of Amberine while they waited for their escorts after lunch, clutching at the frail hope that it was just an empty threat.

Her matter-of-fact reply did nothing to encourage her. "Why do you think the job was open? Arab women certainly can't do them; their brothers or fathers would kill them. It's called honor killing and it happens every day."

"But I thought they were illegal here."

"They are. Darn, they're so Puritanical they even retouch Queen Elizabeth's v-necks before they put her pictures in the paper. So is selling people illegal. So is castrating men. But they figure if it isn't explicitly outlawed by the Koran, it must be okay."

"That international sex symbol, Queen Elizabeth!" They both had a good laugh. Tammy grew serious again. "They won't *let* the other attendants get pregnant, and now, I *have* to."

"That's the others. Don't fight it. In this place, you just can't win. Believe me, I know."

"And please, what's a *jaria?*"

"In its purest meaning it's a young girl, just starting to get ripe. It also means personal attendant. More crudely, it means sex slave."

Tammy couldn't help it. She threw up, all over the tile floor.

"How'd you like to call your folks?" Heineken asked one morning, as if it were the most routine offer in the world.

"Are you *serious?*"

"Sure. I have Sheikh Aziz' code. I can call just about anywhere."

"Heineken, you are amazing. How on earth…?"

He shot her a sly grin. "We can call anywhere except your home town, because they could figure things out real fast. One unauthorized phone call, and you'd be in a wheelchair like Hamida or in a stable at the Ranch. It's a slave prison, by the way, where guys can play with the inmates. And from what I hear, they play rough."

"Daddy has an office in New York, and another one in Geneva. Would they do?"

"Let's think this through. Have to be extremely careful in case the switchboard is listening in. And it often is."

They shot ideas back and forth. Tammy suggested that Heineken ask for Mr. Couillac instead of Mr. Simmons; her father would catch on, but nobody else would understand.

"Only, that's a very hard name to say," protested Heineken, twisting his mouth. "Quack."

"No no, coo-ee-yak."

"That's what I said. Quack."

"Close enough. You know, Heineken, I never thought I'd say this to a, uh, a–"

"Eunuch," he supplied.

"Yes. Sorry." She closed her eyes briefly. "You're really nice."

"You're not so bad yourself. Even though you have friends with impossible names. Quack quack." He duck-walked down the hall while Tammy giggled.

"John, the idiot on line three says his name is Angelo della Misericòrdia," Gina said, making a face. "Not only does he not speak Italian, he has the worst fake accent I ever heard in my *life*. And he insists on speaking to someone named Pierre or Clotilde Quack. I told him he has the wrong number, but he won't take no for an answer."

Angel of Mercy? John raised an eyebrow. And Pierre Quack? What if…? "I'll take it," he said quickly.

"Hello, Pierre? I got-a your Geneva number from your New York-a office."

"This isn't–"

"Angelo" plunged on. "I know. I am thoroughly annoyed-a. You sent-a the shipment to the wrong address. It finally arrived-a in good-a condition, but please, make-a sure you have the correct-a destination. If you continue to screw up-a I will send-a my business elsewhere. Please, note-a the correct one." He spelled it out in German.

"Sorry about that, sir. We'll make sure we get the next shipment right. Thank you very much for your call."

John squinted at the phone as it went dead in his hand. Angelo's Dutch, he told himself, not the least doubt about that. He dialed Abubakr's number. "We've located Bulbul," he said.

As time passed Tammy made tentative friends with a few of the other domestics. She had a pleasant relationship with Nabilah, one of Sheikh Ahmed's three attendants. A strawberry blonde fifteen-year-old Irish girl "rescued" by a freighter after a pleasure boat mishap, she was soon sold to a tanker crew, and then, after an operation to restore her virginity – conducted by a certain surgeon of her acquaintance – to Sheikh Ahmed. "He's nice enough, he is, in his own way. Long as he takes care of me, I'll take care of him, I say."

Hamida was a five-ten German who'd been with five-six Sheikh Aziz for more than a year. He made up for his small stature by being insatiable; she often missed supper or breakfast because he wouldn't release her, and she spent several days a month in the infirmary recovering from his avid attentions. She probably had just had her last blow-up with him. No one was supposed to know what she'd done for fear of giving them naughty ideas, but of course Heineken had all the details. "She took Sheikh Aziz' scissors and tried to turn him into a soprano," he said with a chuckle.

Then there was Alia, a buxom honey blonde of unknown nation-ality, but Amberine guessed her to be Swiss. She was assigned to the Executive Lounge. No matter what you said to her, she'd smile sweetly, nod, and say *"Bahnhofstrasse,"* German for railroad station street.

"She's harmless," Amberine explained, "and the men sure like the way she's built."

Most of the other attendants vacillated between resignation and despondency, but there was one, a Dutch girl nicknamed Namash, Freckles, who loved her job. She was a walking, talking freckle, with bright green eyes and short scrambled red hair that even the very talented Amina had given up trying to domesticate. She'd been with Sheikh Ahmed almost two years.

She'd grown up in Rotterdam as the youngest of six children. When she was thirteen, one of her brothers introduced her to a friend who asked her if she'd like to live in a palace. She thought it would be fun. The brother got a motorcycle, Namash got the palace, and Sheikh Ahmed got Namash.

"This place is so pretty. Silk rugs. I mean, who ever heard of silk *rugs?* And walls made out of jewels. Back in Rotterdam it was so crowded, you know, and here there are only three of us in the room and it's so pretty. Don't you think our rooms are pretty, Hamida?"

"They're okay for what they are," she said with a shrug.

"You'd rather be back on that *farm?* Milking cows and cleaning up horse shit? You're so lucky, Hamida, Sheikh Aziz is sooo handsome. Just think of all the girls in the world dying to go to bed with a gorgeous Arab sheikh and you have one and you act like–"

"Mr. Abdul showed me today,"

"Oh no! How'd it go? Who was it?" everyone wanted to know.

"I don't know," she said, her eyes back on a farm in a forest. "I was stuffed so full of sedatives I could barely stand up. He looked Indian."

Amberine seemed to know something. "Did he ask you to dance, by any chance?"

"Why, yes."

Amberine sighed. "Sounds to me like the Maharajah's Palace."

A stricken silence overcame the group.

It was only when Tammy could get Amberine alone that she was able to ask why everyone had been so upset.

"It's a brothel. Actually, it's just a big house, with a dozen women or so. And it's not as bad as some places, believe me. All the women wear are strings of jewels. A man will rent the entire house and all the women are there to serve him."

"Comparatively–"

"Yes, true, but they're all devocalized, which means they can't talk, and defanged, which means all their teeth are extracted for reasons I will leave to your imagination."

Two days later Hamida was gone. It was several weeks before a replacement was found for her, a seventeen-year-old from Barcelona named Nayirah. She wasn't even pretty, with a bad case of acne, thick-set hips, and a permanently dour expression. She lasted only until the dark roots of her bleached hair appeared. No one – not even Heineken – was sure what happened to her, or why she'd been "hired" in the first place.

One noonday, to everyone's surprise, Carlsberg didn't bring Namash down to lunch. Instead, he brought two very young Slavic girls. They looked so much alike everyone assumed they were sisters, probably eleven or twelve years old. They rarely said anything except to each other, padded around the House on spindly legs, stared at the opulent surroundings through huge eyes set deeply in thin faces. Within weeks they were transformed from frightened skinny children to fright-ened firm-fleshed young women called Laamia and Saamia. They wore the white velvet-bordered uniforms of Sheikh Ahmed's attendants.

Sheikh Ahmed had offhandedly mentioned Namash to a visitor of his, who said he'd always dreamed of owning a cute little redhead. There was nothing Sheikh Ahmed could do, as a good Arab host, but give her to him. Exit Namash.

It was several weeks later before Heineken was able to make contact with John again, who said he had another shipment on its way. "Please call Chopsticks at the number I'm giving you for all necessary arrangements. Thanks, Angelo, thanks a million."

Heineken had spent a great deal of effort cultivating friendships and had earned the trust of one of the drivers, Youssef. Sheikh Aziz was at another "conference" in Bangkok; this meant Heineken could sneak into his bedroom and take calls there whenever he needed to; it was just too dangerous to make outgoing calls. Everybody knew that Aziz' frequent jaunts to Thailand were for kinky sex, but they kept up the charade in hopes that Sheikh Ahmed wouldn't find out.

Youssef didn't mind returning one of Heineken's many favors. "Sure, you can use my phone. Local call only, though."

"Of course." Heineken left a cryptic text message for Chopsticks, who would know which number to call. He raced to Sheikh Aziz' bedroom and rushed to answer the phone that was already ringing. It was the jewelry store. "Yes, yes, I'll be sure to let him know his order is ready. Thank you so much."

A few moments later it rang again, and this time it was Chopsticks. "Hello? This is Central Florist. We have delivery of a large bouquet scheduled for Thursday at 4.30. The truck can only wait for ten minutes, so we hope that someone will be available to accept delivery at the rear loading dock."

"We actually ordered two bouquets; I hope you have the order straight."

"Two? Oh yes, you are correct. Two. We'll see you Thursday."

Heineken gently replaced the receiver and treated himself to a silent whoop. Four days! He had to find Farida and tell her. Wait. Her face was like a picture window; she'd never be able to keep it secret. Even if she didn't say a word, she'd look so excited that everybody'd know something was afoot. Better wait until the last possible second to let her know that she'd be going home.

The eunuchs were hard for Tammy to get used to. Amstel, one of the bath attendants, had been a full castrate his whole life – theoretically emancipated but never released in the early 60's when slavery had been officially outlawed – and as soon as Tammy knew this she nearly gagged whenever he touched her. His waxy, almost transparent skin. His fondness for women's perfume. His high-pitched voice. His oddly proportioned body. As friendly as he was, at first she even treated Heineken like he had leprosy. His condition seemed so unnatu-ral that she just couldn't wrap her brain around it.

Several weeks passed. She'd been paddled twice more, twenty strokes each time, for insubordination. Once she'd been reluctant to answer Mr. Abdul when he asked her to describe her sexual fantasies. She wanted to tell him that it was none of his goddam business, but instead she replied that she only had one, and that was to remove a certain body part from a certain surgeon. Mr. Abdul had eyed her sternly and said sharply, "He just so happens to be my younger brother." Oh shit! The other time was when she hadn't gotten around to reading the required passages in the Koran for Religion.

Mr. Abdul was growing more and more impatient, and she sensed things were coming to a breaking point. Planted as usual on the rug while Sheikh Saud did his work, she took a daring step. If God kept reminding her about going the second mile, maybe it was time to try.

"Sheikh Saud, sir? Would you like for me to help you with anything?" She'd broken a rule by initiating a conversation, but figured it was worth the risk.

He glanced up, startled. "Are you a geologist?"

"No sir. But I can file things, sort things, you know, help you with paperwork. I'd desperately like something to do, and it looks like you could use some help."

"No, I don't need any help." He reflected a moment. "Like you helped Mr. Mohammed with his files? Is that what you mean?" He actually laughed.

"No sir. I mean, really help this time."

"That was unbelievably stupid of you. But it was also damn funny. Damn funny. Thank you for offering, but no, I don't need any help."

"Yes sir." She smiled at him. And he smiled faintly in return.

The next evening he said, "You know, I've been thinking. Maybe you can sort all these receipts for me and log them in? I hate doing that. Come over here and let me show you what to do."

It felt wonderful to have something productive to do, but she had to be careful: she didn't want him to think that she was trying to trap him. When he got too close, she shied away. Maybe nature would take its course, and maybe it wouldn't, but at least she could improve the chances by being helpful. And meantime, she wasn't sitting on the stupid rug doing nothing.

It didn't soften his character; he was just as cold to her as ever. But on the third day, he said he had another pile of receipts that needed logging in, and she delightedly set to work.

"You did a very good job on that. I have another project for you, but I'm warning you, it's a real stinko. See this box? All those dozens and dozens of slips of paper? I need them in date order with the most recent on top. Then I need you to go through them and tally them by work site. The papers are a mess; I've been putting this off because it's such a royal pain."

"Thank you, sir, I'm tickled to be able to help."

In less than three hours she'd polished off the whole box. "What else can I do, sir? That was fun."

"Fun? Okay, if you say so. That's all I can think of right now." After a pause, he asked, "What's the deal here, Farida? Why did you suddenly decide to be nice?"

"Only a few months ago, sir, I thought I was going to be at Georgetown studying diplomacy. Then some ugly stuff happened. I don't want to be here, but it doesn't look like I can do anything about it. You don't want me here, but you can't do anything about it either. I figured well, if I'm stuck with you, and if this is going to be my life, then I might as well make the best of it."

"Don't you hate me?"

She sighed. "I know I acted like I did, sir, and at first I did. I've been really snotty to you and I feel bad. I hate being here, but no sir, I don't hate you. You're not the one who kidnapped me, you're not the one who raped me, you're not the one who sold me into slavery. It's not your fault."

"You're not going to trick me into meeting their idiotic deadline. I don't want you to touch me."

She shrugged. "One thing Mr. Umar has finally gotten through my thick skull, sir – or more accurately, my bottom – is that what you do with me is entirely up to you. And to be perfectly honest, I don't want you to touch me either. I resent the hell out of being thrown at you. But regardless, it would be idiotic for me to sit here bored to pieces while you're drowning in work."

"My father makes his attendants sit at the table with their heads resting on their arms. That is how they spend all day, waiting for him to summon them. So I thought I was being nice by having you at least out here instead of in that stuffy little room. Am I that ugly, by the way?"

"Not at all, sir, you're pretty okay, and I do appreciate being out here. It has nothing whatsoever to do with you. Mr. Abdul is always on my case because I haven't been giving you foot and back massages like, um, a good little *jaria* is supposed to do for her, uh, master." Her brain tripped over the words. "If you would ever like for me to do that, let me know, and I'll be happy to, but it would be to make Mr. Abdul shut up and not because I'd be trying to make you come onto me."

"You're really into flattery, aren't you. Hmm, 'pretty okay.'" He chuckled. "Do you have any notion how tyrannical my father is?"

"I'm getting a pretty good idea, sir; he'd drive anybody absolutely nuts. Sometimes I actually feel sorry for you. I finally understood that you're not the problem; he is."

He studied her intently. "You seem to be sincere enough. I would like to point out, however, that you have overstepped the boundaries of your job description by a shocking margin and that you richly deserve another trip down to see your good friend Mr. Umar. I will spare you this time, but I am confining you to my apartment for the next two weeks."

"Sheikh Saud, thank you for letting me get all that off my chest. I really appreciate it, sir."

"Chest? What chest? You are dismissed." She detected the slight-est hint of a smile before he grew stern again and the Duty Room door clicked shut behind her.

It was Thursday, and Heineken could barely contain his excitement as he went to fetch Tammy for Aerobics. In just a few hours they'd both be celebrating their liberation.

"She's not going anywhere, Heineken. I've confined her to quar-ters for insubordination," Sheikh Saud explained.

"Again, sir? She's a very sweet girl, but she's having a rough time settling in. I'll let Mr. Abdul know. For how long, sir?"

"Two weeks."

"Disciplinary diet, sir? And do I need to tell Mr. Umar to warm up his paddle?"

"Yes to the diet, no this time to the paddle. Thanks, Heineken."

Shit. The best-laid plans… With a heavy heart he reported Tam-my's disciplinary measures to Mr. Abdul. Almost time. He started toward the loading dock.

"Heineken!" It was Sheikh Farook. "How've you been? Haven't seen you for a while." They chatted for a few minutes. Time was going, going, going. He could still make it if he really hurried. "Hey, would you mind running this CD over to Mr. Abdul for me? He's been wait-ing for it."

"Pleasure, sir."

Shit. By the time he got to the loading dock the florist truck was pulling out.

Shit. Double shit.

Dear Heineken scolded Tammy for short-sightedly bringing a lot of woes on herself. "Think of your self-esteem as money," he advised. "You squander dimes and nickels on stuff that doesn't mean much. Hamida threw her ego a party – but look where she is. Did the same thing at first myself. Now I've learned. Past couple years I've been socking my pride away in the bank, making them think I'm a good little boy. Trustworthy. Well under control. And then one morning they'll look around and ask themselves, Where's Heineken?"

"Where would you go? What would you do?"

"Sheikh Ahmed had a valet who left here a few months back. Got sick of being yelled at. Gave me an idea. Got a job at a fancy men's club where he's making tons and tons of money. If I worked there two, maybe three years, I'd have enough for that cabin and plenty to live on." He winked. "I didn't tell you that, right?"

"Tell me what?" She winked back.

He patted her on the back, and to her surprise she didn't mind a bit. She rarely remembered any more that he was a eunuch. He was simply a great guy and true friend.

It was good advice, but hard to put into practice. With a lot of effort she managed to stay just shy of the number of demerits it would take to be sent to Training, but all the deprivations and punishments short of that became a standard part of her life. She wasn't allowed to visit with the other domestics on *al-jum'a* (Friday) afternoons; instead she had to take extra classes in Adjustment. And she almost always got last choice for Alternative Duty, which usually meant that several days a month she'd be sitting for hours on end over the hot mangle in the sweltering laundry room.

The personal attendants were carefully monitored by the bath attendant, or *lawingi,* for the first sign of a visit from Mother Nature, which meant that according to Islamic law they'd be immediately pulled from their regular responsibilities and given Alternative Duty until the visit was over. She'd always hated ironing, but she loved running sheets through the mangle, imagining them to be particular bodily parts of a particular surgeon.

As far as the rest of Islam was concerned, she conformed to what was expected of her, no more, no less. It was funny; she had no idea how important her faith was until someone tried to take it away. She didn't really think God got uptight about what religion you practiced, as long as you loved Him and tried to make the world a better place.

Sheikh Ahmed, however, had his own ideas, so five times a day, whenever the call went out over the intercom at dawn, midday, midafternoon, sunset, and nightfall, she had to recite the *salat* – the prescribed prayer – out loud, contrary to custom, so they could be sure she wasn't saying the Lord's Prayer or calling down curses on their heads. She obediently did the ablutions, draped her head with a *shershif,* opened her palms over her face to shut out evil, bowed toward Mecca, knelt with her forehead to the ground, and rested on her heels while she recited the words. She hoped God was duly impressed; she certainly wasn't.

One morning Heineken came to escort Tammy to breakfast in a roaring good mood. "Sheikh Farook's in big trouble," he said with a laugh, "big, big trouble. Yesterday he had another huge fight with Sheikha Ayissa about Amberine. Eight-point-eight on the Richter scale. Sheikha Ayissa got so mad she stalked out, took one of the Diablos, and zoomed into town." Tammy knotted her brow in confusion. "That's a Lamborghini."

"I know that, but what's the big deal?"

"Keep forgetting how green you are. Women aren't allowed to drive here. Even though she dressed like a man, she didn't have a moustache or beard, and her bare female face was hanging out, which made matters even worse."

"Okay, but I still don't see what this has to do with Sheikh Farook."

"He's her husband. He should have controlled her better."

Tammy laughed. Served the chauvinists right!

"But Sheikha Ayissa is in deep doo-doo herself. First the religious police caught her driving, the crime aggravated by showing her face; it's considered indecent exposure. Then Sheikh Farook beat her up and sent her for an extended visit to her father's, which is about as close to a divorce as you can get."

"Why don't they just get a divorce, for crying out loud?"

"Out of the question. Her father is Sheikh Ahmed's younger brother. Have to keep the money in the family, you know."

"But that makes her Sheikh Farook's first cousin! You don't marry your first cousin!"

"They do it all the time. In fact, in many places in the Arab world, 'uncle' and 'father-in-law' is the same word."

"Aren't the children deformed?"

"Occasionally, but at least the women get to marry someone they might have even met." Heineken chuckled. "Not the first time she's gotten out of hand. When Amberine had the flu Sheikha Ayissa sailed into the infirmary and laced into her. It's one of the rare places in the house where domestics and real people overlap. Pulled hair out, the works. And Amberine had to lie there and just take it."

"Jeez!"

"Look at things from her standpoint. When Sheikh Farook was at the London School of Economics she went with him and stayed five years. Saw how women lived there. Got a diploma in art history. Learned how to swim. Drive. Absorbed a bunch of other subversive ideas. Farook brings her back and she doesn't want to stay cooped up in a harem any more. Then she discovers her father-in-law has given her husband a gorgeous red-haired *jaria*. How do you think an educated, sophisticated, cosmopolitan woman would react?"

"Are the other sheikhs married? I never hear anything about their wives."

"Sure, otherwise they think something's wrong with you. Even if you're gay, you're married. The other wives are very traditional. Sheikh Ahmed is twice a widower. Sheikh Aziz got married last year, but you'd never know it. Sheikh Mohammed is married and has two sons."

"They all have just one wife?"

"Sheikh Ahmed is against polygamy." When she shrugged incredulously, Heineken chuckled. "Hey, let the old man have an occasional attack of liberalism."

This floored her. "But he buys them *jawareen*."

"He'll tell you it's because he respects his daughters-in-law." He threw Tammy a warning look; ahead were Tuborg and Rokhiya, two big sycophants. "Don't you think the new benches in the dining room are nice, Farida?" he asked rather loudly, the picture of loyal innocence. It was all she could do not to have a fit of the giggles, but that had to be the end of the conversation.

"Heineken," she asked one morning. "Why are their clocks always so messed up? I mean, it's weird eating breakfast with a clock that says noon."

"They reset the clocks for midnight every day at sunset. Same idea as the Jewish Sabbath, you know, that starts at sundown. A very ancient way of telling time. You'll get used to it."

"Okay, I know that Sheikh Farook is an economist and Sheikh Saud is a geologist. What does Mohammed do? And Aziz?"

"He's in import-export, specializing in textiles and leather goods. Aziz never even finished school, no surprise, since he had his butler doing his homework. He's basically a full-time playboy, but he tells people he's a financial consultant."

And the surprises continued. Sheikh Mohammed's wife owned her own leather goods business. She worked through her brother who served as a male executor, kept her women-only administrative offices completely separated from the male-only workshop, and employed more than seventy people.

"Why not?" Heineken said. "She was already stinking rich before she married Sheikh Mohammed. She wanted something to do with the money besides spend it on jewelry. Women only inherit half as much as men, but they hardly ever have to spend a dime. Women around here are *rolling* in money."

At times Sheikh Saud was friendly, funny, appreciative, and an actual human being; other times he was arrogant, dismissive, distant, and impossible to please. She never knew which Saud would show up. She began to get a sense that he was struggling with demons that had nothing to do with her or Sheikh Ahmed, but she could only guess. Mr. Abdul kept reminding her what lay in store if she disappointed them, and when the stalemate showed no signs of cracking, Sheikh Ahmed decided he'd scream at her too. At least once a month, when the arrival of her period dashed hopes that she might be pregnant, she could count on being summoned to his gold-and-white office to be raked over the coals.

When they weren't shouting at her, Sheikh Ahmed and Unibrow were yelling at each other. Sheikh Ahmed would telephone and they'd holler at each other, then Unibrow would slam down the receiver and curse. "Like having a damned Mount St. Helen's for a father," he muttered. Once he was so intent on dashing over to scream at his father in person he forgot he just had on his *thobe,* the long white robe, but didn't have on his *sirwaal,* or white duck trousers, underneath. He didn't notice anything amiss until people started snickering; it was the day, of course, that he was wearing red underwear. House domestics giggled for days. Somehow he just didn't strike people as the red-underwear type.

One evening, to her surprise, Sheikh Saud told Nazir to warm up some almond oil. "I've had a rotten day, Farida, and maybe Mr. Abdul has the right idea. Take off that stupid uniform and come over here. Why do I have a *jaria* and then not use any of her services?" She knelt and set to work. "He was definitely right. There's something about a beautiful naked woman at your feet that does good for the soul." She watched discreetly, but her ministrations didn't create a flicker of interest farther north. "My back, please?"

"No problem, boss. So, what happened today?"

"As you know, I've been feeling halfway sick for several days. So I'm already feeling crappy and I have a meeting with a site foreman, and none of my projections had worked, and he's under pressure from his higher-ups, and when the meeting is over he thinks I'm a total zero. Then I go to a presentation where this nincompoop gets a standing ovation for stuff I've been doing for more than four years. Then I have another battle royal with my father. Farida, sometimes I just want to crawl into bed and say, 'I want my mommy!'"

She laughed. "Everybody has days like that. All part of being on the Planet Earth, sir. Tell me about your mother; I think I would've really liked her."

"She was wonderful. I have no idea how she put up with my father, but they were married for nearly 45 years. She was gentle, she was loving, she kept struggling to make Mohammed and me into something even though Farook was always my dad's favorite." His voice broke. "Um, uh, she, uh, even fought for me when I wanted to marry an American girl. A lot like you. She didn't succeed – *nobody* can succeed against my father – but she really tried. She's the one who decorated this House. Without her I'd be a degenerate playboy like Aziz or totally screwed up like my friend Prince Fulaan. She was so grounded, and so serene, despite all the curve balls this society throws at women, that she is my absolute hero. I never in a million years would have achieved what I've done without her."

"What next, boss?" He was just a guy. Just a guy. Just a guy.

"It's okay, just sit there at my feet and look beautiful. Nazir, can you get me some aspirin, please? Farida, tell me about your mother."

"She's also my hero, boss. She's absolutely the most Christian person I know. Very forgiving, very loving, an incredible example. She's a firm believer in the power of love. When we were in Morocco my father had a stupid affair with a belly dancer, and my mother for-gave him. I mean, she forgave him with so much love that now he's the most incredibly devoted father and husband you could possibly ima-gine. She's an interior designer, by the way, and would love this place. She specializes in the mega-rich mansions in Potomac. Quiet opulence. Tasteful splendor. Her watchwords."

"I, uh, I mean this girl, uh, from Denver, uh, she was a lot like you. And I try to picture, uh, what she would've done if, uh, she'd been in your shoes. I mean, one morning you wake up, and you're okay, and the next morning somebody ships you here, and basically you've become just a piece of meat, completely at the mercy of whoever buys the meat. I just want you to know that I'm extremely uncomfortable with this whole arrangement. But, here we are, and as you've figured out, my father is a living, breathing relic of the past. You're supposed to be all shy and modest, and I'm supposed to leap all over you, and maybe we end up like Amberine and Farook. Only problem is, whoever wrote that script didn't know you, and they didn't know me."

Tammy couldn't believe it. He understood, he actually understood. "Tell me about the girl from Denver, boss."

"Her name was Frieda, Frieda Schmidt. Now you understand why my *jaria* is always named Farida. What a coincidence, right? She was working on her master's in mechanical engineering while I was working on my doctorate in petroleum geology. We dated for three years. She taught me how to ski, and it's now one of the things in life I enjoy most. But her family hated me because I was a 'stinkin' Mohammedan,' and my father hated her because her father wasn't a mega-millionaire. Families went into meltdowns on both sides of the Atlantic and we finally gave up. My father and I have been at each other ever since. I'm forty-four years old and he still wants to control my life as if I were fourteen."

"Dumb question, sir, why don't you just move out? And

sir, this is just a thought, but maybe, just maybe, your father is trying to remind you of happier days by naming your attendant Farida. It might even be his way of apologizing about her."

He shook his head. "You don't *do* that, it's unthinkable. But there've been days, believe me, that I've been tempted." He paused and looked at her, cocking his head. "That's actually possible, I never thought about it like that. I know in his own way he cares, he just can't resist trying to control everything I do. All right. Put your dress back on; I have a pile of receipts for you to sort out again, please."

When there were less than two months before the deadline, Unibrow complicated matters by taking a vacation to Switzerland with his good friend Prince Fulaan. He was away for three weeks. Normally, during such an extended absence, she'd have been temporarily reas-signed to the Executive Lounge or to keep houseguests happy, but in her case it wasn't possible because she could've gotten pregnant by the wrong man. Mr. Abdul finally lent her to Housekeeping and she spent her "vacation" in Cinderella mode, vacuuming hallways, polishing acres of brass and mirrors, and scrubbing toilets and showers. She worked from dawn to dusk in the tan Housekeeping uniform, ate silent meals with resentful co-workers who considered her an uppity intruder, slept in the staff dormitory with nine other women. She missed Amber-ine and Heineken desperately. She even missed Unibrow.

Nazir, his Somali valet, had gone with him, which for a while didn't strike her as peculiar. Often in the evenings when she'd been parked on the carpet or sorting receipts, Nazir would help Unibrow into his robe, off with his shoes, pour him another cup of *gawaha*, bring him pomegranates. But now she remembered catching sight of lingering touches, furtive glances. She never saw anything beyond that, but it set her to wondering. And worrying all the more that things were far more complicated than even Sheikh Ahmed could suspect.

Other questions remained to be answered as well.

"Heineken, where is Amberine's Duty Room? Is it–"

"Know what you're asking. Men live on this side, women live on the other side. Do you have any idea how big this House is? You've only seen a little corner of it. And oh, by the way, some fart changed Sheikh Aziz' access code and didn't obligingly write it on the inside cover of the phone book, and I haven't been able to call out for a while. It's just a matter of time before I get it again, though."

Unibrow's trip abroad did nothing to improve his temperament; he'd been particularly nasty for three days. The night before he'd thrown a huge stack of receipts at her, said she'd done a thoroughly incompetent job, and that she was hopelessly useless.

"I swear," she told Heineken hotly as he escorted her to Aerobics, "Unibrow is nothing but a spoiled arrogant brat. Do you know what he–"

They rounded the corner and almost ran smack into a white-faced Mr. Abdul. Rules Twenty-One and Thirty-Seven lay at her feet in smithereens. Mr. Abdul wordlessly gave Heineken a card, and she was taken directly to Mr. Umar.

"You again?" he said. "Sweetheart, when are you ever going to learn? You have the most beautiful backside I've ever seen, and believe me, I see more than my share. I *hate* paddling you. Please, sweetheart, behave yourself." He sighed. "At least it's only 25 strokes this time, could be worse."

Two days later, Sheikh Saud had become friendly again. He had her translate a French-language article on aquifers, which she was overjoyed to do. "Nazir's got the flu and I'm going to be out most of the day, but if you promise to be good I'll let you watch CNN."

"I'll be good, boss, I promise."

She was watching a special on ancient Egypt with one eye, and reading a book she'd found on the coffee table, *Case Studies in Electrical and Radioactive Well Logging and Subsurface Surveys* with the other. Suddenly Sheikh Ahmed erupted into the room.

"Where's Saud?" he demanded.

She leapt to her feet. "My lord, he went to a budget review meeting that he figured would last all morning and then weekly prayers; he'll be back late this afternoon."

"And where's Nazir?"

"My lord, he called in sick today."

"So you're in Saud's apartment, completely unsupervised?"

"He only allows me to be in his room, my lord."

"Entirely inappropriate! And what nonsense are you reading? Give it to me. Now." He hurled the book across the room. "That is not approved. If you want to read something, read the Koran; it will improve your attitudes. Have you touched his computer?"

"No, my lord."

"But it's sitting right there."

"I don't even know the password, my lord."

"I will check nevertheless to see if any unauthorized emails have been sent. Farida, I'm sick and tired of your recalcitrance, your rebel-liousness, your defiance. I'm going to do something I should have done the day you set foot in this House. Security? I want you up here on the double with a full set of shackles."

Tammy threw herself at Sheikh Ahmed's feet. "Please, my lord. I'll do anything you say. Please, please, my lord."

"You haven't obeyed me a single solitary time. For once, you're going to be in the place you should be, the last place in the world you want to be: Saud's bed."

Two guards arrived and practically threw her onto the bed. They ripped her uniform off.

"Not too tight. I just don't want her going anywhere."

A collar went around her neck, irons went on her ankles and wrists. Padlocks clicked into place. Oh God.

"No pillow. No sheet or blanket. No food unless Saud feeds you himself. I will stop by several times a day to check. Depending, I may release you in a week. Or a month. Or never." He turned off the TV and stormed out the door.

Hours later, Sheikh Saud finally appeared. His eyes opened wide. "What the hell happened?"

"Your father came this morning, sir. I was here all alone, reading your book. He blew up. Nobody to supervise me, and reading unauthorized material."

"Are you cold? You're shaking like a leaf. And oh, heavens, we need to get you cleaned up."

"Sorry, sir, I couldn't help it. Been like this for hours. Yes sir. No sheet or blanket allowed, sir. It's these things, sir. I hate them so bad, it's my worst, worst, worst nightmare come true. And I really need to pee again, sir."

"Mush maa uul!" Holy Toledo! "Hello, Infirmary? Bring me up a bedpan, a strong sedative, and fresh bed linens. Pronto." He turned to her. "What? You were reading my case studies book?"

109

"It was actually kind of interesting, sir. It's there under the table where he threw it."

"Subsurface surveys? Interesting?" He treated himself to a good laugh. "You know, of course, what he's trying to do. Sledge hammer."
He slumped in exasperation. "Have you had anything to eat today?"

"Breakfast, sir."

"What would you like to eat?"

"Rice and vegetables is fine, sir. Oh, today's Friday, we get a chicken drumstick too."

"That's not what I asked you. I repeat: what would you like to eat?"

"Really, sir? Thank you, sir. A lamb kebab, and some tabbouleh, and some ice cream?"

"Coming right up." He placed the order with the kitchen and admitted the nurse, who let her use the bedpan and gave her a shot. "I think we're going to need to keep that up here. How long does the sedative last, Ayub?"

"Seven or eight hours, sir." He yanked the soiled sheet out from under her and slid a fresh one into place.

"Can you make sure she gets another shot every eight hours?"

"Yes sir. For how many days, sir?"

"A week. Depending, sir," she replied for him. "He kept the keys himself and said he'll stop by several times a day."

The food arrived. Sheikh Saud started to put a pillow beneath her head, but she stopped him. "No pillow either, sir."

"How the hell are you supposed to eat if you can barely raise your head?" He cut the kebab into tiny pieces and fed them to her, got the tabbouleh bit by bit into her mouth, and finally spooned up the ice cream, which had almost completely melted. "Here's the call button. Can you move enough to use it? No? Here, I'll put it in your hand. Normally it would summon Nazir, but if you need something, press the button and I'll help you, okay? You don't deserve this. I'm sorry."

"Thank you so much, sir. That was delicious. Sorry you had to go to so much trouble, sir."

In the middle of the night, Tammy awoke abruptly to discover Sheikh Ahmed standing in the middle of the room. Saud jumped up from where he'd been asleep on the sofa. The shouting match between father and son lasted a good twenty minutes. Finally Sheikh Ahmed stalked out, slamming the door behind him. Saud hadn't even turned out the lights when the door flew open again and Sheikh Ahmed screamed one last insult. This time it was Saud who slammed the door.

"Nurse?" he bellowed into the phone, "Farida's due for another shot, right? Better bring up a second syringe or I swear, there's going to be a murder."

Next evening Saud was feeding Tammy a hamburger and French fries when Sheikh Ahmed let himself in, but this time, he smiled approvingly. He saw how Saud had to cradle her head to raise it enough for her to be able to eat. He took keys from his pocket, found the right one, and removed the chain from her neck. The collar was still there, but at least she had a bit more freedom of movement.

"Thank you, my lord, thank you very much."

"You take good care of my son, and I mean it." He swept out of the room.

"You see? He really does love you, boss. He wants you to be happy so desperately that he's taking extreme measures.

111

Sledge hammer, like you say. All you see is that he's still trying to control you, and all he sees is that we're being rude to him by not appreciating all his efforts. It's really sad."

Saud swallowed. Sighed. "You have a kind heart, Farida, but we've been feuding for twenty years."

After nine days Sheikh Saud came home to find Tammy sitting naked on the rug. "Finally! I'm glad that's over."

"I never could have gotten through it if you hadn't been so nice, boss. New decree is, I'm confined to quarters for the next ten days, and I'm not allowed to wear my uniform."

"So I'm stuck with the view of a parking lot?" He chuckled.

"'Fraid so, boss."

It was now the month of Rajab and only about six weeks remained before the deadline. Heineken was taking Tammy from Arabic to Religion. He elbowed her and whispered, "Green alert."

Sheikh Farook!

Coming toward them in tennis togs was one of the most attractive men she'd ever laid eyes on. Tall, broad-shouldered, with tousled wavy hair, full sensuous lips, and muscular, hairy legs, Sheikh Farook waved his racket and stopped. Right in front of Tammy.

"Oh," he said with a friendly chuckle when Heineken introduced her, "you're the American who single-handedly keeps the demerit system alive. Amberine told me about you. Somehow, though, she forgot to mention how pretty you were. Where are you off to now?"

"Religion class, sir," she stammered.

"Wouldn't you rather come up to my place for a while? To chat? Or would you rather have a nap while Professor Mumble expounds on the glories of Islam?"

Silently, she begged Heineken for advice. He gave her a look that said, Listen, when Sheikh Farook invites you...

"As you wish, sir."

"I'll take her from here, Heineken. Don't worry; I'll take responsibility. Cheerio!"

When they got to his malachite-and-white marble hallway, she really began to panic. What if Amberine saw them? What if Sheikh Ahmed saw them? And what would Sheikh Saud say?

He acted so natural that she almost forgot who he was. "This room is absolutely gorgeous," she said without thinking. She hadn't said 'sir.' She'd brazenly initiated a conversation. Two rules had already gone up in smoke. She braced herself for a slap. It didn't come.

"Thanks. Mother is the one who decorated the House, you know, before she died a couple years back (may peace and blessing be upon her). Had quite a knack for putting a place together."

"Like my mother," she said. Tears welled up in her eyes and she couldn't help it, rule or no rule.

Sheikh Farook gave her a swift but crushing hug. "I can't fix everything," he said gently, "but I have a good shoulder to cry on. Every now and then it does the soul good to have a jolly good bawl. I say, would you like a brandy?"

No wonder Amberine was in love with the man. "A brandy, sir? A real brandy?"

"I'll take that as a yes," he said with a grin. "Don't you dare tell my father I have alcohol in this place, though, he'd kill me. Although, on second thought, with his spies everywhere I'm sure he knows. Here. Sit down and tell me everything. I want to know what's really going on. Tell me, how's Unibrow?"

She gasped. How–

"Jolly amusing, if you ask me," he continued. "Amberine told me. I call him that now too. So. Cheers!"

For the next two hours she emptied her heart. She told him about her family, Marc, her cat Cleopatra. She described her frustrations, her fears, her sense of futility. He listened intently, handing her tissue after tissue. He ordered an extra plate of roast lamb and eggplant for her; it was such a treat instead of the usual rice with vegetables she almost licked the plate.

"It's so nice to be able to talk to somebody," she said at last. "Even Dr. Ibrahim doesn't seem to be the least bit interested."

Sheikh Farook laughed. "What could he tell you, anyway? He doesn't have an easy job, you know." He poured her some *gawaha* and studied her for the longest time, still holding the pot. At last he replaced it on its tiny table. "You figured out my brother's problem?"

"Problem?"

"Think about it. What's the real situation?"

Think? *Think?* She'd almost forgotten how. She took a swig of the spiced green coffee. "Well, sir, he had a beautiful young wife whom he loved very much," she said tentatively. "He's still profoundly in mourning. Sometimes I think he's even more depressed than I am."

"Go on," he urged. "How did she die?"

"Wasn't it a tubal pregnancy, sir?"

"That's right. And how do you think it would make a husband feel?"

"Sad, sir, that's for sure." He stirred his hands. "And I suppose, guilty."

"Now we're jolly well getting somewhere. What can strong feel-ings of guilt do to a person? A male person, in particular?"

Little glimmers of understanding began to appear. Could it be...? "Sir? Do you mean to say, I mean, men are, um, well, psychologically, um, I can see it would be possible for..."

"Go on," he said with a slanted smile that reminded her of Elvis, "I think you're onto it."

"Do you mean to say that he's so distraught that he's become, well, that he can't..." She ran out of guts.

"Go on."

She gulped and closed her eyes. She plunged. "Impotent, sir?"

Sheikh Farook sat back in the emerald leather chair. "I knew you could figure it out. He's suffering in ways we can only imagine. Be as understanding as you can; I for one would consider it a personal favor."

"And sometimes he tries to cover it up by being mean." She took two breaths, and remembered. "Sir."

Her handsome host laughed.

"Thanks, sir," she said fervently as Tuborg arrived to take her to Sheikh Saud's apartment. "I never could have figured that out without your help."

"Saud doesn't know how jolly lucky he is," he said with a big grin. "Chin up, sweetheart. Cheerio!"

Understanding Sheikh Saud's situation helped her feel more compassion for him, but her relations with him did not improve. As if to keep her from getting the wrong idea about his occasional lapses into friendliness, he continued to scream at her, his father continued to scream at her, and both of them continued to scream at each other.

One day, to her enormous surprise, Sheikh Saud invited her to watch a DVD. She was leery of his intentions, and her suspicions were confirmed when it turned out to be an extremely raunchy porno film in which the female lead spent most of the time strapped to a bed, enduring various torments.

"Did you like it?" he asked, challenge ringing in his voice.

"Not one bit, sir."

"The star was your predecessor."

She'd figured as much.

"They sent copies to her father so he could brag to all his friends."

She raised her chin. "You're not going to do that to me, sir."

"You are my property. I will do with you whatever I damn well please."

She'd been thinking a lot about what her mother always said, When everything else fails, try love. Everything else had failed, so... "Sheikh Saud," she began softly, "I've been thinking. We only have a few weeks left and you and I both know that there's no way we're going to meet their stupid deadline. Samira would've wanted you to stop blaming yourself. No amount of self-reproach will bring her back. You should be living a full and happy life. She'd want that for you, I'm sure. At this point, I have nothing to gain and you have nothing to lose if we call a ceasefire. We don't have to tell anybody; your father and Mr. Abdul can still be utterly convinced that you can't stand the sight of me. I'm pretty sure I understand. I'm just a girl, I'm not a therapist, but I might be able to help you."

To her astonishment, he burst into tears. "I miss her so much," he blubbered. "She was the joy of my life. She'd walk into the room and it was like the sun came out. It's been so hard. So hard." He fought to recover. "I'm sorry. Sometimes it just hits me, and..."

"I understand, I really do." She wiped his tears away. "I know this sounds strange coming from me of all people, but let me sleep on your bed tonight. If nature wants to take its course, so be it, and if not, neither one of us has lost anything."

He stared at her, unbelieving. "I underestimated you." He patted the couch. "Come sit over here. So, you figured things out."

"Yes sir. It took a long time, though. I didn't understand how profoundly you were grieving."

"I'm sorry I've been so stern with you. It was the only—"

"I understand completely, sir."

They sat there for a long time, a few inches apart, not saying anything. At length he rose and helped her to her feet. "I do believe this is one of the nicest things anyone has ever done for me. You're actually giving yourself to me. In spite of everything, you have chosen to give yourself to me, not because you have to, but because you want to. Farida, this changes everything. The way I think of you, the way I think of me. Everything."

"At this point, I might as well."

"What's your angle?"

"Well, if I help you, sir, maybe you'll be so grateful that you'll put me on a plane headed for Washington, give me a king's ransom in jewelry, a million dollars, a villa on the Riviera, and a Ferrari. And, um, let's see…"

"Is that all?" He said with a chuckle. And if you don't succeed?"

She shrugged. "Then I'm absolutely no worse off, sir; I'm sold to a studio that makes dirty movies. It seems to me it's worth a try. I lose nothing, you lose nothing, and hey, it might just work. In a grotesque way, now that we know we can't meet the idiotic deadline, the pressure's off. This isn't a desperate *jaria* trying to seduce her lord and master; this is just an ordinary girl named Tammy giving herself to a grieving guy named Saud."

"This really does change everything. Everything. I'll send for you in a little while."

"Yes sir."

"You may call me Saud, as long as no one else is around." He cleared his throat and grinned mischievously. "Or even, if you prefer, Unibrow."

Tammy wanted to die of embarrassment. The door clicked shut behind her and she lay down on the settee. Somehow the room was brighter, more cheerful. The air fresher.

A couple hours later the buzzer sounded. When she stepped into the bedroom her jaw dropped. Six huge bouquets of roses. The table set with fine china and candles. A bottle of champagne on ice.

"May I have the pleasure of your company for dinner this evening, Miss Tammy?"

"This is unbelievable," she said, hand to her forehead.

"You haven't answered my question."

"Of course, of course, Mr. Saud. And it is still unbelievable. Absolutely unbelievable."

"Take that stupid uniform off. I borrowed this from Amberine." He handed her an exquisite peach negligée with cascades of satin flowers. "Farook and Amberine are sworn to silence; he's the one who ordered everything and all the evidence will go back to his apartment later. Nazir, where's that champagne?"

They lifted their glasses. "To your success."

"To your um, health."

Creamed salmon with garlic and shallots in a puff pastry shell was followed by duck breasts with gorgonzola sauce. A date! She was on a date with a mega-wealthy sheikh. Or, as Heineken reminded her, just another guy.

"I want to know everything about you," he said, refilling her glass himself. "Where you're from, your family, how you ended up here, everything."

She broke down in tears repeatedly as she recounted her story, but he was patient, interested, shocked, amazed, and touched.

When the raspberry dacquoise was a fond memory, he led her to the couch and pulled up photos on his laptop. "Oh my God, she really was gorgeous, Saud. Gorgeous."

"Inside and out. She had a very kind heart and a great sense of humor."

"What's your favorite memory of her?"

"Hmm. Nothing particular, just the way we'd sit in the evening together and play Scrabble – she usually beat me – or the funny stories she'd tell me. She knew more jokes than anybody I ever met and one night had me laughing so hard I literally split my pants." His smile had a faraway look to it.

"Sometimes it's hard to figure out why God does certain things, but know this: when it's your turn to get to heaven she'll be right there to welcome you, escort you to Orientation, Adjustment, Aerobics..." He howled with laughter. "She's in a better place, Saud, remember that, and one day, you'll be together again."

"My brain knows that, but it hasn't yet made it all the way to my heart."

"Or somewhere else a little further south," she added. "Hey, something I've been meaning to ask you for the longest time."

"Shoot."

"Is everything in here burgundy and gold because you're a Red-skins fan?"

"Redskins? *Redskins?* Are you out of your *mind?* I'm a Cowboys fan, through and through. It's burgundy and gold because my mother designed it that way. I never even made the connection before. Oh, my, I'll have to fix that." He turned to his valet. "Nazir, clear everything away except the flowers, and then you take the night off. And if you breathe one word of this to anyone I will personally feed you to the crocodiles."

Nazir winked. "Good night, sir. Good night, mademoiselle."

Nothing happened that night, nor the next, nor the next. It was more than awkward. After months of sparring, here they were in the very place they'd been so determined to avoid. They sometimes snuggled, frequently dissolving into nervous giggles. Gradually, though, they made exploratory forays, and became less and less ill at ease. On the fourth night, he put his arm around her and drew her snugly against him. "Stay pressed against me like this. Don't move." After a few minutes, he chuckled. "Do you feel anything?"

"Hmm, it seems to be getting kind of crowded in here."

The erection didn't last long, but it was a breakthrough. And Sheikh Saud nearly wept with joy.

Heineken checked the special orders card. It was six weeks old, and had Saamia's name on it, but nobody ever really looked at them. He made his way to the Infirmary.

He found Ismail sorting the laundry. "Everything I have to do, and now they dump extra duty on me. Must think I'm made of reinforced concrete." Heineken waved the card.

"Huh? What are you doing here?"

Heineken made a face. "Mr. Mohammed strikes again. What can I say? So, what needs to be sterilized, and what just needs washing?"

They worked together for a few minutes. Almost time for the truck to arrive. Heineken finally inquired, "Aren't you going to the lounge? They say that new Korean is really great."

"Lounge? But I don't get off for two more hours."

Heineken shook his head. "How does Mr. Mohammed keep his job? Hey, it's okay. If you don't want to take the time off, I'll just go back to my regular stuff."

"Are you sure?"

"That's what they told me; I'm supposed to cover for you."

"How the hell I can I do my job when nobody ever tells me anything? The truck's going to be here any minute. Be sure to check the shipment; last time they forgot the surgical dressings and the IV bags. They promised they'd send them this time."

"Of course," said Heineken. "Anything else I should know?"

"Check and see if we're running low on bleach; if there are fewer than twenty liters we need to re-order. 'Bye now."

Heineken had a look around. Aha, an orderly's uniform. It fit, more or less. Some dirty *ghutar* were heaped up in a corner. He only needed one to cover his shaved head. It was wrinkled and smelly, but it'd do. And a surgical mask to cover the telltale beardless chin.

The door opened, and his heart stopped.

"You sign for this?" said the delivery man.

Whew. "You remembered the dressings and the IV bags this time?" The man nodded, and Heineken signed with a flourish. "Here, let me help you get this medical waste onto the truck."

They loaded it together, chatting amiably.

"Hey, my shift's over," said Heineken casually, "and my motor-cycle's in the shop. Can you give me a ride into town?"

"Sure, hop in," said the driver.

The guard waved the truck through. Nobody gave the passenger a second glance.

Next morning it was Guinness who took her down to Hygiene. "Where's Heineken?" she inquired.

122

"Nobody's sure," said the tall, dark-skinned Indian. "He didn't report to the dormitory last night. A bunch of people are being raked over the coals."

He'd done it! Yes! She wanted to jump for joy. And now he'd help her; it was just a question of time.

When she got to Hygiene Amstel smiled. "Big day today, huh?"

She was momentarily confused. How did he know about Sheikh Saud? No no, he couldn't possibly be referring to that. "What exactly do you mean?"

"I'm supposed to get you ready for your screen test. Come on, climb up. Today you get the works."

The euphoria dissolved and the ugly real world came roaring back in.

Dear old Amina took extra pains with her hair, all the while trying to distract her with funny stories. She told Tammy fondly about the old wooden house where the family used to live and the antics of the children when they were growing up, like the story about Sheikh Saud and his buddy Fulaan, who, at age eleven, somehow caught a wild badger, and brought it home in a box. They couldn't resist showing it off, of course, and it escaped into the house, where it stank the place up and terrified everybody for days until it finally got away.

Guinness appeared with another pink Special Orders card.

"Good luck," Amina said.

"Come on, Farida, they're waiting," said Guinness. "We're run-ning behind, as usual."

With concrete in her heart she struggled to keep up with her long-legged escort. He took her to the Garden Room, where Mr. Abdul was waiting with two photographers, one

123

tall and skinny, the other extremely obese. Lights, screens, and tripods were already in place. So were various accessories that she was tied to, knelt on, or stretched across in one obscene pose after another. They put her on a small trampoline and told her to jump up and down.

"Nothing's bouncing," Humpty Dumpty observed.

She thought there could be no further way to humiliate her when they bent her over a bar, strapped her wrists to her ankles, and pulled out an enormous phallus. "Be sure to get the look on her face," Jack Sprat said, and thrust it roughly into her behind. She gasped in pain, clutched at the air, struggling to maintain some semblance of composure. She saw ghosts of Fuad's face and almost came unglued. Video made, they took it out, but immediately put in another one of more normal size. Whew, she thought. But she'd celebrated too soon. Jack Sprat pressed a button on a remote control. She was sent reeling. Oh God! Again he pressed the button, and again she was thrown into the air. She writhed and struggled, trying to get rid of the diabolical con-traption. Electric shocks! Every time he pushed that goddam button it gave her another one.

"Now that's more like it," Humpty said, "ass flying all over the place. Intense movement, and one great-looking ass."

When they'd finally finished photographing each part of her body from multiple angles, they laid her on a table and painstakingly measured her in places she'd never imagined being measured.

"We'll show the footage to the boss and get back to you," they told Mr. Abdul.

All Tammy wanted to do was crawl under the sofa cushions and die.

A week later a very somber Mr. Abdul invited Tammy to sit down. He remained silent a long time before he spoke;

by the time he favored her with words she was a nervous wreck.

"They won't have you," he said finally. "No one is going to pay to look at tits the size of yours."

She waited, not knowing whether she should celebrate or disintegrate.

"There is only one solution, and that is to improve your figure. You unfortunately are not a good candidate for implants, but we know of a facility that does an excellent job without surgery. You will spend as long as it takes to reach the studio's standards before you will be transferred to the studio itself. You are dismissed."

"I flunked," she told Amberine at lunch. "The studio won't have me until I'm curvier. You ever heard of a place that can turn a parking lot into the Himalayas without implants?"

"Yes," she said, "I'm afraid so. Last year Sheikh Aziz wanted his attendant fixed up, so they sent her there. When she came back several months later she'd gone from a B to a D, but she was also practically insane. When we'd asked her what on earth they did, she'd mumble something about an electric bra, a suction pump, shots right into her nipples. We never got the whole story because she was so traumatized they finally had to get rid of her and as far as I know, nobody else has been sent there since."

"Angelo came," Abubakr told John, "and here's the score." He filled him in on the details Heineken had provided. "The problem is, she's kept under such close supervision and security that doing anything for the time being is virtually impossible. However, he's on the outside now, and he's learned that next week she's supposed to be transferred temporarily to another location" – he thought it kind not to mention where – "and we might have a shot during the transfer. We're keeping a close eye on things and will let you know."

"What's the matter, boss?" Tammy asked Sheikh Saud as he strode through the door and threw his keys onto the table.

"You think *I'm* mad at my father? Farook wants to kill him. He's decided to sell Amberine."

"What?"

"She recently turned 28. He let him keep her an extra three years, but now he's adamant about 'maintaining standards.' The son of a good friend is trying to replace Miss Green in his Rainbow Harem, and Dad has agreed to sell him Amberine. Sheikh Fahd is a little bit strange – make that a *lot* strange – but apparently it's a real nice place and the *jawareen* wear fancy gowns and jewelry and there's a pool and a garden, and they're treated very well. At least it's not a brothel like he'd been threatening, but as you can imagine, that's little consolation."

"When is this supposed to happen?"

"Sheikh Fahd's supposed to send for her next week, as soon as the payment arrives." He shook his head. "And there's more. I told him what you did, and how it worked, and asked him to cancel these stupid plans to send you to that boob ranch, but he says the paperwork is already done. I begged and pleaded, and he won't budge. Said if it had happened a few weeks ago, he might have considered it, but now, it's too late. You didn't take his threats seriously until you knew that they weren't joking, that you'd had months and months to act and you stubbornly refused."

He flopped down beside her on the sofa. "Biggest fight we've ever had, and we've had some beauts. There's Farook

126

hollering at him about Amberine, and I'm yelling at him about you, and he's barking at both of us. Farook storms out, storms back in, yells some more, and storms back out. I curse my father and leave. Honestly, I don't know what to do with the man. The older he is, the worse he gets." He looked at the intercom, which had suddenly started playing a religious chant. "What the–?"

The phone rang. He answered, nodded somberly, and dropped the receiver back onto its cradle. "He just keeled over and died," he said in a trembling voice, "while he was screaming at Farook."

"I'm so sorry, Saud, so sorry. I know he drove you nuts, but in spite of everything, he was your father."

"And the last words I spoke to him were curses," he said, holding his head in his hand. "I cursed my father, and those were the last words he heard from me. *Ya Allah!* May peace and blessing be upon him."

The phone rang again. "Okay, sure, I'll be right over." He jumped up. "Farook," he explained, "I'll be back later."

Hours later, he finally returned. He clasped her in his arms as if he were holding onto his last shreds of sanity and, to the sound of religious chants, eventually drifted off to sleep.

The house was draped in white and the public address system played nonstop religious music. All regular activities were cancelled; domestics were confined to quarters except for meals. Of course, everyone was speculating wildly on what was going to happen now that Sheikh Farook was in charge.

Guinness was optimistic. "People are saying that he'll let most of us go. Mr. Ali wants Mardya, and Mr. Abdul wants the Korean. If most of the *jawareen* are released, they won't need eunuchs."

The Korean disappeared.

"Mr. Abdul took her as his third wife," Guinness assured Tammy.

"Mr. Abdul is keeping her in a residential room at a brothel," Kronenbourg said.

"Mr. Abdul is keeping her in an isolation room at a boarding hotel," said Red Stripe. "He'll be the only person she lays eyes on for the rest of her life."

Mr. Abdul himself said nothing, of course.

Amberine disappeared.

Sold to Sheikh Fahd as planned, some said. Others were certain that she'd been flown back to America. Tammy secretly hoped that Farook had finally married her, but there was no way to know for sure.

Laamia and Saamia also disappeared, but this time, there was agreement that they'd been given as a birthday present to Saud's friend Prince Fulaan.

"The plans for you are on hold," Saud told her, "at least until Farook can get stuff figured out. He has a lot on his plate right now."

"He seems quite liberal. Do you think he'll let some of us go?"

"Liberal? Did you say *liberal?*" He threw back his head and howled. "Well, when you compare him with Dad, he's a wild liberal indeed, but... On a scale of one to ten, Dad was a minus six. Farook's probably a four. On second thought, more like a three-point-five."

"What are you?"

"Hmpf, never really thought about it. Probably something like a five-point-five, maybe a six."

Two weeks after the funeral, Sheikh Farook called a meeting of all the remaining domestics. They filed into the House theater, nervous and excited. The flame of hope burned brightly.

First he made a short but touching speech about his late father. Then he got down to business. "Several announcements," he said, eyes dancing. "First, no more weekly enemas."

They cheered.

"Instead they'll be daily," he joked. When they booed he feigned surprise. "Oh? Well, then, if you insist..." They all got a good laugh, something they never dreamed of doing around Sheikh Ahmed.

"Second, I want you all to know that I have relieved Mr. Moham-med of his duties, effective immediately."

More cheers.

"Third, I have replaced the Rule Book by this." He held up a single sheet of paper, and the assembly gave him a standing ovation.

Hmm, thought Tammy, if we still have rules, we still have domestics. But Farook hadn't finished.

"It is most unusual to do this so soon after I buried my father, but these are most unusual circumstances. May I please present to you my bride of two days, Lady Amberine."

She appeared from behind a curtain, wearing an emerald green *suit* and high-heeled snakeskin *shoes*. They cheered until they were hoarse. For her part Amberine stood next to her husband, tears of joy streaming down her cheeks. It had happened. It had actually happened.

"Please join us in the garden for refreshments."

Honey-drenched cakes, and soft drinks, and chocolate-covered strawberries, and platters piled high with apricots and dates.

She'd moved into Sheikha Ayissa's old apartment in the House and had drivers and cars at her disposal. "Hang onto hope," she told Tammy with a big hug. "See? The fairy tale came true."

Farook hadn't finished surprising everybody, though. Less than a week after the little reception, Tammy was amazed to see a new 15-year-old Norwegian, wearing the green-bordered uniform that Amberine used to wear. *What?* She was beginning to understand why Saud had laughed when she'd said he was liberal.

Next morning after breakfast she was escorted in to Mr. Abdul's white-draped office and was invited to sit down.

"As you know, we are making some alterations in our domestic staff assignments," he said cheerily. "I am very pleased to announce that, because of your diligence and devotion, and due to eloquent interventions on your behalf by Sheikh Saud, we have cancelled arrangements for the enhancement of your appearance and the contract with the studio."

He'd done it, bless his heart. He'd–

"Instead, you will become the new Miss Green in the Rainbow Harem of Sheikh Fahd. The limo will be here in twenty minutes. You are dismissed."

PART FOUR

THE RAINBOW

August 2006 – September 2007
Shaban 1427 – Ramadan 1428

Tammy was loaded into a silver double-stretch limo. Well, she told herself with a heavy sigh, if the new place turned out to be anything at all like Saud had described, it'd be a hell of a lot better than wearing electric bras and having dildos stuck up your rear. She'd had such high hopes, but here she was on her way to be a toy for another sheikh.

She didn't have much time to pout, since it was only a ten-minute ride from the House to Sheikh Fahd's enormous walled estate. She was swiftly and efficiently processed by the pleasant major-domo, who turned her over to a bare-chested bejeweled eunuch named Delta. Straight out of a movie set, she chuckled to herself. He accompanied her through a long underground passageway to the Rainbow Harem.

A beaming middle-aged matron was waiting for her. "Welcome, dear, I'm so glad you've arrived. We'll be having lunch soon, but would you like some juice, perhaps? Or some *gawaha?* Oh, palpitations, where have I put your papers? You're American, I believe? That's very nice. You're quite beautiful and I'm sure you'll make a perfectly lovely Miss Green."

Tammy followed her through clouds of perfume and billowing scarves across a sunlit tiled lounge walled on three sides, overlooking a flower garden bursting with fragrant roses. She showed her to a perfectly stunning large green room. "This is where you'll be staying. No air conditioning today, but it's quite pleasant, don't you think, Miss Green? Why don't you get out of that hot *abaaya* and freshen up, and

I'll send Maryam for you when it's time to eat. In fact, dear, why don't you put on one of these?" She flung open a carved armoire stuffed with formal gowns that looked like a rack at Lord and Taylor, except for the fact that every last one of them was green.

How could she possibly choose? Silks, brocades, velvets, satins, taffetas. After standing transfixed for the longest time she finally just closed her eyes and grabbed. What she had in her hand was an apple-green satin ball gown with appliquéd yellow roses and yellow insets in Snow White-style sleeves. She ripped off her plain homespun traveling dress and let the smooth cloth glide over her. Sleek. Sensuous. Sophis-ticated. She twirled round and round, exulting in the luxury. No boring uniform. Real clothes! Gorgeous clothes!

Everything else in the room thrilled her too. On the dressing-table were French cosmetics and perfumes. Hers! She finally decided to drench herself in Chloé to match the roses; later she could put on the Madame Rochas or the Joy. Space! Luxury! A real double bed! Sunlight! God, she breathed, thank you. If I'm going to be stuck in a stupid harem, I'm glad it's a nice one.

Shortly there was a soft knock on the door. "Miss Green?"

The Rainbow Harem was filled with miracles; the door didn't even have a lock on it! She made a ceremony of opening a door herself for the first time in more than a year.

A smiling Somali was on the other side. *"Ahlan wa-sahlan,"* she said, Welcome welcome.

"As-salaamu aleikum. Peace be upon you. Do come in."

"Aleikum salaam. No thank you, it is not allowed, but peace be also upon you. I am Maryam, and I have come to show you to the dining room. The Rainbow is anxious to

133

meet you. Oh, Miss Green, no jewels? You must wear a complete *parure,* it is the rule."

The rule? To wear *jewelry?* Sheikh Ahmed would have a heart attack for sure! In a corner she found a chest overflowing with exquisite pieces in little velvet cases. She chose a set of emerald-cut citrines, which met with Maryam's enthusiastic approval.

"I couldn't find any shoes," she told Maryam apologetically. "I feel funny, all dressed up like this, and barefoot."

"The silversmith will soon fit you with ornaments for your feet."

Oh. Well, there had to be *something* wrong with the place.

She followed Maryam to the dining room, which faced the right side of the lounge. Sayida, the matron, was waiting at the door.

"Oh, here she is, Rainbow, our new Miss Green!"

There were nods and pleasant murmurs. Her eyes darted from one richly-gowned young woman to another, each one in a different color, struck by the beauty of the idea, dazzled by the quality of the clothes.

Then she really saw them. The girl in the lavender dress had purple hair. The one wearing peacock had blue hair. The one in orange had orange hair... A purple hand waved a friendly greeting. A red hand reached for the bread.

"Sit down, dear. Oh, isn't it nice to have a Miss Green again, Rainbow? She's originally from – oh, now what did you say? Austria, is it? Do sit down. Your place is there between Miss Blue and Miss Yellow."

"America," she supplied, still trying to absorb the scene.

"Ah. The land of round doorknobs," commented Miss Purple, in English.

Tammy stumbled over and took her place before a green plate, having difficulty keeping her balance. A bright blue hand and wrist dripping with diamonds and aquamarines reached up to steady her.

"What's the matter?" asked Miss Purple with traces of New York in her voice. "Haven't you ever seen colored people before?"

She gawked. Purple hands, purple feet. "They dye us every couple of months. It doesn't hurt," Miss Purple added quickly, "and it will be months before the chemicals destroy your nervous system. Here. Have some chicken with red olives. It's excellent. My name is Fritzi, but you can call me Moby Grape if you like."

Tammy couldn't remember if she ate anything or not.

Next morning it took Sayida only fifteen minutes to explain every last one of the rules to her and show her all around. "You'll like Sheikh Fahd. He's young and fun-loving, as you will see."

Saud had called him "a lot strange," and she was beginning to understand why.

There were no required prayers. No tiresome adjustment classes. The *jawareen* could keep their own names, their own faiths. Tammy immediately deconverted, unaware at the time that renouncing Islam was a crime punishable by death. Nobody cared.

"Go wherever you like, dear. Do whatever you please." Only one problem: there was nowhere to go and nothing to do. Tammy ate and bathed and dressed and freshened her perfume every three hours as required and wore the requisite pieces of jewelry.

But the walls were twelve feet high and the access doors, carefully guarded by suspicious eunuchs, led deeper into the complex. Within a few days she was wandering aimlessly around the garden, claustrophobia already setting clammy hands upon her. Colorful birds sang in the branches of fig, apricot, lemon and orange trees – and flew brazenly over the wall. Clouds, pompous and vain, lingered mockingly over the garden – and traveled on. Even the scorpions threw supercilious looks at her before disappearing over the wall.

"We've located Bulbul," Abubakr told John, "thanks to Angelo and his amazing contacts. She's in what is reputed to be the most beautiful harem in the entire area, the Rainbow, with incredible gardens and pools floating with flower petals, considerable freedom of movement, and, I'm sure you'll be happy to know, one of the finest private libraries in the entire Middle East. The ladies wear designer ball gowns and fabulous jewels all day long. It's really nice. She's Miss Green, so she wears green gowns and green jewels." He sort of forgot to mention anything else.

"Well, could be a lot worse, a lot worse. Do we know anything about um, about, the man?"

"A little strange but pretty much hands-off. She's reasonably well off, which is a good thing, because security is extremely tight. Short of a commando operation, there's little chance, realistically, that we can do much. Angelo used to work with one of the eunuchs there, so we can keep an eye on things. Just remember. She's alive, she's healthy, she's in a beautiful place, and she has tons of books to read. I know it's not the news you wanted to hear, but all in all, pretty positive."

John sighed. "Her mother is in the hospital. Again. Maybe this news will help, I'm not sure. All she wants is her daughter back. Thanks, Chopsticks, for all your help. I know you're trying very hard."

"You're one of the rare fathers who knows exactly where she is and how she's doing. Most of the time they just plain vanish and no-body ever knows anything."

"Sometimes I think I'd rather not know. But then I realize how grateful I am–" here his voice broke – "that she's alive. And somehow, I know in my heart that in spite of everything, she still finds a way to laugh."

Less than a week after her arrival she found Fritzi in the lounge. "So, how do you like this place?" Fritzi asked.

Tammy shot her a scathing look. "It's perverse. Perverse. Tell me about Sheikh Fahd."

"He's what they call a private collector of specialty livestock. This is just one of his eight *hareem*. The one he's building now is for his collection of genuine Italian nuns. We hardly ever see him, and when we do, we're just decorations. I used to think that if you were a harem slave you were a sex object, but no, you're actually just an object. Being a sex object would be a major step up. Anyway, he's totally fixated on a tall redhead. Don't worry about kinky sex; I haven't had any sex here at all."

Tammy wasn't having an easy time wrapping her mind around all this.

About a month later, it was time for Tammy to participate in the dye cycle.

"We who are about to dye salute you," said Fritzi.

Elli spent most of the time coughing. Margot vomited all over the tank cover; it was flecked with red glitter and blood. After a 14-step process of precisely timed conditioning, dyeing, setting, redyeing and fixing, Tammy became kelly green from the neck down. Then the *halaakh,* or hairdresser, cut off half her hair, dyed it to match the rest of her, and styled it like the others, full on top and softly curled on the sides. When she got back to her room and saw herself in the dressing-table mirror she fought down nausea. With green hands she put her green nightdress over her green skin and slid between green sheets. Dear God, she prayed, help me get through this; I'll never, ever make it on my own.

Kermit, she discovered, knew exactly what he was talking about; it's *not* easy being green. It took weeks for her not to gasp every time she'd catch a glimpse of her own green legs – even if she were face to face with a girl who was vivid orange. Fritzi had been correct that the process wasn't the least bit painful – at least not while she was in the dye tub. "Oh yes, but give those chemicals time," Fritzi said cheerfully. "The traces of aniline gradually change hemoglobin to methemoglobin, and this interferes with how oxygen gets to your central nervous sys-tem. In a few weeks or months you'll feel depressed. Then you'll feel tired all the time. Then you'll start getting dizzy spells. Then–"

"Oh shut up!" Tammy snapped.

A startled Fritzi tipped her head to one side, perhaps to evaluate Tammy's intelligence, or, as Cleo used to do, size up how much she could get away with. "Oh, and a little bit of trivia, here, just to improve your morale. The dye tanks are actually the same big glass pots that they use at the Rodeo when they boil people to death."

"*Boil* people? Oh my God. I'm sorry, Fritzi, I really am. I'm having a hard time getting used to all this." She hadn't heard from her demons for a while, but now they were having a heyday. *Look at you. You're green. Bet even your blood is green.*

The Rainbow Harem was indeed the loveliest of prisons. The airy tiled lounge was graced with big tubs of flowering plants, an enormous skylight, and fat tasseled floor cushions atop thick oriental carpets begging for relaxation. The fourth

138

wall was composed of open arches beside the large walled garden, at the far end of which was a bathing pool of perfumed water strewn with multicolored flower petals. The arched portico continued down the garden wall where *chaises longues* offered places to enjoy the garden from the shade. In the middle of the garden was a multi-level fountain where water splashed from basin to basin, each tiled in a different Rainbow color.

"I know you feel strange at first, dear," Sayida said, "but green is a lovely color on you."

Fritzi, who'd been in the harem the longest, three years, appointed herself Tammy's hostess, showing her the ropes, explaining pro-cedures, giving her advice.

"How'd you land here?" Tammy wanted to know.

"My father's a cellist," she said, "and my mother's appointed purpose in life is to lose five more pounds. I grew up in New York, Berlin and Milan, mostly, wherever Papa could get a job, but I have – I mean I had – an American passport. Papa wanted me to study music, and Mother wanted me to do languages, but I always had my heart set on chemistry. I was in my second year at Columbia when I answered an ad for a Nordic-type ski instructor, hoping to make some extra money during winter break. You can fill in the blanks."

Miss Orange was a Dane named Elli, not quite 18, who'd been in the harem for five or six months; previously, she'd spent almost two years as one of 21 devocalized blondes belonging to a prince. Whenever he had a guest he wanted to honor, he'd place the entire harem at his disposal, which he referred to as the "21-blonde salute." Tammy instinctively liked her, but conversations with her were an adventure. Since Elli had only a smattering of English and had never learned to write in Arabic, she did her best to laboriously reproduce the sounds in one language or the other according to Danish spellings. Sometimes it took all their combined ingenuity to figure out what she meant, while Elli wept in frustration. Tammy naively thought that Miss Red, another Dane, would be willing to translate for her, but they'd quarreled months before and this courtesy was out of the question except when Sayida ordered it.

"How," she asked Fritzi, "do you stay so cheerful with nothing to do? I know I ought to appreciate the relaxed pace here – it's like a vacation – but another week like this and I'll be a basket case."

"You could continually argue over carom like Smurfie and Redbreast," Fritzi suggested, "or maybe cough all day and play solitaire like Agent Orange." She made a face. "Personally, I spend my time thinking up ways to poison Sheikh Fahd," she said nonchalantly. "Did you know, for instance, that roasted apricot pits can be turned into a lethal poison? There's mandrake growing near the fountain, too."

The flip tone of voice Fritzi used made Tammy nervous. "Fritzi, do you know what they do to people who even *attempt* murdering an Arab?"

"Sure. Sometimes they're beheaded, sometimes they're sewn into a bag and drowned, or there's that snuff club called the Rodeo where they're whipped to a pulp and then fed to crocodiles or roasted alive. I know."

"But how can you even *think*, I mean–"

"I'm not going to get caught. I've had a thousand ideas I haven't used because they weren't absolutely perfect. I've been planning this for more than a year."

"And what happens even if you succeed? Sheikh Fahd has sons who might be even weirder, or maybe they'll dump us somewhere worse. Look, Fritzi, I know exactly how you feel; there's a miscreant out there I'd dearly love to kill myself. But it's so hard, they take so many precautions, and it's so risky. Do be careful."

140

"Listen, Tammy, Fahd's killing us one layer of skin at a time. I'm going to get him before he finishes getting me, that's all. And I won't get caught. Trust me." She fingered a book she'd been carrying around on applied chemistry.

"Just where did you get that book?"

"His library. He has gobs of books."

Library? Tammy couldn't get to Sayida fast enough.

"Oh, did I forget to mention that, dear? On *al-ithnain*, Monday, if you like I can give you a pass during women's hours."

She waited the three days like a four-year-old before Christmas. Gamma, a dour black eunuch with skin-tight red pants and a chirping voice, inspected her pass, nodded gravely, and guided her through the underground hallways. She was checked and re-checked at several points along the way, but oh, was the destination ever worth the trouble! The six-room library was bursting with books in Arabic, English, French, and German. She was allowed to stay for three hours, reading just about anything she chose, and then select up to ten books, which she submitted for approval to the elderly eunuch Lamda, who sent them over later.

Books! She wanted to bury herself in their words, press herself between their covers. Books! She leapt over the walls. Walked the streets of long-forgotten cities. Laughed herself silly. Dreamed. Stayed sane. Tammy read classified ads in two-week-old newspapers as if her life depended on knowing the price of used cars. Reviews of *The Departed* as if she could get front-row seats. Laughed when Pluto was demoted from full-fledged planet to dwarf. It was reassuring to know that the world was still there. She was determined that when the time came, she'd be ready to rejoin it.

One day Tammy and Fritzi were at the fountain, trailing their fingers in the water. Tammy finally got up the nerve to ask what had happened to the previous Miss Green.

"Drowned herself. Cute girl. I hardly knew her, though. Nor-wegian, sixteen. She'd only been here a couple of months."

Maryam interrupted them. "Miss Green, Sheikh Fahd wishes to see you." Maryam took her to a small rich salon where Sheikh Fahd was laughing with Sayida, drinking cup after cup of *gawaha*, and polishing off a huge box of chocolate cordials. He was engagingly ugly: short, dumpy, nut-brown, mustachioed, with a huge nose, heavy brows, and a goatee showing signs of gray. He was younger than she'd expected, probably in his early forties. She curtsied nervously.

He gave her a grin and held out his hand. "No, no, don't be afraid, my little one, come over here." She got within a few feet of him and he motioned for her to sit on a blue and gold paisley cushion nearby. "Let me guess," he said, stroking his moustache, "might you possibly be the new Miss Green?" He roared with laughter.

Sayida shot her a martyred look, but Tammy didn't mind; he was no worse than Fritzi, who punned shamelessly in four languages. She chuckled.

"That's right, my little one, I like smiling faces." He sank back in the sofa and watched while Sayida refilled his cup. "I just wanted to meet you, Miss Green, and welcome you personally into my household. Have a chocolate. Please. How do you pass the time?"

"I was delighted to discover your wonderful library, sir."

"It is intended for your enjoyment. What are you reading?"

"*Desperation* by Stephen King, sir. And *National Geographic* since 1951. You have an amazing collection of books on international development. And every last newspaper I can get my hands on."

He laughed approvingly. "Now. Tell me honestly, my little one, how do you like being part of my beautiful Rainbow?"

He demanded honesty, he got honesty. "Really peculiar, sir. In fact, I feel like a Martian."

To her relief he threw back his head and roared. "You'll get used to it in time, and I must say, you look absolutely stunning." She was in an emerald green gown with a velvet bodice and full satin skirt. Her necklace, earrings, bracelets and rings were teardrop emeralds set in antique silver. "There's another ring that goes with that set, as I recall. Next time make certain that you wear it."

"Yes sir."

"Return to your book. And again, welcome."

"Thank you most kindly, sir." She curtsied and raced to find Fritzi. "He didn't seem so bad."

"Oh, he's positively charming. If I saw him on the street and had no idea he owned 74 women, I'd probably like him a lot. His daughter must be doing okay if he was in such a good mood. She's been fighting leukemia for the past three years and she's barely ten. He dotes on her. Whenever she takes a turn for the worse he gets depressed and builds himself another harem." Tammy's confusion must have been evident. Fritzi let loose a sarcastic laugh. "The Rainbow was his first one, and the least bizarre, if you can believe that. And I think that the only girl he ever sleeps with is a six-foot-two redhead, who's kept in the Blue Harem all by herself. She's Danish, absolutely magnificent, and is positively crazy about him too."

"Where are all the others?"

"The Garden of Prosperity is where he keeps eight girls in cages and fattens them to grotesque proportions. When

143

they finally get too big for the cage he sells them to a brothel that specializes in the obese. Another is for his collection of fifteen Asians under one meter fifty – that's about four-ten – he calls it the Nursery and dresses them in diapers and they can only eat or drink by sucking pacifiers shaped like dicks. The Zoo is for fourteen tall, buxom girls that he tattoos with animal designs; you know, one is a zebra, another a leopard. They don't wear anything else.

"Oh yes, and then there's Poseidon's Realm where, for twelve hours a day, all eight girls are dressed like mermaids with spandex fish tails, pearlized torsos and arms, and they have to keep particular poses in this elaborate set he had built that looks like the bottom of the sea. Let's see, and now he's building the Order of Saint Fellatio, where he keeps his Italian nuns; he only has three right now but has orders in for another nine. I'm missing one. Oh, yes, Bookoo Bazoula, which is slang for big tits. He takes already extremely well endowed girls and sends them for implants. Then recently he has them wearing special bras that produce electric impulses and makes the tits get even bigger. Some of them have honkers so big they can hardly walk. How's that for you. Glad to be in the Rainbow?" She shook her head. "And to think most people are perfectly satisfied collecting *stamps.*"

Tammy felt dizzy and returned to her room. Its splendor did little to cheer her. About twenty feet by twelve, it had lattice-covered clerestory windows set close to the high ceiling. The walls were tiled in a green ivy pattern, the built-in sofa was upholstered in green satin, and the bedspread was dark green velvet. A green and ivory Chinese rug with carved flowers softened the floor. Lattice-covered windows over-looked the lounge, and provided not only cross-ventilation when the air conditioning wasn't on, but also some natural light.

"Tonight is film night," Sayida reminded them during her announcements at dinner. "Tonight, *Carousel.*" Most of them were Shir-ley Temple or Nelson Eddie classics or musicals from the 60's, but they did help pass the time, and reminded Tammy of how she spent happy evenings with her grandmother.

There were few other scheduled activities, so Tammy would get up early while it was still relatively cool and sit near the fountain and read. By mid-morning Maryam would have set out platters of bread and fruit and a samovar of strong tea, and they could help themselves whenever they felt like it. After a dip in the flower-petal bath, a *lawingi,* or bath attendant, would rub her down with fragrant oils, she'd select her gown and jewels for the day, and find a shady spot where she could read. And read. And read.

Often, she'd be so absorbed she wouldn't be aware of the dining room bell, and Maryam would have to come fetch her. No leftovers here! And nobody cared if she decided to treat herself to an extra piece of baklava or turn up her nose at the turnips.

For supper they were on their own. They could reheat anything left over from lunch, or make a meal of yogurt and bread and hummus or eggplant dip. There was no prescribed diet; nevertheless, the colors were under the strictest obligation to maintain their weight between 55 and 60 kilos (about 120-130 pounds). They were all very close to the same height and were all small-boned and small-breasted, which, as Fritzi pointed out, made clothes purchasing a very simple matter.

At the end of her first month, she weighed in more than a kilo low. Sayida gave her a gentle lecture. At the end of Ramadan, despite making a conscious effort to take extra helpings and eat regular snacks, she'd only gained 200 grams, so Sayida took a drastic measure: she withheld Tammy's library pass for an entire week and threatened that she'd suspend it for the whole month every time she weighed in low. This struck such terror in her heart that she gorged herself on avocados and pistachios and managed, by the end of Shawwal, to get back within the authorized range.

145

On the other hand, Fritzi said all she had to do to gain weight was to wave at a piece of baklava, and at Shawwal she came in at 1750 grams over. The worst punishment Sayida could think up for her was to veil her, which in Rainbow terms meant, being forbidden to talk and be spoken to. It was also terribly trying for Tammy, because during the exact same week she lost her library pass neither could she converse with her only friend.

Fritzi was already on the second level of probation, and being veiled put her perilously close to the third and final level, after which she'd be sold. "Just two weeks after I'd been dumped here Sheikh Fahd came to the harem to visit, and I didn't know he could understand English. There was a Canadian here then, Miss Blue – that was a couple months before the aniline killed her – so I said Oh look, here comes the pot belly at the end of the rainbow. He didn't think it was very funny, and so right off the bat, I was on level one."

Usually, Tammy could count on Fritzi to cheer her up, but every now and then Fritzi had a bad day herself.

"Today is November 30th, my birthday. Papa always wrote a special piece for me. I know he's still doing it. He had such dreams for me, and if he knew I was dyed goddam purple and locked away in a goddam harem he'd crawl off in a hole somewhere and let himself die."

"Gisela says within a year or two you're going to be free, don't forget," Tammy said.

"Oh right," Fritzi shot back, "and those coffee grounds of hers say you'll end up with a handsome prince. You believe that nonsense? Sometimes I don't even know why I should bother murdering him. You know, it's been several months since I've noticed a lump in my breast. But no, they won't even have it examined, because it might be malignant, and that might mean surgery, which would spoil my *looks.*" She was shaking with rage. "And get this; things used to be worse. The dye-master changed the formula because the girls were dying like flies. They use mostly soy dyes now with just a few chemicals to add intensity – believe me, I've checked. We're also damn lucky that the dye-master put his foot down when Mr. Fahd said he wanted fluorescent colors. But mark my words, I'm going to kill the man. I am absolutely positively going to kill him."

Tammy decided it was hardly the moment to announce that her urine had turned black.

Before she knew it, it was time to freshen the colors. This time, Gisela refused. Sayida begged her, pleaded with her. Threatened her. Gisela wouldn't budge.

Omicron, Lamda, and Theta dragged her to the pavilion, stuffed her into the vat, and bolted the lid down. She cursed them, cursed Sheikh Fahd, cursed Sayida, cursed the entire Arab world.

"One more peep out of you and I'll have you devocalized," said Sayida, "and I mean it."

As soon as the process was complete – with the eunuchs transferring Gisela from recipient to recipient as needed – they dragged her to the fountain. Omicron and Theta held her down, and Lamda gave her fifty strokes. Her screams reverberated through the entire harem. When it was finally over they left her lying on the patio in a heap, sobbing miserably. She remained thus for more than two days, until Sayida had her transferred to the infirmary, then to solitary confinement in the Black Room. She returned to the harem three weeks later, much subdued.

One morning Tammy had gotten up much later than usual with a sour stomach and an overwhelming sense of futility. If it'd been up to her, she'd have slipped into some sweat pants and a tee-shirt, but instead she dressed in a green-and-gold Shakespearean dress, peridot and diamond jewels, and Chanel No. 5. She intensely hated the Rainbow Harem that morning.

"You're looking a bit green around the gills today," Fritzi started in as Tammy dragged herself to the *chaise longue*.

"Oh, shut up."

"We're getting testy, too, aren't we? Your eyes are bloodshot, and your nose is red. Capillaries are hemorrhaging. Wow, and they've only dyed you twice."

Omicron, the elderly gardener, rolled his wheelbarrow to a flower bed and began setting in pansies. "You ought to go help Omi, you know? Of all the people I know you have by far the greenest thumb."

Tammy groaned, but the silly pun did make her smile.

"Jealous that you can't pun like me? Look at you, positively green with envy."

This time Tammy shook her finger at her.

Tammy had been Miss Green for more than five months and, except for the day that he'd welcomed her, had not laid eyes on Sheikh Fahd. So it came as quite a surprise when Sayida rang the gong. "Everybody to the studio! Quickly!"

"But it's movie night," whined Margot.

Tammy didn't much care for the way Miss Red flounced around, but Fritzi told her not to be too hard on her; after eleven years in *hareem,* maybe she had the right to be temperamental. At sixteen she'd eloped with a Russian sailor, who immediately sold her. She subse-quently spent nine years as one of more than 40 women in the harem of an "obese, smelly, utterly revolting" sheikh whose great pleasure was lining them up and urinating on them.

Sigma put sticky color-coordinated make-up on their faces and necks and Zeta stuck colored glitter to it.

"Ready, Rainbow? You look beautiful. Come along, now, dears, you know how he gets if we're late."

They waited in an anteroom, like so many Easter eggs, for the buzzer. After about forty-five minutes, it sounded three times. He had changed his mind.

They all trooped back to the salon. "The goddam bastard," Fritzi said, angrily swiping off her make-up. "It's going to take days and goddam days to get the goddam glitter off, and meanwhile you can forget about getting any goddam sleep."

Tammy cleared her throat. "Why, just look at you, Fritzi, you're purple with rage."

"Touché," she said with a chuckle.

Fritzi was right about the glitter, though. It got in their mouths, their ears, they breathed it up their noses and sneezed glitter for days.

Paula, Miss Yellow, fainted three times in one day.

"A year ago she was vivacious and fun," Fritzi said, "Now look at her. Between cadmium messing up her liver and captivity messing up her mind, she's not long for this world, believe me."

In a few days the glitter more or less wore off. Redbreast went back to loudly accusing Smurfie of cheating at carom, Yellow-Belly stared into space, Agent Orange played solitaire, Tammy read, and Moby Grape resumed plotting the murder.

"I'll hold him down and you pelt him with puns," Tammy offered. "He'll never stand a chance."

"Hmm, that would be the punnacle of my career."

"Oh gawd," said Tammy, making a quick dash for the lounge.

"It would cause pundemonium! And the punalties would be terrible!"

Next morning Tammy awoke later than usual, so it was already hot when she started across the courtyard toward the fountain. She felt her book slide from her hand. The garden swam before her eyes.

When her eyelids fluttered open Gisela was crouching beside her. "Maryam, bring her some lemon-water, and a cooled Turkish towel for her forehead."

"The heat," Maryam said, "the heat."

Fritzi arrived on the scene. "Of course. The heat. Of course."

Early one morning, Sheikh Fahd appeared unannounced and made a beeline for Tammy's chaise. She quickly set her book aside and rose to curtsy. She stood up too fast, in fact, and had to fight off another dizzy spell.

He waved off the formality. *"Sabah al-khayr."* Morning of abundance. He took a seat on the blue *chaise* next to hers. "You're the only one up, my little Martian?" Maryam raced over with tea and he began stirring it round and round.

"Sabah al-noor," morning of light, she responded.

"I wanted some company, so I thought I'd come bother you. Do you mind, Miss Green?"

"Of course not, sir. By the way, my name is Tammy. Tamara, actually."

"Nice name," he said, still absent-mindedly stirring his tea. "Tamara? Isn't that some kind of Italian spice?"

"My parents told me that Tamar was a daughter of King David, and that in Hebrew it means palm tree. A symbol of life."

"In Arabic tamar means a soft ripe date, sweet and ready to eat. Like you." He smiled at her in a way that made her nervous. Quick, time to change the subject.

"Tell me about yourself, sir."

"Huh?" He was taken aback. "I do believe you are the first girl to ever ask me that. What do you want to know?"

"I don't know, just you, sir. What kind of work you do, things like that. Your library covers such a wide range of interests that you must be a really fascinating person."

"What are you reading today, Tamara?" He looked through the books she had lying next to her. "*Case Studies in Psychological Disorders, Mayan Peoples of the Yucatan,* and *Easy Magic Tricks and Special Effects.* Oh, I haven't seen that book since I was a teenager. What's that one you're reading?"

"A study by the OECD on rural development projects in Sub-Saharan Africa, sir. I notice that you have a ton, a ton of books on this subject. I think I've read just about every last one."

"Really? I used to work for our foreign assistance program."

They chatted for nearly an hour. She learned that his father had sold fine jewelry, which explained his interest on that score, and that he grew up wanting to be the next Elvis. He regaled her with stories of when he was a horticulture student in Germany, how he fell in love with a Congolese poultry specialist named Yvette, and how she'd introduced

151

him to a fascinating part of the world that he knew little about. And the conversation came full circle.

"So that's how I got involved with rural development projects; horticulture is often a big part of them. But rural society can be extremely risk-averse, and, as a colleague of mine used to say, 'change-proof.' There was one project in the uplands of Guinea that we always use as an example of what not to do. There, men do the plowing and women do the cultivating. So the project introduced traction animals, that is to say, horses pulling the plow instead of a guy on his own. Result: the men plowed more than three times as much land as before, but the women were already working 18-hour days and had no way to cultivate three times as much land. But the men expected them to. So the women got mad at the men. Then, the project decided to teach the women how to make soap and grow onions so they could have some income for themselves. This infuriated the men, who felt that they were losing control. So all in all, the very best of intentions, but everybody was mad at everybody."

They laughed. He gulped the last of his cold tea, and rose.

"Sir? May I ask, how is your little girl?"

He didn't look up. "Six sons I have, and one daughter. The sunlight of my life. Sometimes the will of God is hard to understand. The doctor gives her six weeks to two months."

"I'm very sorry, sir, I know it must be extremely painful for you. My mother used to have a sign over her desk, Don't pray for an easy life. Pray to be a strong person."

"Good advice, coming from a Martian. Thanks, Tamara. Inter-esting conversation. Keep reading, and see you around."

Just a guy, as Heineken would say. A guy with a suffering heart. She found it impossible to hate him.

In Zul-hijjah, right after the 'Id al-Kabir celebrating Abraham's willingness to sacrifice his son (except Muslims believe it was Ishmael, the first-born son, and not Isaac, the first-born legitimate son, whom God demanded); Sheikh Fahd appeared in the harem with a huge crate.

"Come, my little ones, gather round. See, I have brought you gifts."

As the women exclaimed over the fairy-tale dresses, Gisela, as if on cue, went into seizure. She was barely over it when Elli had a colossal fit of coughing. Sheikh Fahd was offended, as if they'd gone out of their way to be rude.

"The dye still has very unhealthful effects," Sayida said gently, much bolder than Tammy had imagined. "I am sure your dye-master can continue his excellent experiments so your Rainbow can be beautiful and stay healthy too."

He laughed indulgently. "Don't be silly, old lady. These are the new formulas; none of the colors has died for more than a year. Female nerves are very fragile. They were just overcome by the excitement of my visit. Here, chocolates flown in from Belgium. Aren't they won-derful?"

Chocolate! How many months had it been? Chocolate! Tammy made a pig of herself. She didn't care one bit that the others were looking at her reproachfully.

When Tammy told Fritzi about the sheikh's daughter, Fritzi fell silent.

"Something wrong? It's been fifteen minutes since you told a joke."

"No, just feeling a bit punsive. I've got to do something. Fast."

"You've been saying that ever since I've been here."

"I've been saying that for years. But the moment has to be just right. I'm not anxious to be ripped apart by hyenas at the Rodeo, you know."

In the year 1428, the day of the Feast of Ashoura, Paula suffocated herself. Maryam found her with a pillow over her face held in place by a bed leg. Her body was removed quickly and without acknowl-edgment. Sayida never mentioned the incident.

"I never had the guts to do that," Tammy told Fritzi. "There's something stubborn in me that makes me want to live despite every-thing."

"I tried to hang myself once," Fritzi said. "The sheet didn't hold my weight, and I fell into the dressing-table, and perfume bottles went flying everywhere, and I sprained my ankle. Attempting suicide is considered attempted escape, so they beat the soles of my feet. That's when I decided to murder him."

Several weeks later a seventeen-year-old French girl named Martine became the new Miss Yellow. She was dyed less than a week later and kept trying to rub it off. *"C'est fou, c'est complètement fou!"* This is nuts, completely nuts, she said dozens of times a day. Tammy tried striking up conversations with her, but she stared into space and rarely said anything to anyone.

During the month of Safar, Elli fell so ill she was almost too weak to cough. Maryam had to spoon-feed her, and despite careful tending, she grew worse and worse. "It seems like a case of poisoning," Maryam told Tammy one morning, worried and puzzled. "Who would possibly want to poison sweet Miss Orange?"

Tammy had a funny feeling. "Fritzi, I thought it was Sheikh Fahd you were after. Why take out your frustrations on poor Elli?"

"Agent Orange'll get better. I had to make sure I had the right formula."

Tammy decided not to ask any more questions.

Elli gradually did improve, but had missed a dye cycle, and her color was fading. About a week after she started eating with the Rainbow again, the gong sounded so early in the morning that everyone except Tammy was still in bed.

"To the studio, Rainbow, to the studio!" called out a yawning Sayida.

Maryam dashed from door to door like Paul Revere, and soon sleepy-headed colors were heading for the studio. Gisela yawned just while Theta was dusting her face and got a mouthful of glitter; there was a short delay while she gagged and spat.

"You deserved it, you cheat," Margot sniffed.

This time, when Sayida pressed the button in the anteroom, the door opened almost immediately. As they passed through the gold-tooled leather door, Sayida gave each one an ostrich feather that matched her color.

Sheikh Fahd's bedchamber could have been a throne room, opulent with navy, burgundy, and gold paisley. Seated on the gold-tasseled couch was The Redhead, with rippling waves of fire-colored hair cascading to her waist, creamy white skin, beautiful full breasts, long shapely legs. Although she was completely naked except for gold foot ornaments hung with sapphires and rubies, she acted like an em-press.

Sheikh Fahd had eyes only for her. "Dance," he ordered.

It'd been weeks since they'd practiced, but they swayed their hips and waved their feathers. The sheikh mounted his redhead. When there was a cry of victory, they stopped abruptly and lay still on the carpet. Soon there was the soft sound of peaceful snoring.

"You are dismissed," said The Redhead.

"How asinine is that?" Fritzi said. "It took us 44 minutes to get ready to do a ridiculous five-minute dance. I'm not sure my system can bear all the excitement."

Next day, Martine was gone. Fritzi, whose room was next to Sayida's, had overheard that The Redhead had concluded that Martine had too many freckles.

"It sounded like she was going to the Prince Macabre like several of his other discards."

"What makes him so scary, anyway?"

"I'm not really sure. All I know is, he's extremely handsome and so kinky that he's a major embarrassment to the royal family. They've excluded him completely from any possibility of succession."

Sold to a sicko because she had too many freckles. Jeez.

As she lay there in the semi-darkness she calculated how much it must have cost Sheikh Fahd for those five minutes of entertainment. First, the purchase price of seven women, one of whom was a Rolls Royce, then maintained in luxury for months. There were Maryam and Sayida and Omicron and Sigma to pay. The guards. The dye-master. The dyeing equipment. The Redhead's six servants. Her house. The beautiful ball gowns, the expensive jewels. It was mind-blowing.

Ten days later, two days short of Tammy's anniversary in the Rainbow, they were all treated to a celebratory luncheon in honor of the grand opening of the Shrine of Saint Fellatio. They were not, however, invited to the festivities, even as *objets d'art*. Apparently it had created quite a sensation when the Genuine Italian Nuns were presented to the guests; they wore full-length habits and wimples, but there was no skirt below the waist in the back.

156

Suddenly the gong started sounding at two in the afternoon, four in the morning, even once while they were having their colors refreshed. They'd spin around and get ready, and then, he'd decide not to see them. When he did open the door, the Redhead would reprimand them for taking so long or for not having a Miss Yellow. As soon as they got rid of the glitter from one summons, he'd call them again, and round and round they went.

"His weirdometer's gone completely out of control. He decided it would be fun to inseminate the nuns so all twelve will be pregnant at the same time. I need to act quick, before he does the same thing to us."

Tammy sighed sadly. "Poor man, he must be suffering so much."

That day at lunch Sayida was more distracted than usual. "My dear Rainbow," she said at last, the way she did when she had bad news, "Sheikh Fahd has been very disappointed that it has taken us 30, even 45 minutes to be ready. You must henceforth be ready for his pleasure at a moment's notice. You must be glittered and made up at all times, so that we can be in the anteroom within seven minutes during daylight hours and within fifteen minutes at night. His orders will be strictly en-forced. Starting tomorrow."

That night Tammy cried. The library wouldn't let her in unless she was glitter-free, because it ruined the books. Glittered all the time meant itching like mad and sleeping sitting in a chair, because otherwise it turned sheets into sandpaper. But she soon felt ashamed. What was missing a few days of reading compared to losing a child? When she said her prayers she made a special request to comfort Sheikh Fahd and to give him strength.

After three days of nonstop grumbling, Sayida finally relented and let them wear loose dressing gowns during the day, but warned that if they missed the deadline, she'd have to rescind the privilege. They had to stay fully glittered, however, because that was the most time-consuming part of preparation.

Everybody moped around, trying not to touch anything. Tammy begged Sayida to have Lamda send her books – any books – and with the condition that the books be protected by plastic covers, he sent her Arabic-language treatises on standards of proof in Islamic criminal law. She was so desperate, she actually read them. What she gleaned from them was that two female witnesses carried the same weight as one male; she was surprised that women's testimony in the overwhelmingly male-dominated society was worth anything at all.

One afternoon they were sitting around sulking when Sheikh Fahd unexpectedly walked in. He found Gisela first, filing her nails. "I buy you silk dresses and you wear *this?*" he bellowed, ripping the dressing robe off her. "All of you! Ingrates! Look at you, slovenly and lazy, still not properly dressed and it's almost lunchtime! Sayida, I expect you in my office at once. Be prepared to explain this shocking disregard of my orders." He threw Gisela's robe at her and stormed out.

"Oh, palpitations," said Sayida.

Tammy figured that his daughter must be on her deathbed. Extra prayers tonight.

Margot threw another temper tantrum when Sayida announced that henceforth, Sheikh Fahd required them to be in full array and fully glittered at all times.

"I'm sure he has absolutely no idea how complicated it is," Tammy told Fritzi, "He just wants us to look pretty."

Wearing the glitter drove them crazy, and they were all red-eyed from lack of sleep. Gisela and Margot even had to stop playing carom. Elli stopped playing solitaire. There was nothing left to do but pick fights with each other, and Sayida got so tired of the bickering she veiled the whole Rainbow for a week.

"Amazing what some peace and quiet can do for your thought processes," said Fritzi when the veils were finally removed, "I know just what I'll do."

The little girl died, and Sheikh Fahd was mad with grief. One week he sent for the Rainbow eleven times, including four times in a single night. Even Sayida cried herself to sleep.

"He's gone clear over the cliff," Fritzi observed.

He began appearing in the harem several times a day, convinced that as soon as he turned his back they broke all his rules. He poured an entire bottle of perfume on Elli's head because he couldn't smell her fragrance from three feet away. He ripped an emerald necklace from Tammy's neck and threw it in her face because the pendant was a half-inch off-center.

He called them all to a meeting in the salon, and Maryam served him *gawaha*. As Fritzi was seating herself, she accidentally knocked over the coffee pot. "I'm so sorry. Allow me to bring you a fresh pot, sir." In a moment she was back and his cup was full again.

"I'm thinking about closing the Rainbow," he told them. I've been very disappointed in your disrespectful behavior, your refusal to adhere to my standards, your slowness in responding, and your shocking insolence."

This announcement took even Sayida by surprise.

"I'm putting all of you – including you, Sayida – on probation for an entire month. If things do not substantially improve, I will sell all of you to my friend the Prince. And you, Sayida, will go back to changing diapers in the nursery. Understood, my little ones?"

A chorus of "yes sir."

Three days later Sayida was called out in the middle of lunch. When she returned, she was manifestly distraught.

"My dear Rainbow, oh, palpitations, palpitations. Sheikh Fahd has just joined his daughter," she finally announced, blinking back tears. "May peace and blessing be upon him." She began to bawl. "I held him in my arms when he was a baby. I kissed skinned elbows and watched him proudly as he grew. Now he's gone from this earth. I know he is happy in the arms of the angels."

The official cause of death was a stroke brought on by sedatives he'd been taking.

Whew.

The harem was draped in white. They were covered in white robes and forbidden to talk, laugh, play games, read, or otherwise be disrespectful to his memory. Professional mourners were hired to read aloud from the Koran round the clock.

During the month of Ramadan, 40 days to the day after Sheikh Fahd's death, Sheikh Issa, the principal heir, came to the harem. "I'm closing the Rainbow," he announced brusquely. "You will hand over everything to Sayida immediately for inventory. Good day."

Next morning all the girls were assembled in a large salon in the main building. Mr. Abdullah, the merchandising consultant, explained his approach. "I identify the best feature—"

"I don't care what you do," Sheikh Issa said, "just give me an empty room and a check."

It didn't take Mr. Abdullah long to figure out what Tammy's best feature was, and she was soon lying backside up across a gold brocade pillow. Before long, all the women were arranged among fringed blue brocade draperies, lengths of tulle artistically positioned around an ankle here, softening

160

the look of a shoulder there. The air was fragrant with spicy incense and the dim salon lit by clear tubes of sparkling lights.

"Yes, complete dyeing instructions are included," Mr. Abdullah confirmed to the scratchy-voiced man who bought Elli and Margot.

"I love Danes," he said, "Now I have fourteen of them."

Gisela cried when they led Margot away. Then Fritzi was taken and Tammy was the one who cried.

"No noise!" barked Mr. Abdullah, and touched her thigh with an electric cattle prod.

A few minutes later he was back. "Here's a cute little piece for the man who likes to get to the bottom of things," he said, pinching her rear.

"She's a very nice piece," he said, kneading some flesh apprais-ingly. "Turn her over."

A commercial blunder. He guffawed. "If I took those tits to His Highness, he'd have me fired." He moved on.

She was repositioned as before, but was now facing the wall, with instructions to stay perfectly still or the cattle prod would come back out.

She could hear another group of customers. She began to tremble as several people stopped right beside her.

"A nice investment for the man who likes to get to the bottom of things, don't you agree? Here, sir, let me turn her over for you."

Dr. Hassan was grinning from ear to ear. "I'll take the green one," he said.

PART FIVE
THE OFFICE

September 2007 – March 2008
Ramadan 1428 – Rabi al-awal 1429

Dr. Hassan came to the holding cell the following morning. "So! How long has it been since you graced my humble clinic? A year? Two? I hardly recognized you. I spent all last evening wondering how I could advance your career, and I've come to the conclusion that you'd make a great whore. The training and discipline will be most beneficial to your attitudes, so I've reserved a place for you at The Office, a high-class men's club with an excellent training facility where they teach whores to swallow their pride. Teach them how to swallow something else, too."

He smiled smugly as Tammy shuddered. A whore!

"Besides, I'm Chairman of the Board and could request your attentions whenever I want. You'll be so popular there with that rump of yours that you'll hardly get any rest at all." He lifted her chin with a possessive finger. "Now, won't that be fun?" He stood very close. "The Office keeps only the finest; there are other clubs on the circuit where the ladies aren't, shall we say, as pretty when they come out as when they went in. Now, let's have a little taste of what you'll be doing. On your knees." He lifted his *thobe* and started undoing his trousers.

He had to be kidding.

He eyed her victoriously, reveling in her discomfiture.

She knelt. Tried to do what the miscreant wanted.

"Haven't you learned anything?" he demanded, holding her roughly by the hair. "Don't just slobber, you idiot, suck!"

She was overwhelmed by disgust. Against her will, tears streamed down her face. After a few minutes, in spite of herself, she started catching on to what he expected, and he grunted approvingly. Good, she thought, if I do it halfway right maybe the sleazeball will leave me alone.

That's nonsense, the demons chirped, *If you don't get it right he'll keep after you until you do, and once you do it the way he wants, he'll torment you all the time.*

"Oh, sometimes I'm too brilliant for words," he said. "I just thought of the perfect way to guarantee you years of exquisite misery. I'm going to make a phone call." When he returned he brought her hands behind her back and cuffed them. She tried not to let him know how frightened she was.

"Don't like handcuffs? Just wait until they put you in a full har-ness. Or in shackles. They're kept in every room." A wave of nausea surged through her. "But this time I'll give you a sedative so you won't scare off the customer."

She was taken to an atrium garden where a fawning Dr. Hassan welcomed a slight goateed man reeking of cologne. "This is the piece I mentioned to you, my dear sir. She was part of Sheikh Fahd's fabled Rainbow Harem; her natural skin color will return by the time she has completed her training. With firm handling she will be a very profitable investment indeed."

"No tits," sniffed the officious snob, "and no real work experience. His Highness has high standards."

"She requires careful training, that's all, and an owner who knows how to keep her under control. What better place than The Office, and what better master than His Highness? Look at her plump little ass, a nine-three, maybe even a nine-four. His Highness' exquisite collection is famous; he's sure to find hers quite pleasing. Whether leased as a revenue-generator or gracing His Highness' own harem, you can't go wrong, my dear sir, not with this piece."

"His harems are presently stocked to capacity, thank you, but it is true, she might be a money-maker. Very well, we'll take her. You may make the necessary arrangements with The Office."

Dr. Hassan showed the man out. He returned, ecstatic. "I did it. Your doom is sealed."

Tammy clenched her teeth. She wanted to strangle him. "I hate you," she said evenly.

"I know," he said delightedly, "but you don't yet realize the full extent of my genius. You see," he said, "you have just become the property of the Prince Macabre. I'm sure that one day he will call you into his own harem, where you will no doubt be served up at one of his famous orgies. You see, His Highness is a necrophiliac. He has a weakness for fresh blonde corpses."

Tammy lay on the examination table in the Induction Room, where Mr. Ali, a supervisor, had finished taking complete – complete! – measurements. He was dictating. "All right, Adham, this is Ass 421. Beauteous Gluteus. Hourly rate, $628. Specialty, sodomy. Boobs, 1.3. Ass, 9.4. Torso, 7.8. Arms, 8.0. Thighs, 8.2. Lower legs, 8.1. There's no point in photographing her yet for the cuntalog; we don't want to scare members away. Daily training schedule is as follows: 1 hour toning, 4 hours sodomy, 4 hours traditional, 2 hours dancing, 3 hours BJs, 1 hour erotic massage, 1 hour variety. Take her to Personnel and then to Screw U."

A metal ID anklet engraved with T 421 AI and The Office logo was soldered around her right ankle. She understood the T stood for *tisee*, ass, and 421 was her inventory number. But she had no idea what AI stood for and no one explained. Then she was ushered to the train-ing room. At first glance it looked like a sports club.

The training was a combination of live instructors, DVDs, and what she soon called "those goddam infernal diabolical hellified" simulation machines. Over the next six weeks she was taught how to jiggle-walk wearing five-inch pumps; do an express BJ (blow job) in 90 seconds or less or make one last for 30 minutes; do pole, lap, and other erotic dances; how to assume twelve different pleasuring positions; how to writhe, grind, wiggle, and thrust; and all the rules about how to accommodate members' special "variety" requests, make them feel manly, and show appropriate respect. The training department itself had one rule: if you acquired enough points, you were allowed to eat; if you got too weak to perform, you were dismissed.

It was the toughest school she'd ever attended; anything below 90 was unacceptable. "We only keep the best," they kept saying, and they meant it. She positively hated doing BJs and only got an 84 on the exam, but fortunately, she'd received such high marks elsewhere that she managed to squeak by. Of eighteen trainees in Tammy's class, only four had scores strong enough for The Office; the others were sent to less stringent clubs.

The dye gradually faded and they could finally photograph her for the cuntalog. Three views of her rear were accompanied by the blurb, "a succulent asshole for discriminating tastes, surrounded by plump alabaster mounds of sweet eager flesh." Mr. Adham decided that her already very fair skin tone should be even paler, so she was covered in lightening cream each morning when she got off duty. They stained her with an exaggerated dark red mouth and exaggerated black eyebrows. They also accentuated her nipples dark brown. When she caught sight of herself in a mirror, she barely recognized herself. She sighed. Of course. She was no longer an individual, a human, just an anonymous piece of female meat for rent.

The first two months, Tammy was assigned to the waiting room, where she entertained executives while they were waiting for their rooms or other club services – sports, restaurants, cinema, etc. She knelt and performed BJs, washed and massaged their feet, lap danced, changed DVDs of dirty movies, served refreshments from the bar, and obligingly retrieved all the key chains, pens, cell phones, and other things that the executives kept dropping. And dropping. At first she wondered why they were all such unbelievable klutzes; it took her more than a week to realize that they just wanted to see her bend over.

She was then promoted to apprentice. In this capacity she might provide a stimulating view for the member to enjoy while he was using another whore, or provide any other service the member desired. After two months, she was considered capable of handling assignments on her own.

She sank dejectedly into the routine, still unable to believe that the wholesome majorette named Tammy had become a high-class whore named Beauteous Gluteus. The two things she particularly hated, BJs and sodomy, were the very things the executives demanded the most. Worse, maybe one in five would strap her down, and she'd be so terrified she could barely function. Workdays lasted between fifteen and seventeen hours, and she figured that on average she spent four or five hours giving BJs and six to ten hours being sodomized. In other words, the vast majority of her time she spent doing things she abhorred, were downright painful, or that positively sickened her. She'd be proud of herself for having made it through one horrible job without completely breaking down and then immediately be sent off to one even worse.

It wasn't that the men were mean – most of them were perfectly normal guys with perfectly normal tastes – they just wanted services they were reluctant to demand from their wives. Since she was a slave, a whore, she did what they wanted. And because poor performance or attitudes meant a disciplinary transfer to a club lower on the food chain, where life expectancy was counted in months or even weeks.

Her survival instinct was strong, but there were days that she doubted it'd be powerful enough to overcome the disgust she felt as she knelt to do yet another damned BJ, or the repulsion that overwhelmed her as another damned Fuad assaulted her backside. Enthusiasm? They had to be kidding. She cried herself to sleep almost every night, dismayed every time she'd wake up and realize that she faced another day serving men who treated her, as Honey Buns put it, with all the respect they gave toilet paper. Do you ask its opinion? Of course not. It just silently, uncomplainingly, fulfills its intended purpose, no matter how revolting.

Her dad always said, Look, you can't control what happens to you, but you can control how you react. Choose to be happy, and you will be happy, regardless. She was trying her darnedest, but things around her kept getting worse and worse.

She'd occasionally catch glimpses of Dr. Hassan and positively dreaded the day that he'd send for her. Whenever she appeared at Central for her next assignment, she stopped breathing until the rumps' supervisor, Mr. Ali, or his deputy, the pompous Mr. Adham, announced the executive's name. If it weren't Dr. Hassan, she could exhale.

Don't worry, the demons crowed, *Dr. Hassan will send for you soon – unless, of course, the mental case takes you into his harem first.*

And she was scared to death of her owner, whom she still had not met. The normally tolerant Mr. Ali grew impatient with her periodic seizures of panic about becoming a fresh corpse. "Nothing but hear-say," he insisted. "He's actually a very nice man. Considerate, funny, and from what I hear, knows a thing or two about action between the sheets."

"But Dr. Hassan is the world's best clearinghouse for people's dirty secrets," she protested. "That's exactly the kind of thing he knows."

168

"Both he and His Highness are on the Board here and you will not speak disrespectfully of them. Now, Glute, if you don't let silly rumors affect your attitudes, you could be Rump of the Month."

A dubious honor. The good news was that the winner got a day off – a real treat – but the downside was that her "99 Attributes" were featured in embarrassing life-size photographs displayed in the reception hall, enticing men to try her out, and not incidentally, pay a hefty surcharge for the privilege. Her natural inclination to excel locked horns with her equally strong reluctance to debase herself. She was petrified that if she became a good little whore, the prince would reward her by taking her into his harem; on the other hand, she was just as fearful that if she rebelled, The Office would punish her by sending her there.

Then it happened: Dr. Hassan sent for her. "Mr. Ali, please, please, send somebody else," she begged, wiping away tears. "I abso-lutely hate that man. Send me on ten other difficult assignments, but please, please, sir, not this one."

The slap was not a complete surprise. "I forbid you to speak like that. He specifically requested you. And you will take proper care of him. He's Chairman of the Board here, and Vice-Chairman of the holding company that owns all the clubs on the Circuit. If you don't absolutely delight him he has the power to transfer you with the stroke of a pen, including the Ranch and the Falcon Club. In fact, considering his scathing comments in your file, I'm amazed he hasn't transferred you already."

"Because he wants to keep me where he can humiliate me again and again, sir."

"He often goes to the Ranch; I remind you; he especially enjoys the branding parties. You will be polite, you will be respectful, you will smile and show appropriate enthusiasm, and you will do whatever he wants without complaint."

Carlo admitted her to the Salle de Versailles, where Dr. Hassan was sitting on the red silk couch, reading a newspaper.

She hated herself as she knelt and squeezed out the standard formula. "What will be your pleasure today, sir?"

"Ah, my golden treasure. You will address me as master. Come over here, my dear. Don't you look cute in that French maid's outfit. Oh my, they seem to have forgotten the skirt in the back. How terribly embarrassing."

She was boiling with hatred but kept her mouth shut. Even managed the semblance of a smile.

"I've planned a wonderful afternoon. First, you will give your master a bath. Carlo, please run the Jacuzzi. Then you will give your master a full body massage, followed by a long and extremely luxurious BJ. You may begin by disrobing me."

"With pleasure, master," she intoned. She programmed her sanity, her self-control, by the minute. Just get through the next few seconds, she told herself, and the next few, and the next. She gave him his damned bath. His damned massage. It took every last ounce of self-discipline she had to give him his damned BJ, but she got through that too. His blow tasted extremely bitter. It was never a pleasure to swallow ejaculate on the best of days, but some was a lot worse than others. It was fitting that Dr. Hassan's would taste the worst of all.

"Carlo, shackle her spread-eagle to the bed. Oh look, you're shaking. Shaking with desire for your beloved Dr. Hassan." He lifted her chin with a possessive finger. "Too bad you don't like shackles. I happen to like them on you very much. That look of terror. That look of utter misery."

She wanted to weep with humiliation and pain as he sodomized her, dry and rough. Most executives accepted "standard lubrication," but some didn't, and of course, their requests were always honored. She'd gotten to where she

170

could almost, almost tolerate it if she were well lubricated, but when they wanted her dry, it just plain hurt. He knew damned well – he was the one who'd stitched her up after Fuad – and he reveled in it.

At length he finished but left her shackled to the bed. He knows how much I hate these goddam things, she thought hotly, and he's doing it just to make me miserable.

"Carlo, take a picture. Make sure you can see both her face and her pussy. How'd you like for me to send that to your father? I still have his contact information, you know. I'm sure he'd be delighted to know what you're doing. Have it enlarged. Show it to all of his friends." They took a dozen other poses. "What a beautiful portfolio. I strongly suggest that you be the perfect little whore, or we might give it wide distribution."

Perhaps an hour later, Carlo released her, but just because it was time to get back on her knees. "You did a nice job on that, so I will reward you by allowing you to lick my plate. Carlo, set it over there on the rug. You will kneel and bend over while you lick it, and keep your ass raised. Higher. Excellent. Now, wasn't that fun?"

Then another damned BJ, this time with clamps holding her tits. And another damned foot massage.

"Not bad, my golden treasure. Satisfactory. You do need to work on your enthusiasm, which was completely absent, and your respon-siveness. I will be monitoring other executives' comments and if we need to take corrective action – that you may not enjoy – we will not hesitate to do so. Now you must repeat after me: Master, I am honored that you requested my attentions and I eagerly await the next time you summon me."

"See? You survived," Mr. Ali told her. "Six hours and fifteen minutes. He was easy on you; he often goes for twelve, fifteen hours."

"All he does is torment me, Mr. Ali, sir. He enjoys humiliating me."

"If it is his pleasure to humiliate you, then you will graciously submit to being humiliated. You're here for the members' pleasure. All part of the job, Glute."

She slumped with despair. Of all the people in the world to have to kowtow to! All right, she told herself, do whatever the bastard wants. And one day, you'll get back at him big time. Dear God, she prayed, please forgive me, but I would really, really like to murder that man. She held onto that thought with both hands and managed to stagger through the many times that he called for her. She danced for him, massaged his feet. Did stupid games like ass-walking across the floor before a bell sounded. He'd rigged things for failure so that he could punish her, either a spanking or a certain amount of time chained in an uncomfortable position, or a one-hour BJ, or painting his jewels with shit-flavored sauce and making her lick it all off...

"A nine-hour Unsatisfactory from Dr. Hassan? He says that you sassed him. What happened?"

"Oh, Mr. Ali, sir, I tried so hard, but he kept provoking me. After hours and hours of making me miserable he said I needed to show him more respect, and I told him he knew exactly how much I respected him. He slapped me, like, five million times, and threatened to transfer me to the Ranch if I ever showed him disrespect again."

"Glute, babe, listen. He's Chairman. You do not, do *not*, want to displease a member of the Board. Mr. Suleyman, Dr. Hassan, Prince Ibrahim, Mr. Daood, Sheikh Faisal. You are perilously close to losing your spot here at The Office, so you'd better improve your attitudes, especially with him. Tell you what. If you can get at least a three-hour Outstanding from Dr. Hassan, I'll give you a day off. All right? You'll try harder? Okay, next assignment is with Colonel Aziz. You'll like him. He loves being teased, and your playfulness will go over well. He does have one special request: he enjoys having girls suck his big toe. Off you go."

Suddenly, Dr. Hassan stopped sending for her. She wasn't exactly upset, but she couldn't help but wonder why.

One afternoon Mr. Ali sent her on an assignment with a new member, so he couldn't brief her on his tastes. "Sheikh Hussein is a highly regarded banker, extremely handsome. He's already worn out one asshole today and wants a fresh one. Take good care of him."

She headed off nervously for the Venetian Room. Jiggle-Tits passed her in the hallway, putting her hand on the top of her head, the staff members' private signal for "dreadful meeting." Tammy responded by scratching her hip – new executive. Jiggle-Tits rubbed her cheek to wish her good luck.

When the valet opened the door she heard screams of pain – nothing at all like the shrieks of pleasure they'd been taught to make. She saw her classmate Chesterfeel strapped spread-eagle to the bed, her face twisted in agony.

"Please don't, sir! Please!"
Sheikh Hussein leaned toward her, a lighted cigarette in his hand, a half-smile on his face. "But I'm not finished yet, my dear little slut." He bent closer.

There was the smell of burning flesh and another horrible scream. The room swayed, and the rug flew up and hit Tammy in the face. She came to in the infirmary, where in the bed next to her Chesterfeel was being treated for 29 cigarette burns. Sheikh Hussein had been writing the word *sharmuta* (slut) across her torso, but only got as far as "sharm" before he was interrupted. Since he was in violation of the strict rules against anything that would leave permanent marks, he was required to pay a breakage charge and was strongly encouraged to patronize other clubs on the Circuit. Nevertheless, poor Chesterfeel was too damaged to meet The Office's high standards for "prime meat" and was shipped off to the sadistic New Frontier.

Shaken staff members just about wore their cheeks out wishing each other luck.

A month or so after she'd started working assignments on her own, Tammy reported for her regular meeting with a rotund executive named Mr. Abdul, who showed up every *al-arbi'a* (Wednesday) evening, always asked for page 37, and spent half the meeting showing her sketches of his recent inventions. She didn't have a clue what most of them were supposed to do, but she rather liked him, because he was kind, terribly insecure, bumbling in an endearing way, and loved being teased. She enjoyed watching him glow with pleasure when she told him they were works of dazzling genius. He always gave her an Outstanding for a five-minute BJ, another reason she wanted to keep him happy.

Much of the staff members' fate, in fact, rested in the hands of individual executives, each with his own more or less arbitrary set of rules. Ratings were multiplied by the number of hours the meeting had lasted; to increase their motivation, Unsatisfactories carried twice as much weight as Outstandings. Every month their composite score was then multiplied by a Pleasurability Index, a complicated computerized system that compared the shape, size, and allure of various body parts against a given standard of perfection, as well as ratings from members themselves and anonymous quality control inspectors. They were graded on enthusiasm, technique, respectfulness, and ability to deliver maximum sensation. Prizes, as well as premium hourly rates, were dispensed for high scores, and low ratings resulted in tough disciplinary measures.

When she arrived in the Tahitian Room the valet, a curly-haired blond, was exclaiming over one of Mr. Abdul's designs. His long-tailed morning suit couldn't disguise the familiar pear-shaped body. She almost whooped with joy, but instead pinched him slyly on his leg. He winked at her, mouthed 'later,' and pretended to be blown away by Mr. Abdul's drawings of kellies and slush pits and gate valves.

"Cute little rump they sent you today, sir," Heineken commented, as he helped Mr. Abdul into his red silk robe.

"Ah yes, Pierre, my favorite. Sweet, sweet piece of ass. Just between us, I've put in a bid for her, but they tell me she's on lease, and I won't know until the middle of Muharram if they'll let me have her or not."

She shot "Pierre" a look of surprise; it was the first she'd known about an offer. She briefly wondered whether or not she should be flattered, but the thought was quickly shouldered aside by a wave of powerlessness. Maybe someday she'd get used to being bought and sold as casually as a potted petunia.

After the meeting Heineken was waiting for her. They made sure no one was looking and hugged until they could scarcely breathe.

"That's the last of that," he warned, "Never let on we know each other. Good to see you, dearie, missed you a lot!"

"I was so happy you got away I could have burst!"

"Every security system has a soft spot," he said with a wink, "and at the House it was the infirmary. Things are going great, making tons of money. Another year or so and I'm off to Colorado. What's new in your zoo, dearie?"

She caught him up rapidly on her news, ending with how Dr. Hassan had sold her to the Prince Macabre, who'd leased her to The Office.

"That puke-bucket used to come here all the time, but now I hear he's hiding out in Belgium. Somebody tipped off Interpol about a blonde baby brood-farm, and he has to lie low for a while." His eyes narrowed. "The Prince Macabre? That sicko? Just sank in. Oh! Sorry, there goes the call light.

175

Mr. Abdul will never find his way into his clothes all by himself."

"You're the best, Heineken."

"Pierre," he corrected, huffing himself up and trying his best to look snooty.

She exploded with laughter. It was the first time she'd laughed in months.

She wasn't assigned to meetings at The Tahitian Room very often, but just knowing Heineken was there buoyed her morale. Her ratings soared, much to her astonishment. What? Tammy Simmons? A top-notch whore? It took some getting used to.

Abubakr held his head in his hands. How, just how, could he break the news to John that Tammy was in a brothel? A high-class brothel, but nonetheless, a brothel. In all his years of fighting on behalf of these girls, he still hadn't found a way to let a father know without absolutely breaking his heart. Calling it a gentlemen's club would soften the blow a little, but John was far from naïve.

Of course, that was bad enough, but Angelo said she'd been leased there by her new owner, Macabre himself. Volatile. Unpredictable. Arrogant. Mount Vesuvius temper. Power-driven. Vengeful. Host of lavish orgies where, it was said, there were at several girls for every guest. Not counting a corpse or two, which was always blonde, always scented with Giorgio, and always called Lucia. How could he ever let John know that Tammy was in the clutches of a major mental case who'd been known to have seven or eight slaves put to death in a single day?

Not a phone call he wanted to make, but better let him know.

John's voice was warm and upbeat. Oh boy, was that about to change. "How's it going?"

"Well, could be better, but not too bad. She's been moved again. This isn't easy to tell you, John, but she's in a high-class men's club." He shrank at John's horrified gasp. "As far as these things go, she's in the best possible place. No violence, no brutality. Very elite clientele, we're talking generals and princes and ambassadors and mega-millionaires. I realize that's little consolation, but I needed to give it to you straight."

"Oh," said John painfully, "oh, my baby, my poor baby."

"By the way, her new owner is one of the best-looking men on the planet."

"I don't care what the hell he looks like, I just need to know that he's a decent person. *If* there's a slave-owner who can be considered a decent person. My poor baby, my poor, poor baby."

"Angelo's there, he'll let us know if there's any news."

"Well, thanks, I suppose. Oh, my poor baby. I feel like a total failure as a father, as a protector. I want in the worst way to mount some kind of commando operation, get her out of this hell."

"Don't beat yourself up, Simba. I understand; I have three girls of my own. But realistically, there's very little we can do. She's kept under very, very tight security. The building is a fortress and there have been no escapes or rescues in the last seventeen years. Only two girls smuggled out since 1978. Listen, in my early days I tried four commando operations, and every last one of them was a complete failure. We're talking automatic weapons and dozens of guards. In three of them, the first thing they did was kill the girl. In the fourth, they weren't sure which girl we were going after and they killed seven. Made me lose my enthusiasm for commando operations. Hey. She's alive.

177

Considering everything, she's all right. And like you say, since you raised her so well, she's almost assuredly found something she can laugh about."

"My poor, poor baby." He was close to tears.

"You're the third-ranked rump in The Office now," Mr. Ali congratulated her at the end of Zul-Hijjah, only her second full month on duty. "Next month you should go after a prize."

Tall and wiry, with a near-permanent grin stitched under a bushy moustache, Mr. Ali positively bowled her over when he mentioned he had a doctorate in human behavior from Tufts. He loved thinking up clever names for the staff — although the English puns were lost on many members — and was proud of the way he took recalcitrant, resentful teenage girls and turned them into recalcitrant, resentful disciplined professionals. He made sure that no matter how busy they were, there was always time for a brief weekly coaching session, to go over per-formance, compliment achievements, and suggest ways to improve weak points.

Normally he was reassuring and supportive, but even Mr. Ali couldn't resist teasing her about the pathetic 1.3 star rating her front bumper got, the lowest he'd seen in his four years at The Office. She didn't mind an occasional gibe from him about her "two mosquito bites"; on the other hand, executives tended to have very little sense of humor about it. On several occasions members were so outraged they actually sent her back untouched.

"It's so humiliating," she told Mr. Ali.

"Hey, you can't blame executives if they want a couple of nice grapefruit along with their meat. But they do love your playful nature and your great ass."

Usually, members simply ordered a rump; if they were willing to pay a surcharge, they could specify page 37 of the cuntalog, request Beauteous Gluteus by name, or order number 421. It hurt to realize that even after four or five meetings with the same men, they often showed no signs of ever having seen her before. Even when they spoke to her they looked through her, not at her. Just an anonymous piece of meat.

Despite her misgivings, for the months of Muharram and Safar, she did win Rump of the Month, and spent her prize day off each time catching up on her sleep. It wasn't quite the way she'd dreamed of celebrating her twenty-first birthday, but it sure beat running from meeting to meeting.

The day before she reached full majority she was on her way   to the Jungle Room, wearing a backless one-shoulder tiger print number straight out of a Tarzan movie. Heineken was waiting for her in the hallway and slipped her a little gold box. It contained four Godiva chocolates.

"Happy birthday, dearie. I liberated these for you. You remind me of the gal on the seal, wearing lots of pretty hair and not much else."

Tammy devoured the chocolates right on the spot. "I can't believe you still remember my birthday," she said, wrapping her tongue around a luscious hazelnut crème.

"'Course I do. You remember mine?"

"November fourteenth. See? Did you hear I won Rump of the Month again?"

"Must be absolutely bursting with pride," he said with a straight face.

Mr. Ali thought it was quite an accomplishment. "Keep it up. I think you should even shoot for Grand Pussy."

Oh yeah, she thought, sure. The prize, three days off, was taken month after month by Superboobs, whose breasts, measured from the center of the nipple to the underfold, were a colossal 194 millimeters, dimensions achieved after four harrowing trips to the Boob Camp. It was hard for a paltry 48 like Tammy to compete. Tammy was surprised that Superboobs wasn't completely demented.

"My grandmother survived Birkenau where the SS sent her for hiding a Jewish family," Superboobs explained. "If she could get through that, I can put up with that damned hellified electric bra. Although frankly, I don't know why they just don't do implants like everybody else."

"Surgery leaves scars," Tammy reminded her. "Even Dr. Hassan isn't perfect. And sometimes the implants leak, or get hard. Customers complain."

Superboobs was 30, by far the oldest staff member, but by acclamation given an exception to automatic retirement upon turning 26. Since "grandma's" figure caused near-riots every time she ventured into the hall, she was usually confined to the Booby Trap, a room on the second floor where every conceivable object resembled the female bosom. Time with her cost members more than $1200 an hour, but even so, she was booked up weeks in advance.

"You'll be meeting with a new executive today," Mr. Ali said as he adjusted her cowgirl suit. "His name is Mr. Taymoor. He's a distinguished architect, and since today is his first time, all I can tell you is that he wanted a sweet blue-eyed blonde with a juicy caboose. Make sure you take good care of him."

Mr. Taymoor was very devout, so to guard against any risk of adultery, he'd taken the precaution of making a *zawaj al-mit'a,* a temporary marriage, which normally would automatically be termin-ated as soon as it could be ascertained that no pregnancy had resulted. But since The

Office gave staff members contraceptives, its validity ended when the meeting with her was over.

The main problem with new executives was that many of them hadn't yet realized how serious The Office was about enforcing its rules. Executives could use restraints and give "playful" smacks, but anything that would leave marks for more than three days or compromise health was strictly forbidden. After the incident with Chesterfeel, The Office decided that whenever restraints were used, the valet had to remain in the room. The way they sold it to the executives was that the presence of a valet would help protect them from vengeful staff mem-bers. Indeed, every few months a staff member would snap and attack an executive. Nearly always, the damage was minimal and the Rodeo got more meat, but every now and then a staff member actually managed to commit murder. It had only happened once at The Office, fourteen years before, but it had happened.

Just the week before, a new executive had ordered a "liquor licker," or sucker, as an accessory. He'd ordered her to lick him clean after he'd been to the john. She threw up, which earned her an Unsatis-factory. Mr. Suleyman astounded the staff and enraged the members by not only fining the executive but also overruling the grade.

So it was with considerable apprehension that Tammy knelt before the unknown Mr. Taymoor. "What is your pleasure today, sir?" she intoned mechanically, still panting from racing up two flights of stairs. Running was highly recommended, since staff members arrived breath-less. Anything to please the customer.

"You look exhausted," a tenor voice said pleasantly. "Are you all right?" She raised her eyes. There on the sofa was an exceptionally attractive man with sandy hair, friendly brown eyes, and an endearing boyish smile. "Come over here."

Rumps were forbidden to sit down since it interfered with the view, so she started arranging herself on a cushion on the floor.

"No no, here. On the couch. Beside me." Mr. Taymoor's eyes were fastened on her costume as she edged over and took a seat. "Is that idiotic outfit supposed to turn me on?" he said with a chuckle.

It was mostly fringe, with plastic holsters and a tiny bolero. And of course, no back to the skirt. It really *was* idiotic. She laughed.

Damn. There she went again. Laughing had frequently gotten her in trouble. Too forward. Insinuated that she was remotely the execu-tive's equal. She closed her eyes, bracing for the inevitable slap.

It didn't come.

"Why are you so afraid of me? Relax. Or, let me guess, they charge me extra if you do?" Tammy felt disconcerting cracks in her carefully cultivated façade of detachment. "This place has made an art of extracting currency from members' pockets, that's for sure. Sixty-six dollars for a shot of Johnny Walker Black. Eighty-nine for a Chivas. Now tell me your name and give me a smile."

"Beauteous Gluteus, sir."

He groaned. "No no no no no. Your *real* name. A woman as beautiful as you deserves a beautiful name."

Woman? She warmed to the word. "It's very kind of you to say that, sir," she told him. Then words jumped out all by themselves. "I don't see many like you here."

He studied her, and there wasn't a trace of accusation in his voice when he spoke. "How long have you been doing this?"

She gulped. "Eight months. It wasn't exactly my idea, sir."

"So how did you get here?"

"It's against the rules for me to say, sir. I'm sorry, I can tell you I'm originally from America, but other than that I'm forbidden to reveal anything about myself at all."

"I insist."

"I must respectfully decline, sir. Both of us could get into big trouble."

She didn't add that The Office frequently had inspectors pose as executives, who tested staff members' adherence to the rules. Boomin' Bust had recently fallen into one such inspector's trap when he promised to help her escape. She was placed on two months' probation, which was bad enough, because it doubled the value of any Unsatis-factories. While she was still on probation she let another undercover inspector give her some brandy, and therefore was, with much fanfare, given a disciplinary transfer to the sadistic Falcon Club.

"I don't understand why you're still so scared of me. Relax. Please."

Most men didn't care whether she was afraid or not; the ones who noticed how ill at ease she was flattered themselves into believing that their overwhelming virility had made her shy, or that she'd taken one look at their dominator and completely lost her nerve. This man, though, seemed different. She looked far into his warm brown eyes and saw kindness. Generosity. She began to relax.

"That's better. I need to find a nice name for you, though."

They sat there on the couch together and talked. Several times, she felt herself strongly drawn to him, but she forced herself to stay aloof. He kept making her laugh, and would grin at her in his disarming boyish way, and it became harder and harder to keep her guard up. She soon heard all about his green-eyed, scorpion-tongued wife and two sons, as well as the pretentious sheikh whose new palace he was designing.

"I show him plans that are so gaudy they're almost comical, and he just laps them up. God is great, but I've noticed that sometimes He creates people without a single tasteful cell."

"Except for people like him, Mr. Taymoor, do you usually like what you do?"

"Oh, I love it! It's very satisfying to take a vague idea and turn it into plans, and plans into buildings. Next time I come I'll bring you some pictures. The only time I hate is when I'm dealing with someone like this sheikh, and I find myself saying 'yes sir,' 'of course, sir,' when I'm really thinking 'take your vulgar plans and stuff them you-know-where.' Makes me feel like a filthy whore."

Her heart momentarily lodged in her throat; Mr. Taymoor lay an apologetic hand on her shoulder. "I'm sorry, my sweet, that was a poor choice of words. It's not like you're a volunteer here. I admire your courage." There was a moment's hesitation while he blew some dust off some mental files. "First time I ever said that to a woman, now that I think of it." He rose. "Well, I didn't come here just to talk, although it's been wonderful. Would you care to give this tired fellow a nice massage?"

"With pleasure, sir."

The massage, of course, soon led to other things. He wasn't a particularly good lover, but she felt a certain contentment lying next to him as he rested in a mellow afterglow.

"I know, Kiwi! My favorite fruit. Only it's not as sweet as you. I think I'm in love with you." He patted her rear.

"You've got a wonderful body, and you're a sweet, sweet girl. How do I make sure I get you next time?"

She outlined the possibilities, and he stored them in his phone. He put his card in the slot in the service terminal and gave her an Out-standing. Before he sent her off, she said, "I think I'm in love with you too."

Three and a half hours! Hooray! Yesterday's Unsatisfactory from Col. Kamal was already neutralized.

"Give me a kiss, my sweet, and I'll see you again soon."

Oh, how different life suddenly became! She wanted to shout to the world how happy she felt. On a more realistic level, though, slogging through the daily routine was harder than ever, and the strict prohibition against communicating with anyone on the outside became a fresh and bitter vexation.

She had fleeting thoughts of Marc, and almost laughed. The ideal-istic naval cadet and the equally idealistic majorette. What a clueless couple they'd been, in that safe place called Bethesda, in that far-off time when she'd belonged to herself. Marc, she thought, I'm sorry. I'll always love my memories of you, but now I need someone who can understand the complicated person I've become.

For a time Mr. Taymoor came every *al-ithnain* (Monday) night, but soon he started reserving her for *al-khamis* (Thursday) mornings as well. Oh, how she craved his visits! He was tender, if a little awkward, very thoughtful, and was interested in everything. She finally trusted him enough to confide in him. He wanted to know all about Dr. Hassan, Sheikh Khalid, the Rainbow, The Office. How did they operate? How did she live? Why wasn't she keeping a journal? Where were all these places? How were the women forced into them? Who ran them? She told him everything she knew.

"They mustn't treat women like that," he said. "It's scandalous. Islam says men are supposed to protect women, not abuse them."

"Then, Taymoor, please, darling, tell me how you justify coming here."

He was taken aback. "Actually, that's a fair question. I respect my wife, Kiwi, but there's no passion in marriage to a cousin. She's dutiful, nothing more. Here I can relax. Go a little crazy if I want. Do you know the names my wife would call me if I spent an hour making love to her? In this country it's almost impossible to have a mistress, and besides, they get expensive and have the nasty habit of causing trouble." He rolled his eyes, and Tammy smelled a story. "You pay a lot of money at playgrounds like The Office, but you get a safe haven, and men need that. Lately, though, I've noticed one big drawback," he said, pulling her close to him and covering her face with melting kisses, "I didn't mind so much at first, but now, my sweet Kiwi, I very much resent sharing you with others."

"Being with you is all that keeps me going," she replied, snuggling happily against his shoulder. "You know, it's funny, but Dr. Hassan actually did me a favor by sending me here. Otherwise I never would have met you."

When Taymoor couldn't come she withered. Then he'd return, and drench her in affection, and she'd have the strength to get through another few days.

"I've had it up to here having to make appointments to see you," he told her one day, his breath precious against her cheek. "I've got to get you out of this infernal place. I try to divert myself by using other club services. I go to the bowling alley, try to play squash – I'm terrible. But I have to admit, all I want here is you."

"You could buy me," she suggested. Not only would she be off the Circuit, but she'd be protected by a kind-hearted man. "They have boarding rooms here, you know, where I

186

could stay. I wouldn't have to see other men, and you could come and visit whenever you pleased."

He shrugged without enthusiasm. "Turn you into a *mukaddara?* Keep you totally secluded from everyone but me? I couldn't do that to you, my sweet. When does that ridiculous annual review of yours come up?"

"The eleventh of Muharram. Please, Taymoor, if you could get me out of this wretched place I'd be indebted to you for the rest of my life. Please please please please."

"I'm not looking for gratitude, my sweet, I just want you for my very own."

Then he was off for 27 days visiting a distant construction site. She relapsed into deep discouragement.

"God, I hate this place," Tammy told Heineken, "Even Mr. Abdul was crabby last night."

"Hey. Stuff happens, dearie, things change. Hang in there." He was still trying to help her escape. "These folks have taken everything into account, even sneaky valets. I'll keep working on it, or maybe I'll just work a little extra and buy you." He cocked his head and looked her over appraisingly. "Great butt, but most eunuchs I know have bigger tits. And betcha can't even split logs or scale river trout. Think they'll take fifty cents for you?"

"Fifty cents? Just one minute here! Since I was Rump of the Month these guys are paying nearly eight hundred dollars an hour, and you think you can buy me for a measly fifty cents?"

"Okay, okay, a buck-fifty. But don't let it go to your head. By the way, I checked the auction book. There are three bids for you right now; the lowest is sixty-six thousand and the highest is ninety-four. I've saved up enough money, I can top that."

187

"You'd spend your hard-earned money to get me out of this place? Honest?"

"Honest injun." He shrugged. Blushed. "Course, I'll get it back. Rent a room over a saloon and charge the fellas a buck apiece. Might take a while, but…"

"One stinking dollar?"

"You got no tits. There's the light, gotta go." He winked and made an extra-snooty face.

Giggling, she rang the chime to start her meeting with Sheikh Abdullah. She quickly sobered; the man was nothing but elbows.

Later she was sent to service Mr. Abdulaziz, a sixteen-year-old. He sat arrogantly on a stack of three staff members, with one more massaging his hands, one more massaging his feet, and one behind him massaging his back. When Tammy appeared he pointed arrogantly with his sparse goatee to the bed. "Full harness," he told Vinod. "Frog position."

"She's ready, sir."

"Where are the spurs? And the riding crop?"

"Full harness, yes sir, but the other accessories aren't used here."

"What? I use them at the Frontier all the time! It's no fun without the spurs, no fun at all."

Reins slapping against her back, annoying bit in her mouth, she was ridden roughly and hard, so hard she was reminded of Fuad. A brute in training.

"Vinod, now spray her with that bitch-in-heat stuff and send for a German Shepherd."

Make that, a brute and a pervert.

188

"Uh, sir, uh, we don't have dogs here."

"Why the hell not?"

"This is a very high-class club, sir."

"Are you insinuating that I'm not high-class? How dare you insult me, you wretch! Come here!"

And he slapped Vinod hard on both cheeks.

Make that, a brute, pervert, and tyrant. The future of The Office was assured.

The 27 days inched past, filled with good and bad appointments. Dr. Jibril, for example, sang opera arias to her, especially from *Aïda*. He'd order a pharaoh's costume for himself and a Cleopatra costume for her, and he'd reserve the Ramses the Great Room and sing away. She was no expert, but in her opinion he was a darn good tenor.

Then there was one of the (dozens of) Mr. Mohammeds – the one they nicknamed Mohammed the Bald – who wrote limericks. Tammy reminded him of a girl he once knew in Edinburgh, so he always called her Gwen. One day he proudly showed her a limerick he'd written in her honor. She was very touched – until she read it: There once was an asshole named Gwen/For whom Mo had such a yen/He'd fuck her just fine/But in ten minutes' time/He'd want to fuck her again. A few weeks later he had yet another one. Mo was a very nice guy/Who loved to watch asses fly/Gwen was a nine/and oh, she was fine/An asshole that he'd like to buy.

The easiest executive of all, however, was the ever-smiling Mr. Musa. He'd satisfy himself in forty-five seconds and then fall asleep on her. His naps would often last for several hours, she could sometimes read newspapers or watch CNN while he slept, and he distributed Outstandings like water.

Sheikh Mustafa always requested a *raqiisa,* or dancing girl. He never said a word, sitting on the couch, neglected cigarette between his fingers lifting strings of smoke into the air, watching her, smiling wanly, distant. When the cigarette became uncomfortably small he'd light another, and let it burn unsmoked and unnoticed, while he watched her dance, a look of profound melancholy in his eyes. He never touched her, never spoke to her, and she never learned the reason for his sadness.

Finally, dear Taymoor returned. She bounded into his arms like a lost puppy. He swept her up and swung her around.

"Oh, my sweet! How good to have you back in my arms! Sometimes I forget how much I love you until you're not there." He pressed her close, then held her by the shoulders and inspected her, eyes twinkling. "How am I supposed to keep a straight face around someone wearing half a pirate outfit? Here. Put this on." He handed her a box wrapped in silver paper tied with a gold ribbon.

"I'm not allowed..." she began.

"I know I know I know I know! Open it anyway."

"Oh! A dress! A real dress!" An Arab dress, but a real one it was, a *fustan,* with bands of exquisite gold and red embroidery down the front and rimming the sleeves. It was beautiful. Almost.

"Do you like it?"

"Words can't begin to describe what it means to me, Taymoor. It's the first dress I've seen in ages. It's beautiful. And so...*green.* How's that? Do I look anything at all like a real person?"

"You look absolutely stunning, my sweet. I want you to wear it every time I come. Now come here and put your head on my knees." He stroked her hair pensively for a few minutes. "I want you to tell me your name. It's important that I know."

She hesitated. She trusted him, but there again, she'd trusted Dr. Hassan. She took a deep breath. "My name is Tamara Lynne Simmons and I'm from Bethesda, Maryland, right outside Washington, D.C."

"Thank you." He paused. His hand trembled slightly. "Tamara Lynne Simmons, I want you for my wife."

Her head was swimming. Marriage? Had this wonderful man actually proposed *marriage?*

"Are you serious?" she sputtered at last. It wasn't at all what she'd intended to say, but she couldn't get her brain to stop spinning.

He sighed, slumping in disappointment. "I've never been more serious in my life. My sweet, this past month without your touch has been miserable. You were always on my mind. This is no life for you, and my joy is incomplete without you. Kiwi, I mean Tamara, you're a kind and gentle woman, an honest and brave woman, a remarkably beautiful woman. I will know paradise on earth with you, my sweet."

He was always quoting the Koran at her, and she decided to tease him a little. "I thought in paradise they only had dark-eyed women."

He laughed. "'They shall sit with bashful, dark-eyed virgins, as chaste as the sheltered eggs of ostriches.' Well, God has sent *this* mortal a blue-eyed blonde."

"Oh dear! If I have to be bashful, and have dark eyes, and be a virgin, we'll both be out of luck."

He laughed, but quickly sobered. "You haven't given me your answer."

"Dear, dear Taymoor, you're wonderful to even think of marriage with me. I don't have to tell you how much I want

191

to get out of this place, but aren't you afraid that marrying a wh–, uh, someone like me, might compromise your reputation?"

"I've already thought of that." He smiled, touched at her concern for him. "You didn't choose this job, that's for sure. Besides, you'll be a respectable wife. Only a handful of people will even know you exist. I don't think it'll be a problem."

Of course. A respectable Arab wife. Well guarded. Cloistered. Not her idea of paradise. Too, she recognized a subtle change in his tone of voice. Authoritative. Even, she hated like the dickens to admit, some-what patronizing. What was there about the word marriage that made men so possessive? *Anything,* though, would be better than stay-ing on the Circuit.

"Could I have a kitty?" she said abruptly, trying to distract herself from niggling doubts. At that very moment she missed her soft friend Cleo so deeply that tears welled in her eyes. "A gray long-haired kitty?"

"A hundred cats, if they'd make you happy. A million, even. Well, maybe not a million."

She started misting up. "I'm so lucky to have met you, Taymoor, you're a precious dream come true."

"You still haven't actually given me an answer."

What else was there to say? "Yes, of course, yes yes yes!"

He bounded across the room like a three-year-old. "You truly are a gift from God."

"So I'm not dreaming after all?"

"Nor I?"

They laughed. Kissed. Made love.

Later, they lay tenderly in each other's arms, filled with content-ment. He unleashed a loose rolling chuckle. "I never thought I'd see the day that I'd be buying myself a wife," he said.

She sat bolt upright, suddenly very worried. "What if he won't sell me?"

"Lie back down, my sweet, I just want to enjoy looking at that beautiful rear of yours. Listen to me. If the price is right, he'll sell, and I can guarantee you that the price will be right. How much are you going to cost me, anyway?"

"He's making a fortune off me, and I really don't know at this point what he thinks I'm worth. There are a couple bids in for me, and from what I understand the high one right now is ninety-something. I believe he paid $113,000 for me."

"Not even as much as a decent car, I'd say," and if he hadn't touched a playful finger to her nose she'd have been thoroughly miffed. "I'll offer him three hundred thousand. That ought to do it."

"How can I ever thank you, Taymoor?"

"You're giving me yourself, and there's no finer gift than that. You're worth it," he said simply. Her heart swelled with love. Then, eyes gleaming, he added, "Think nothing of it, my sweet. I've paid a great deal more for thoroughbreds."

Over the next few weeks Tammy alternated between heady daydreams about her future life with Taymoor and an unrelenting sense of impending catastrophe. Her nightmares returned, and she dragged the demons around after her like a leaden shadow.

He'd be insane to sell you, they hooted, *because you generate more than $75,000 a week for him.*

She did her best to put the demons out of her mind. The prince was going to sell her, and she was going to marry Taymoor. Period.

"What's gotten into you?" Mr. Ali wanted to know. "One day you get two Outstandings and the next, three Unsatisfactories."

"I guess I'm just in a slump," she said, not wishing to elaborate.

"That's dangerous, this close to your annual review. Muharram's only a month away. We're not obliged to renew your lease, you know."

She was jolted back to reality. Taymoor didn't own her yet. As much as she hated The Office, it was by far the least objectionable club on the Circuit, as Mr. Ali frequently reminded her. To underscore his point he'd shown staff members videos of other locations where they could be reassigned. The Oasis specialized in freaks, many of whom were designed by a mad but extremely imaginative surgeon named Dr. Rasheed. He was fond of grafting nipples onto buttocks, creating Siamese twins, grafting boobs onto backs, fusing the soles of feet together, grafting a right wrist to a left ankle, and many other unthinkable creations. At the Ranch, "fillies" and "heifers" were kept silenced and handcuffed in stables and hot-iron branded. The New Frontier was a B&D, or bondage and discipline club, where "filthy sluts" were tied up and beaten, or "insufferable bitches" were chained down and whipped. There was also reputedly a six-foot-six Angolan dominatrix who would obligingly whip or spank naughty members who felt the need. The Falcon Club catered to blood-and-gore sadists. And most horrifying of all, the Rodeo, a snuff club, where people were whipped to a pulp and sub-merged in habanero pepper sauce, then dropped into boiling oil, drowned in shit, or put on a spit and roasted.

She asked Butter-Butt, a Danish rump also leased by the Prince, what his criteria were for taking girls into his harem.

194

She shrugged. "Nobody knows. He is completely capricious. Two years ago he was planning an orgy, so all seven of his rumps went to his harem. Usually it's only one or two. Who knows?"

The demons were positively overjoyed to have this information, and for three sleeping-shifts running Tammy had screaming nightmares again. Always made for popularity in the crowded dormitory.

With constant fear enshrouding her it took real effort to show requisite amounts of "enthusiasm" to the executives, particularly since Butter-Butt had also mentioned that the prince used an assortment of names and that any of the men who sent for her might in fact be His Gruesomeness himself.

"But this man owns us. Shouldn't we at least know who he is?"

"You are thinking that Mr. Ali will be telling us, 'this is the Prince Macabre'? Mr. Ali is wishing we remain alive. If we know the man we are meeting is enjoying dead girls, perhaps our hearts are collapsing and we are becoming dead girls too soon."

Even though she hadn't wanted to mention her hopes about marriage to Mr. Ali, she did, of course, share her good news with dear Heineken.

"Mr. Taymoor? Nice guy. Big tipper, too," he said approvingly. "Gave me a thousand dollars one time." Then he shrugged sadly. "Guess you're better off in a fancy house here than in a dumpy little cabin in Colorado."

Guilty tears sprang to her eyes. "But – I didn't realize – oh, Heineken. I'm so sorry! I didn't understand that that's what…that's what…you had in mind. I should have, oh, Heineken." Her remorseful kiss on his cheek made him blush furiously. "Can you ever forgive me for being such a dolt?"

195

"Understand," he said thickly, stuffing his hands into his pockets. "Big-city gal, anyhow. Can't even split a log."

"Heineken, please forgive me. I just...I mean, I didn't..."

"S'okay. Shouldn't have teased you so much. Sorry 'bout that."

"No, that's not it at all. I was just too dense to understand what you were trying to say."

"What's important, you get out of here."

"Heineken..."

"S'okay. He's got tons more money than me anyhow. If you're okay, I'll be happy. Gotta run."

"Heineken..."

"Pierre," he corrected with a half-hearted grin.

She wanted to race after him and fling her arms around him, but she'd already pushed her transit time to the limit, and Col. Kamal was ill-tempered even on his good days.

The meeting was a disaster. She didn't have her mind on what she was doing and wound up with a two-hour Unsatisfactory, with the review less than two weeks away. Damn.

On one of the last days of Zul-Hijjah 1429 she was lying beside a napping Taymoor, reading a *Vogue* he'd thoughtfully brought her, watching Wolf Blitzer on CNN, trying not to let melancholy over hurting her truest friend ruin her prospects with the generous man beside her. Was she really going to get a life again? Decide all by herself what she was going to eat, have a pretty kitty to love, and read read read?

Almost as if he'd read her mind Taymoor awoke, yawned, and pulled out pictures of a walled estate that would make a movie star drool. "I've found a house for you," he said. "The pool needs work, and the windows in the bedrooms are too small, and eventually I'll want to reconfigure the women's salon, but for now it'll do."

"Darling, it's incredible. Absolutely incredible. I'm touched. I'd have been perfectly happy with something simple; I never dreamed it would be so lavish."

"A wife does not question her husband's judgment." Those brown eyes suddenly took on a steely look. "She does not question her hus-band's orders. I'm very traditional in that regard. And I'm giving you fair notice, if you disobey me I'll be obliged to correct you."

"You mean, beat me?" Her voice sounded thin and tight.

"Of course. 'As for those from whom you fear disobedience, admonish them and send them to beds apart and beat them.' When I become your husband I become responsible for your behavior, and I take my responsibilities seriously. I won't beat you very often, or very hard, but I most assuredly reserve the right to do so. Now, about this house."

Her mind was hardly on the pictures. She rarely had felt so depressed, so guilty. Had she been so caught up in her selfish chance for escape that she'd ignored her best friend's feelings? She wished a thousand ways that she hadn't been so insensitive, so deaf. She had to get out of The Office, but was marrying a man who was going to hit her and jail her in a palace the only way to do it? It took a painful quarter of a second for her to decide: it was.

She glanced uncomfortably at Taymoor. Merchandise to the highest bidder. When she got off duty she cried herself to sleep.

Tammy awoke the eleventh of Muharram with lead in her stomach.

197

Mr. Ali assembled all five of the prince's trembling rumps in the Garden Room, wearing nothing but their anklets. Butter-Butt pressed her thumb to her cheek. It was generous of her, since as she was only two months short of her 26th birthday, she needed good luck worse than anyone.

The cologne-soaked goateed snob Tammy recognized from before appeared, arranged himself importantly on a sofa, and withdrew some files from a hand-tooled leather case. Without courtesies or preliminaries, the review was under way.

"Number 188."

Butter-Butt stepped forward. Tammy prayed silently for her. It was almost a foregone conclusion that she'd be transferred, but she was terrified of being turned into a freak and sent to the Oasis.

"Boobs 4.5, Ass 7.6, Pleasurability, 6.2, Performance 3, average 5.3. She's had a disappointing year," Mr. Ali began, "her attitudes have deteriorated and we've only had two offers for her all year. Moreover, she's nearly 26. The Office does not wish to renew her lease."

"Amortization?"

"Returned more than seven thousand percent on His Highness' investment in four years."

"Auction. Number 241."

Tammy didn't dare give their sign of relief – they were forbidden to move – but she tried to send some sympathetic thought waves. The executive who currently had the highest bid for her was fat and ugly, but apparently wasn't too bad a sort. As much as she could hope for.

Jiggle-Butt had had a good year and her lease was renewed, but Moonbeam's performance was only a 2, and worse, she was only seven months from retirement age. "She's sagging everywhere, Dreadful. Brood ranch."

It was Fabulous Fanny's turn.

"Boobs 7.1, Ass 8.1, Pleasurability, 7.6, Performance 7, average 7.5. Excellent year, twice Rump of the Month, eight offers for purchase. The Office is prepared to renew her lease."

"Age?"

"Twenty-four and three months."

"Experience?"

"This is her first year at The Office, sir, but she worked five-and-a-half years at the Candlelight Lounge."

"Defer temporarily. 421."

"Boobs 1.3, Ass 9.4, Pleasurability 7.6, Performance 7, Average 6.3. Rookie. After a slow start she has generally performed well. Twice Rump of the Month. Six offers, including one at more than seven times the purchase price. The Office is prepared to renew."

"Age?"

"Twenty-one and eight months."

"Experience?"

"This was her first year at The Office; prior to that she was privately owned."

"Seven times the purchase price, you say?"

"Yes sir."

Tammy held her breath. Please please please please.

"Nine-point-four?"

"Yes sir, there's only one other nine-rump in The Office, and she's a nine-point-zero. Turn around, let him see."

"Indeed."

Okay, she thought, here it comes. Blood thundered in her ears.

"What did you say, Mr. Ali? Another nine-rump? How long has she been here? And why wasn't I immediately informed?"

"She's not a blonde, sir, she's Indian."

"He has the right of first refusal for nine-rumps. Whether His Highness accepts or rejects the *dawaab* is his decision, not yours, Mr. Ali."

Tammy stiffened. He'd referred to them as livestock.

"I did indeed ask Sheikh Azzedine if he'd be willing to sell her, sir, but he will entertain no offers."

"Sheikh Azzedine's business now runs the risk of encountering, shall we say, unexpected reversals. I will inspect her before I leave here today. And next time, you will not neglect informing me."

It was almost fun watching Mr. Ali squirm for a change.

He inclined his head. "Of course, sir."

"With regard to 398, a limo will pick her up at sunset to take her to the prince's harem. And with regard to 421, I checked and even as a rookie she has generated more than two million dollars in revenue this past year, so the lease will be renewed. I expect to be shown the Indian rump immediately. Good day."

Fabulous Fanny, who'd been admirably composed, fainted. Butter-Butt wept. Moonbeam stared emptily into space. And Jiggle-Butt and Beauteous Gluteus were hurried back to Central.

"Mr. Taymoor is waiting for you in the Salle de Versailles," Tam-my was informed as she put on a French maid's uniform that presented, she thought wryly, very little threat to the world textile supply.

The dear man rushed to open the door himself. She couldn't get any words out, but her shrug and doleful look told him everything.

"I'll go see him myself and offer ten times what he paid for you," he moaned, punching his pillow. "I'll do whatever it takes."

Tears streamed down her face. "I'm going to end up in that weirdo's harem, I just know it. Oh God, what are we going to do now?"

"I don't intend to give you up that easily, that's for sure. Just give me a little time."

The $500 champagne in the cooler went undrunk. They clung to each other, joined in defeat, united in despair.

Her ratings plummeted. Mr. Ali was baffled. "From third to twelfth, in one month? Are you *trying* to be the bottom of the bot-toms?"

"This is a really hard job," she said lamely.

"Maybe you'd rather be at the Falcon Club. All you have to do there is scream." He paused to let this sink in. "You get back up to fifth place by next month, or else I'll send you back to Screw U."

Not that again, please. The "honey"-sauced food, the infernal simulation machines that never got tired, the porn films projected onto every wall twenty-four seven, the infuriating dildos. The "appreciation" class where they had to groan, squeal, ooh and ah, flatter, express grati-tude.

201

Her ratings improved.

Mr. Ali still wasn't happy. "Fifth? Come on, come on, you used to be Rump of the Month." Suddenly he seemed to catch onto something. "Are you deliberately lowering your performance ratings so you won't be sent to the prince's harem?"

"Not exactly," she stammered. "The truth is, sir, I'm afraid of what'll happen to me if I'm sold off, like Butter-Butt. I'm afraid of being sent to the Oasis. And I'm scared to death he'll call me like Fabulous Fanny."

"The higher your ratings, the more likely it is that you'll stay here, and you know it. Now fix them."

She tried, she really tried. But it was so hard.

The rumor mill corrected itself. Now it appeared that Butter-Butt was sold to a sheikh with an obsession for BJs. If you didn't please him, he'd have your lips sewn shut, put you in a small cage in the corner of the stable, and let you slowly starve to death. And, Tammy thought with an icy shudder, he wasn't even the Prince Macabre.

Not that she didn't occasionally enjoy her job. Some of the members were rather fun.

Mr. Ayub was a world-class klutz whose generous nature and heartfelt apologies hardly compensated for the destruction he wrought. In less than ten minutes, Tammy saw him break a door handle and crack a lamp while he was bumbling about the room looking for his keys. As it turned out, he'd left them in the dumbwaiter, where they'd become lodged in the gears, and the maintenance engineer had to come to repair the damage.

Early in the month of Safar, she crossed Heineken, his morning suit drenched from head to toe. "Mr. Ayub," he said, rolling his eyes. No further explanation needed.

She was still smiling when she got to Central. She toweled off after her shower, submitted to the standard douche and lube job, and reported to Mr. Adham. "New executive today. Not at all bad looking, not at all. African ambassador, veterinarian by profession, formerly with the UN in New York, extremely well connected. Name's Prince Yerima. Go. He's waiting."

Oh no, she thought, that's all I need, a new executive. "What costume, sir?"

"You're wearing it."

Stark naked, already a very bad sign; in her experience men who ordered her naked were five or six times more likely to want to strap her down. In other words, terrifying. The Hall of Mirrors, which magni-fied humiliations a thousand times. A raw new executive who might not know all the rules. Any one would be scary enough, but all three at once?

She started down the hall with dread in her heart.

PART SIX
YERIMA
March 2008 – April 2009
Rabi al-awal 1429 – Jumada al-awal 1430

In any room Prince Yerima would have been striking, his ice-blue African robes breathtaking against his lustrous dark skin. He sat easily on the royal blue velvet sofa, his left arm draped casually over a gold-tasseled pillow, as if he were only vaguely conscious of how splendid he looked.

"Come here." His voice shone like hammered copper.

A thousand Prince Yerimas were reflected in a thousand mirrors, making him a thousand times more magnificent. She caught her breath.

Pretty is as pretty does, chirped the demons. *You were terrified of him for good reason.*

She was trembling with fear, but felt strange sizzles in female places as her bare feet crossed the mirrored floor, leaving little foot-ghosts behind them. Intense masculinity oozed from his pores.

His dark Saharan eyes narrowed, and his smooth brow folded into neat furrows. "Turn around."

He burst into laughter. "I felt sorry for you until I saw your *derrière*, but I see that Almighty God, in His justice, compensated you richly for His lack of generosity in other regards." The statement was made without a trace of malice.

In the blink of an eye he'd disrobed and was stretched out on the silver silk sheets. Oh, she thought, what beautifully sculpted shoulders, what a finely muscled torso. "You're absolutely gorgeous, sir," she heard herself saying.

He shook his head. "Don't try that fake stuff on me. Whores are supposed to say things like that. Come over here and lie down."

"True, sir. Most of the time I don't mean a word of it, but honestly, sir, you're the second-most handsome man I've ever laid eyes on. And sir, your shoulders are especially awesome." She'd often thought of the man with the silver streak in his hair she'd seen out the harem window at Sheikh Khalid's.

He smiled, his even white teeth luminous against his dark lips, eyes dancing. "That's sincere enough, even coming from a whore. Who was the most handsome?"

The twinkle in his eye told her she could probably get away with being saucy. "Whores never say, sir." Besides, she had no idea who he was.

The prince treated her to rich coppery laughter. "I know from your accent that you're American – one of my wives is from Michigan – but do you happen to speak French?"

"Yes, sir. It's a bit rusty, I'm sorry to say, but I'd be glad to get some practice."

"*Très bien.* I'm much more virile in French, you see. Now lie down, I want to take a good look at you. Why are you so afraid of me?"

She hesitated.

"Be honest. I really want to know."

"Okay, sir, several reasons. First, you're new here, and a lot of new executives don't follow the rules about not causing permanent damage." She told him the story about Chesterfeel and he shrank back in horror. "Second, sir, you requested me naked, and in my experience it means you're a lot more likely to use restraints."

"Bad experience?"

"Yes, sir, I'd call three weeks in the hospital, a ruptured rectum, and four months before the knots on my back were gone a pretty bad experience."

He closed his eyes and shook his head. "No wonder. So basically, you're scared to death of being strapped down."

"Absolutely terrified, sir, but nobody cares. They want me in chains, they put me in chains. Just part of my job."

"Don't worry. I have no plans whatsoever to restrain you." He looked at her sideways. "And?" She swallowed uncomfortably. "Look, I'd really like to know, because the more I know how you're put together, and the more I know about your background, the happier I can make you."

"Yes sir. Please forgive me, sir, I mean no offense, but you requested a frank response. The way you look at me makes me feel way more naked than I've ever felt in my whole life. It's disconcerting. Kind of like an automobile enthusiast checking out a new car."

He roared with laughter. "You're right, except I'm a beautiful woman enthusiast. I like what I see, I like what I see very much. May I proceed?"

She used a line from Appreciation class that members always ate up. "You are my lord and master today, and you may do with me whatever you choose."

Instead of nodding and beaming like he was supposed to, he went into gales of laughter. His voice went electronic. "Your phone call is very important to us. Your call is now 627th in line and hold time is approximately two hours and fourteen minutes." He laughed again. "Wow, was that ever a canned line. Don't tell me –" he was still sputtering – "that it ever actually works?"

"Works great on everybody but you, sir." She too dissolved into giggles. This dude was different. Waaay different.

"Listen, uh, I'm feeling a bit strange here myself. This is the first time in my life that I've been to a place like this; I usually don't have much trouble getting girls into my bed, but in this society... Well, anyway, here I am. They tell me that all the girls here are slaves, and that short of hurting them, I can do anything, absolutely anything, I want. My imagination started going a little wild. So, I, like, push a button, and a few minutes later this beautiful naked woman appears in my room. I didn't seduce you, I just ordered you, like lamb chops from a menu. I even have no idea what your name is. And I have no idea if you're going to like me at all. What spooks me is, you might even hate me, but you have to do what I tell you anyway. I want a girl to be in my arms because she *wants* to be there, not because she's obliged to. Tell me honestly, are there men here that you hate?"

"A couple, sir, one in particular, who loves to torment me. Just comes with the territory." He looked like such a dominant male, and it was touching how he let her see some faltering confidence.

"So, can we forget for a while about this slave thing? Will it be okay if I treat you just like a regular girl?"

"I *am* a regular girl, sir. The only difference is, I'm owned by a prince I've never met, and he leased me here. And I do like you, sir. You're an extremely attractive man."

"Thank you. You're a beautiful, beautiful, um, automobile." He winked and ran his hands up and down her length, leaving molten trails. "Nice fenders." He sucked briefly on a nipple, sending shimmers coursing through her. "Hmm," he said approvingly. "Headlights might be little, but they're in excellent working condition." He grinned at her, impossibly handsome, and she knew he'd noticed how she'd sucked in her breath. "Turn over, I want to see your trunk and

207

your exhaust pipe." His fingers explored places they had no business being. Like...like...he owned her. She started getting nervous again. When he looked between her legs, he darkened. "It's been a very long time since a man has taken proper care of you, I see. Well, don't worry, we'll fix that. Now I want you to do some work. Give me a bath. A cat bath, with your tongue. Straddle me, start with my shoulders, then my chest. Then I will give you additional orders. Don't miss a single spot, or there will be conse-quences. *Dire* consequences." He winked again.

"Yes sir." It was as interesting as it was awkward. Arabs tended to have a great deal of body hair, but he had virtually none, and his skin was extremely fine-grained. And she felt little quivers in places she hardly knew were there.

"How do I taste?"

"Influential, sir, sexy as hell. And a little salty."

"Suck," he said, when she reached his nipples. "Work them." He drew in a breath. "Nice job. You may continue."

As she moved lower, it became more complicated, because there was something – a very big something – in the way.

"Now I want you to become acquainted with the little prince and his two bodyguards. Bury your face in them, know how they feel, how they move under your touch. Be nice to them and they will be your very, very good friends. Now give them a cat bath and don't you dare miss a single square millimeter."

"Sir?"

"Yes?"

"I can't find the little prince, sir."

"What?" The raw manly power in his voice made her feel intensely female, but it was also scary. This man had a temper.

"No sir. There's this, um, this baseball bat in the way."

He roared with laughter. A few minutes later, he said, "Finished? Excellent job. Now. In my bed there are only two positions you may assume unless specifically ordered otherwise: the position of supplication, and the position of complete surrender."

The demons started to snicker.

"Lie on your back, your knees at least as far apart as your shoulders, arms at your side, palms upward. This says to me, Master, my body is at your absolute disposal and I will gladly surrender myself to you. Now, if you wish to ask me anything, you lie prostrate, knees apart, palms upward next to your head. This says to me, Master, I wish to ask you something. Then you wait quietly until I acknowledge you. Assume the position of absolute surrender." When she had complied, he continued. "In my bed, you must address me as master or lord. In other places, sir or lord is fine, but when you are in my bed, you must know that I am your master. Is that understood?"

"Yes, my lord."

"You're just mouthing the words, say them like you really understand what being under the complete rule of a lord and master means."

"Yes my lord." The arrogant, good-for-nothing bastard. He'd seemed like so much fun, but this was getting to be outrageous. This is how he treated a regular girl? How would he actually treat a slave?

The demons started guffawing.

"No, I'm still not happy with the way you say that. Repeat after me: in his bed Yerima rules over me, and I will submit to whatever he requires of me."

She felt strangely but not disagreeably humbled as she repeated the words.

"Much better." He awarded her a slight smile. "It's my favorite game. I'm your loving lord and master, and you're my devoted little harem slave. It's meant to stimulate both our appetites. Problem is, in this place you really are my slave, and I really am your master, and it kind of messes up my system. Can you pretend for a while that you don't actually belong to that prince and that you really belong to me? That I've captured you and whisked you away to darkest Africa? And you're frightened beyond belief? But then you see that I might just know a thing or two about the secret of life, and that if you are a very, very obedient harem girl things might turn out a lot better than you thought?"

She laughed. "I think every girl has a fantasy a little bit like that, master. And it really happened to me a couple years ago, but my master was 81 years old, and he didn't like me one bit, so I figured I'd scratch it permanently off my list. But to please you I'll dust it back off and try my best to be your very own harem girl. You rule over me completely, master, and I will submit to whatever you wish."

"Good. The brain, you know, is the most important sex organ we have." He spread her legs wide, looked briefly between them, scowled, and lay down beside her. "Plaster yourself to my back, as much contact as possible. Put your arm around me and hold tight."

After perhaps five minutes pressing against him she wanted his body so badly she didn't know what to do. She'd always wondered exactly what they meant, but she finally understood what the romance novels called "frantic with desire." She wanted to ask him a question, but he was holding her wrist and she didn't dare break his grip. How could she tell him she needed to ask him a question if she couldn't move, and couldn't ask him a question? She squirmed.

"So, you want to ask me something? You may rub me lightly three times with a finger to let me know that you'd like to assume the position of supplication."

"In other words, master, request permission to request permis-sion?"

"Quite correct, if you want to put it that way. Don't forget, you're under my absolute rule."

She groaned and lay prostrate, palms upward.

"What did you want to ask?"

"Um, master, my lord, sir, um, do you plan to do something?"

"Do something? Now just what would that something be?" He sat up and looked at her sideways, eyes dancing.

"Um, I sort of, um, thought that you sent for me to have sex."

He whacked her rear. Hard.

"Master. Sorry, my lord."

"That's more like it. Well, it might surprise you that I didn't come here to have sex with a whore at all." A dramatic pause. "I came here today to make love to a beautiful woman, but that beautiful woman isn't nearly ready yet. The pot's on the stove and the water's heating up, but it hasn't yet started to boil." Another pause. "All right, turn over." He clasped her feet and ran his tongue up and down their soles. Then he licked between each toe. Every place he touched turned to molten gold. "Now you do the same for me."

More delay? Oh no! But even his feet were beautiful. She was so crazy with longing she could hardly concentrate on what she was supposed to do, but it was fun making him suck in his breath and gasp. She bit her lips, trying to maintain some self-control. She rubbed him three times.

"Did you want to ask me something?"

Trembling now, she lay prostrate.

"Master, please, please, please make love to me."
"Hmm, that doesn't sound much like a whore talking."

"It isn't, master, it's my pussy." Her voice was ragged. She was almost in tears. Never in her life had she wanted a man so badly.

He chuckled. "And just what is that pussy of yours saying?"

"She says, would you please tell that incredibly gorgeous hunk to hurry up and come visit me?"

Whack.

"Sorry, master, she says, would you please tell your gorgeous but extremely annoying master to hurry up and come visit me?"

"Turn over and let me see. Oh, yes, we're getting there. Another twenty or thirty minutes should do it."

She whimpered.

"Are you absolutely positive that you want me? Absolutely positive?"

"Please, master, another thirty seconds and I'll be completely insane."

"All right, my dear, if you insist." He took the quivery trembling jumble into his arms tenderly, masterfully, and filled her as no other man had ever filled her. She gasped, closed her eyes, and held on for dear life. There was scarcely time to grab her breath as her legs were pulled this way and that, her arms immobilized in a muscular grip, her heart at a standstill. She wasn't sure she'd ever be able to unscramble her limbs. At last she sensed he was arriving at his destination. Time to writhe and shriek just the way she'd been taught.

Her reward was a volley of stinging slaps, and he threw her unceremoniously onto the floor. "Damned whore," he said through clenched teeth. She cowered in fear as he rose and stood over her. "How dare you insult me like that? Insult my masculinity?" More slaps. "Get the hell out of here. Tell them to send me a whore who knows how to show proper respect for a man of my rank."

"Yes master," she said, completely baffled. "As you wish, my lord. May I rise, master?"
"I said, get the hell out! Crawl, for all I care. Out!"

The knot in her stomach rose halfway up her throat. Another Unsatisfactory. Damn. Mr. Ali had threatened a paddling if she got another one this week, and she still had two days to go. Hating herself, she prostrated herself, palms upward, trying to figure out how she could keep a difficult customer satisfied, Mr. Ali placated, and her bottom unwarmed.

You look so cute when you grovel, the demons snickered.

"Dammit, whore, what is it now?"

"Master, I'm very sorry. Believe me, master, I'm here only for your pleasure. I beg you to tell me what I did to displease you, master, so I can make it up to you any way I can."

Now Prince Yerima was the one who was perplexed. "You honestly don't know?"

"No, my lord and master."

Black desert eyes bore through her. Each bone, each sinew, each thought, was laid bare. "Look at me." He studied her for a moment. She'd never felt so much like a slave. He did rule her completely, and it was no game at all, and it was scary as hell. *"Ça, alors.* You really don't." A burst of full-throated laughter shook the room. "I owe you an apology. I assumed that a whore would know when she was faking it. You're totally, totally clueless. Tell me, how long have you been a whore?"

An apology? From her all-powerful lord and master? "A year and a half, master."

He shook his head sadly. "And in all that time you haven't come across a man worthy of the name?"

Taymoor certainly was a man and a fine one at that. "I see six or ten men every day, master, and some of them are very nice."

"Nice?" he spluttered. *"Nice?"* He threw back his head and howled. "No wonder you shot me all those murderous looks. Look, when I issue commands to a naked woman I feel very manly, and when I feel manly, that naked woman has a very good time. What a pity. The world is so big, and we Africans are so few. Well. I need to redeem the honor of the masculine race, and you need to learn what it's like to be a fully, ahem, educated, ahem, woman. Get back in bed. Don't move a muscle, now, my little virgin whore, just relax, and let me take you on a splendid journey."

Long slender fingers found tropic places. Explored shadowed valleys. Rustled quiet pools. Traced fiery pathways. Once again, he brought her to the brink of insanity. It was unnerving, how much he knew about her. It put her completely at his mercy. To her utter amazement, it felt wonderful.

He pinned her beneath him and stretched his full length out upon her. "Complete surrender, now. Accept my control, and I can take you places you never imagined. No, you're pulling back again. Don't panic, I'll give you back after a while in a much improved condition. Relax. That's more like it. One of these days I'll indeed ask you to resist me, but not until you know how to give yourself over to me. No no no, I won't hurt you. *Au contraire.* Just let yourself go wherever I take you, and this time, don't do anything unless your body absolutely screams at you to do it."

There was no choice now, no escape. She ceased resistance. He summoned her yet, and she released herself to him. He acknowledged her surrender with a knowing smile.

He finally decided she was ready, and plunged. Yes, oh God yes! She found his rhythm and matched him; her body would let her do no less. She clung to him, hungering for his muscled form, raw with the need to seek refuge in his power.

She fell softly, deliciously, through space and time. A gust of whispering wind cradled her and gently bore her up. Her body turned to fire. To steam. And still she fell, drawn inexorably into a pulsing pool.

The world exploded into shimmering light.

"Yes," a deep coppery voice said proudly. "Yes indeed."

The puddle of warm butterscotch in Prince Yerima's bed soon had to reconstitute itself into an Office staff member and get back to work. Tammy staggered around, awed by her sudden feeling of being worthwhile, resentful that no one else seemed to care about the startling change that he'd wrought in her. She was filled with even more con-tempt at the heaving, wheezing executives, but no less was the contempt she felt for herself for demeaning, however unwillingly, the beautiful gift that Prince Yerima had bestowed on her. Whenever she closed her eyes she felt his touch, heard his molten voice, remembered the feel of his velvety skin, felt an urgent quickening.

"Did they change your skin cream?" Honey Buns asked when she saw Tammy in the hall. "You look great."

"What happened to you?" Tittylation asked. "Suddenly you're smiling to yourself all the time."

"Happy Thursday, dearie," said Heineken, who'd liberated some more chocolates for her. "Gee, you sure look pretty."

"What's the matter?" Taymoor asked as she lay in his arms. "You seem so far away."

Panic momentarily clouded her thoughts. "No, nothing, really, darling," she said, as reality returned. "I was just wondering if you'd been able to speak to you-know-who."

"I'm afraid not. He's still abroad and may not be back for weeks. But I did raise my bid for you to $800,000." He sighed deeply.

She sighed too, but not for the same reason. Dear Taymoor still owned her heart. But all the rest of her?

It was nearly a month before Yerima sent for Tammy again.

"Who showed up today, the whore or the newly minted woman?" His black eyes twinkled with mischief.

"They think they sent you a whore, sir, but you get a woman too. No extra charge."

"*Mon Dieu,* spare me. A politician." His intense gaze warmed her, and every place his eyes rested seemed somehow glorified. "You look different. Before, you were sort of dried up. Now your skin cells are plump and happy. There's even more bounce in the way you walk."

"Really, sir?"

216

"Indeed. It shows." He motioned her to her knees. "Did you think about me?"

She shrugged nonchalantly. "Nah, no more than 150 times a day, sir."

"Keep those palms up. I own you now, you know."

She looked up sharply.

"No, I didn't buy you. But indeed, you belong to me, and you know it."

"Sort of, sir."

"Oh, I know," he said with a chuckle, you're in love, but not with me. Let me guess. A *nice* man, right? Does he want to carry you off on his white stallion?"

She couldn't decide whether to be impressed by his perceptiveness or outraged at how he kept knowing things he had no earthly right to know. "He intends to marry me, sir."

"Marry a whore? Is he out of his mind? Oh, but I forgot. He's *nice*."

She glared at him, which made him laugh all the more.

"Well, I'll just settle for owning your body, for now. They tell me there's some cream over there in the drawer. I want you to start by massaging my feet, then my back."

She worked happily away, feeling intensely female.

"Now I want another cat bath, this time, my legs."

"With pleasure, sir. You know, in a previous incarnation I was a cat."

"You're in my bed now; don't forget that I'm your master. Me too. I was a lion in Luxor. I'm still trying to figure out, by the way, why I was demoted to a mere human."

217

When she was finished he said, "Now you are going to massage my chest, just using your nipples."

This project was complicated. Several times she lost her balance and fell against him. She swallowed, remembering… She was breath-ing heavily, and it wasn't from overwork.

"Good. Back on your knees, now. Give the little prince some loving attention. Make it last a long, long time."

The stirrings within her grew more insistent.

After thirty minutes or so he pushed her away. "There, that's enough for today. You are dismissed."

"Master?"

"I said, you are dismissed. I have an appointment at the café downstairs." He cocked his head to one side, eyes twinkling. "Some-thing wrong with your ears?"

"My ears aren't exactly the problem, master."

"Oh," he drawled infuriatingly, "what seems to be the matter?"

She threw composure out the window, along with the scraps of dignity she had left. She knelt. "Prince Yerima, master, I want you. I need you. I've waited almost a whole month for you, and…"

A boom of delighted laughter. "Beg me."

Again? The cells that loathed his arrogance were shouted down by the ones clamoring for his touch. She'd strangle him – afterward. "I beg you, master, please make love to me. Please."

"Prepare to receive your lord and master."

She beat him to the bed and looked up and him, trembling and quivery.

"You sure you still want me?"

"Well, on second thought, master, maybe I'll just leave like you said."

"Oh no you don't!" He gathered her in his arms and pressed her to him. "What happened to the naïve little whore who was here last time?"

"You know perfectly well what happened to her, you arrogant, irresistible, good-for-nothing, sexy-as-hell bastard. Master."

Much later, the molten lava in his bed finally began to cool and take on the shape of a woman.

"You screamed," he said.

"Smpf," she protested thickly, mouth dry, brain all steamed up.

He roared. "You screamed, my dear, you screamed." Prince Yerima put his hand on her thundering heart. "No whore can fake that," he said.

An after-shock quivered through her.

"Enough?"

"Of you, master? Is that possible?" She raised her head and looked at her legs.

"What are you looking at?"

"Just checking. I figured you'd turned me into a pretzel."

"Get ready," he said with a chuckle, "because I'm just warming up."

Almost five hours later he whacked her fondly on the bottom. "How many times did you come?"

"I'm not sure, I lost count. Five? Eight? Do you have a bone in there?"

She thought he was going to laugh, but to her surprise, he slapped her. *"Master.* That's the second offense. Third time, I spank."

"Is that a threat or a promise? Master?"

"Both." He tweaked her nose. "I'd like for you to disobey me sometimes, though. It's no fun bossing somebody around if they're nothing but a jellyfish. I love your playfulness. I'm nuts about your body. Maybe one day, my sweet little whore, I'll take you back to Africa with me."

She needed to ask him something, so she prostrated herself.

"Yes?"

"Master, I'd really appreciate it – please don't take this wrong – could you, I mean, I'd feel happier if you didn't always, um, call me a whore."

His laughter was tinged with incredulity. "But that's what you are."

"Not really, sir. I'm a slave forced to work as a whore. I never would have chosen this life."

He waved her off. "That's what they all say. By profession I'm a veterinarian; in my heart I'm a horse rancher. My cousin sucked me into being a diplomat. I hate it. But my office is in the embassy, my car has diplomatic tags, and everybody calls me His Excellency the Ambassador. Whether I like it or not, I'm a diplomat."

She drew designs on the sheet with her finger. "Yes, master."

His disarming grin made her forgive his bluntness. "You lost your freedom; it's not your fault. You became a whore;

it's not your fault. I'm sorry to say that the result is still the same. Your request is, however, well taken. If the word bothers you, then I won't use it, because when you're with me I want you to cherish every minute. I need to call you something, though. Reminds me. I haven't given you a name yet. When a man owns a woman he gets to give her a new one." He reflected a moment. "I'll call you Sudari. In Fulfulde it means 'jewel'; only you and I will know precisely to which part of your anatomy it refers." The mischief in his smile made her blush. "What name has the *nice* man given you?"

How, she wondered, did he always *know* these things? "Kiwi, master."

"Kiwi?" He turned the word over in his brain a few times. A slow smile became a grin, then amused laughter. "He likes your ass a lot."

The accuracy of his statement completely floored her. "Yes master."

"All right, Sudari, I'll let you go today, before they send up the Mounties. Next time, I'll make you faint, so be ready."

She turned to leave. "Sir?"

He elaborately ignored her until she assumed the proper position. Grrrr.

"Yes?"

"What does a kiwi fruit have to do...I mean, master, how do you *know* things like that?"

"I'm sure it's subconscious, Sudari, since he's so *nice,* but have you ever looked at a cross-slice of kiwi? What does it look like?"

It took a moment for her to figure out what he meant. She blushed. "You're amazing, sir."

"I know. Now get out of here before the little prince needs another snack. Seven hours will have to be enough for today."

Tammy got four steps out the door and had to sit down. "What's the matter?" Wilson asked.

"I can't walk."

"Horrible meeting?"

"To the contrary. But I can't walk a single step. I just can't."

Wilson called for a gurney and rolled her back to Central. Mr. Adham took one look at her flushed cheeks and dispatched her to the infirmary for a blood-alcohol test. When it came up clean Nurse Musa examined her. "Hmm, looks like a severe case of over-enthusiasm. Last time this happened it was a Nigerian," he said, suppressing chuckles.

"Ambassador of Cameroon."

He threw his head back and laughed. "It's a good thing there aren't very many Africans here, or we'd have a serious personnel shortage." He promptly gave her a sitz bath, put her to bed, and told Central to put a red alert on Prince Yerima's file. Normally this would have entailed a substantial increase in his rates, but in his case, because of "connections," he wasn't charged for most club services. It was nearly two days later when Musa cleared her to go back to work, and every time he passed her bed he'd burst out laughing again. She soon became such a regular visitor that he threatened good-naturedly to station a stretcher outside Prince Yerima's room door just to save time.

Some weeks later, Nurse Musa passed her in the hallway. "Hey, wait, I haven't seen you for a while. Your ambassador friend stopped coming?"

"No, sir, he sent for me two days ago."

"Well, I suppose like all muscles, the more it's exercised, the stronger it gets. Especially if it's exercised, and exercised, and exercised..." He chuckled and shook his head.

Tammy really liked Nurse Musa, who treated his patients as if they were actual humans. She told him a story. "In our family we have a picture of my great-grandfather and great-grandmother that was taken right after their honeymoon in 1904. He was sitting down, and she was standing up, very unusual in those days. The story in the family goes that he was too tired to stand up, and she was too sore to sit down."

He howled with laughter.

"The ambassador told me that officially, soccer is their national sport, but that everybody knows what it really is."

"I gotta meet this guy. By the way, I think you'll be well enough to go back to work tomorrow. I'll give you a test drive just to be sure." He winked and patted her on the bottom.

Yerima's startling insights were thoroughly stimulating, but Tammy intensely needed him on a far more basic level. True to his word, he did make her faint from pleasure; she soon came to expect it, as did he, and on the rare occasions she didn't pass out in his arms, he actually apologized.

"Master, all men should have such a problem," she told him.

After one particularly delicious encounter, she stretched lan-guorously, her body filled with light, her eyes feasting on the beautiful man beside her. She loved the liquid natural grace of his movements, his athlete's conditioning, the way his skin lay proudly upon him, as if it were conscious of the splendor of the man beneath.

"Prince Yerima, sir? May I ask you something sir?"

223

"Get one thing straight. Nobody ever pays any attention to me, but for some reason I still try. *Yérima* is our word for prince. My name is Adamou Abdoulaye, but the only name I've ever used is Abdoulaye. Call me Prince Abdoulaye, if you want, or Yerima Abdoulaye, or just Yerima, but please, no more of this Prince Yerima stuff. It's like saying Sahara Desert." Mr. Ali had accented the second syllable of Yerima, but Yerima himself accented the first syllable, YEH ri ma. (In Arabic, *sahara* means desert.)

"I've been meaning to ask you about that too, sir. Except for the Zulus, I didn't realize they still had kings in Africa."

"You'd probably think of my father as a sultan, but to us he's a *lamido*, or king, and the line goes back several hundred years. Now, my darling little Sudari, what did you wish to ask me?"

"I don't know quite how to say it, but I'm really confused. You make sex so beautiful, sir, that now it seems all wrong when I give myself to someone else."

"You don't give yourself. They take you. You're a, uh, you have a job to do."

"Only now that I know...what I was missing, sir, I hate this job more than ever."

His coppery laughter made her smile. "I think I know what you're trying to say. Great sex does wonders for self-esteem, doesn't it? It makes you feel like you deserve the best of everything. Right?"

"Exactly, sir."

"I'll tell you a story. I have four wives, and four times I've watched a metamorphosis. When I married the first one, Aïssatou, she had no self-confidence and only four years of education. Now she's a judge, and a damned good one, too."

"Wow," she said.

"The second one – a French countess named Alizée, by the way – found enough satisfaction, on a level you would recognize, to give up a sizeable fortune and follow this poor nigger to Africa. She's no intellectual, but she's very gifted with her hands – *very* gifted," he added with a wink, "and now she's a highly regarded sculptor. The third one, Amsaou, was so headstrong, everybody was convinced she was going to turn out to be a world-class bitch. These days she's the sweetest of the four. She's the manager of a large hotel and so popular that she makes our president nervous. And the fourth one, JoAnn, the one from Detroit, broke off a six-year relationship after one night with me. Eleven years ago she was selling shoes in New York. Now she's a botany professor."

"Just like a man, sir, if you permit me to say so, to give himself credit for women's success."

He shifted with annoyance. "Just a goddam minute here. I'm not the one who went to night school pregnant. I'm not the one who got up at four in the morning to study for exams. My only role was to give them the infusion of self-worth that nature intended. Then I stood back, tried to keep out of the way, and watched them make me proud." He smiled at her. "You're smart, Sudari, you'd make something of your life too, if you had the opportunity. What would you be if you had a choice?"

It'd been so long since she'd allowed herself the luxury of such thoughts it took her a second to reply. "I wanted to be a diplomat like my father," she began, enjoying the stunned look on his face. "Now, I think I'd like to teach."

He looked at her sideways. "Haven't you forgotten something?"

"Sir?"

"You didn't say a thing about being your *nice* man's wife."

Tammy swallowed. "Before I met you, I thought I loved him." His intense look made her squirm. "I do feel very tender toward him, sir, and don't forget, he's the only person who's offered me a way out of this place."

"Are you that desperate?"

"I'd do practically anything, sir; this place is horrible horrible horrible." There was a pensive silence and she could sense he was considering new possibilities. She didn't want him to think she'd noticed, or that she was pushing him – he *hated* even the slightest hint of manipulation – so she changed the subject. "I can't help but wonder how amazing women like your wives are adapting to life in this society. It must not be easy on them, sir."

"Oh," he said breezily, "they haven't had much trouble, mostly because they all knew how women were treated here and refused to come. Four gorgeous wives and nine of the best children a mortal was ever blessed with, and here I am, a bachelor again." He grimaced. "So, I'm stuck here without them. You see why I hate this job?"

"Yes, Mr. Ambassador," she replied with elaborate innocence.

He tweaked her nose. "Don't you dare call me that, you naughty little, um, whore."

He propped himself up on the pillows, hands clasped behind his head, and she lay on her side pressed close against him with her arm across his chest and her head resting on his shoulder. Her skin rejoiced at being so close to his own, as if it could absorb some of his wonderment. She closed her eyes and sighed happily.

"Tell me about yourself."

She told him about Marseilles, and Dr. Hassan, and Sheikh Khalid, and Sheikh Saud.

"Wait a second. Does Saud have a brother named Farook who's an economist and another brother who's a playboy?"

"Yes, master."

"I know Farook a little. He gave a presentation a few weeks ago and we had a nice chat afterwards. His brother Saud was with him. Good guy." He grinned. "Your type, too. Farook, I mean."

So she also told him about Amberine, and then Sheikh Fahd, and how Dr. Hassan had sold her to the Prince Macabre who leased her to The Office.

"You must see some really strange types here."

"Strange, master?" She laughed. "There's the guy who stuffed hard-boiled eggs up me and made me cackle and lay them while he sat there and masturbated. And another one who puts a dog collar on me and attaches the leash to his ankle, so I have to crawl around after him and bark. I don't really see him trying that on his wife. Oh, and the one who makes me suck his thumb – just his thumb – until he ejaculates. Or the one who wears the watermelon falsies and wants me to suckle him."

"*He's* the one wearing the falsies?"

"Yes, my lord. Breast envy." They both started to laugh. "Or the one who just sticks his fingers in me and masturbates. And then there's the guy who has the valet lock him into a chastity belt and I lick his nipples until he comes."

"Chastity belt? For a man?"

"Oh, yes, my lord. A sheath that keeps the dominator pointed straight down. Mr. Umar, the flogging-master at The House, used to have to wear one too. Or how about the fat guy who dresses up in a tutu and ballerina slippers, with the hairiest legs you ever saw. Should I go on?" Yerima was chuckling. "The disagreeable, and the strange. That's how I spend a lot of my time."

"Disagreeable? As in giving BJs and being sodomized?"

"Yes, master," she squeezed out. How –? Of course he knew she hated them. He was Yerima. And she'd just broken the rule that for-bade her to tell an executive that she objected in the *slightest* to doing something that he wanted her to do. "But, it comes with the territory."

"So let me see if I have this straight. You spend hours and hours a day providing services you hate to men you don't like, who in return slap you and kick you. And you still find a way to stay playful and laugh."

"If it were fun, they wouldn't need slaves. But there are occa-sionally extremely nice fringe benefits, master." She planted a line of kisses down his chestbone. "Extremely nice."

"You notice I've stopped using your exhaust pipe," he said, "because I sensed that you really hated it. But I'm going to pull rank about the BJs. You're just too damned good at them."

"I really don't mind with you, master, because they're just a little part of a lot of things we do. I honestly don't mind. And I know you aren't going to leave me out of the party."

One day Yerima seemed preoccupied, and Tammy asked him what was the matter. "When I was at the UN I was in charge of livestock projects in the Sahel. I told them then that the projects were poorly designed, poorly staffed, and of too short duration to be able to properly evaluate results. Now I've just read a report where they're basically blaming me because the projects were poorly designed, poorly staffed, and of too short duration to be able to properly evaluate results. All just part of the game, I guess."

"What would you have changed, sir?"

"Well, for one thing, make the projects at least three or four years long. For another, refuse to accept personnel whose only qualifications are their politically connected relatives. And third, get a real hands-on subject-matter expert to design the projects instead of an ivory-tower UN bureaucrat."

"Were there any provisions, master, in any of these projects to take women into account?"

"Good point," he said, "but hey, how do you know so much about this stuff?"

"At the Rainbow, Sheikh Fahd had an incredible library. In the year I was there I read more than five hundred books, and probably twenty or twenty-five were about rural development. I read books on Mayan hieroglyphs. On sexual deviants and psychosexual disorders, because I was trying hard to understand him. Then I realized he wasn't a pervert, just really weird. Magic tricks. Pre-school education. Greenhouse horticulture. Ancient Egypt. I sure did love the library."

They shot ideas back and forth for nearly an hour. Taymoor considered world affairs an improper topic for a woman – he kept tossing out a quote from the Koran that said that women were "powerless at disputation" – so she glowed with pleasure when Yerima asked her for her opinions and took her comments seriously. The only problem was, she still had to request permission to change position, she still had to hold her palms upward, and in general, continue to follow the numer-ous rules of his dozens and dozens of sexual games.

His indomitability was extremely exciting as long as their relationship stayed on a strictly physical level, but after an extended discus-sion about the condition of women in Africa, they had moved to a higher plane. In order to petition him to suspend his rules, though, she had to prostrate herself, which immediately destroyed the intellectual rapport, made the relationship revert to a sexual one, and made the answer to her request a foregone conclusion. She kept trying to work her way around the way he'd rigged things, but every time she sent up a test balloon he saw it coming and shot it down.

"May I make a request, sir?"

"You know what to do."

She lay prostrate and waited for him to acknowledge her. She felt ridiculous. The same person who'd just given such a scintillating analysis of incorporating the needs of women into development projects was now lying prostrate, begging permission to beg permission.

"Yes, Sudari?"

"Sir? I request authorization to suspend calling you sir when we're having an intellectual discussion, sir."

The reply was instantaneous. "Of course."

What? Her heart warmed. There was hope for the man after all.

"Actually, when we're still in bed, you should be calling me master. Or, if you prefer, lord. Or, if you like, *jaumu,* which means master in Fulfulde."
She drooped in defeat, steaming.

"Oh, Sudari, I love the way your eyes flash when you're mad, like ice-blue lightning. Now get back in bed and lie prostrate. Your master is about to show you how to use some particular muscles in a particular place for a particular purpose."

It never failed. She made a face at him, collected an amused smile, and climbed back onto the bed. "Master? Don't you see that your rules make it impossible to have a relationship with you on anything except a sexual level?"

"Of course," was the reply. "Why do you think I insist on them? Seeing you on your knees or prostrating yourself really turns me on. And I don't come to here for intellectual stimulation in the first place."

His Excellency Ambassador Dr. Prince Yerima Abdoulaye con-tinued to amaze her. Every time she saw him there was some other technique, some new game, he wanted her to learn. She was an eager student, and the skills he taught her soon translated into improved ratings from other executives, although she could have sworn that she gave as little of herself to them as she could.

"Don't you ever run out of new things to teach me, sir?" she asked him one day.

"Sudari, so far we've covered eight, maybe ten percent of the curriculum. You're still only partway through the introductory course."

Her mouth dropped open. This man was ten times more amazing than she'd ever imagined.

"Sorry, Simba, no real change," Abubakr told John. "She's still there. Apparently quite involved with a top-drawer architect and with an African ambassador. She's a classy girl, that's for sure."

"Chopsticks, do you have any idea how hard this is?"

"I've devoted my life to getting them out because I know, and I hate, how hard it is. Last week we managed to spring four girls from one of the worst clubs on the Circuit – the pretext, a so-called off-site party. It felt so good, because sometimes I go weeks on end without any results. Just remember this: if it's hard on you, it's nothing like what she's going through. You raised her right, you made her strong, and like you always say, I'm sure that in spite of everything, she's still finding a way to laugh."

231

"Why is it," Tammy asked Yerima one day as she happily massaged his long, finely formed feet, "that you order me to do something, and some other executive orders me to do it, and with you I love it, sir, and with him, I resent it like hell. The same exact thing."

"Like what?"

"Like kneeling. Before I met you it positively made my blood boil. Only with you, sir – and this is what I really don't understand – I actually, I don't really know how to say this, but actually like it."

"The first day you were here, and I told you to kneel, you thought I was an arrogant jerk. Right?"

"Yes sir. Exactly."

He went into gales of laughter. "You were so pissed, it was hilarious. You thought I'd be like everybody else and just boss you around for my own pleasure."

"Yes sir. Only I thought I'd disguised my feelings pretty well."

"Nope, not with me. And what happened?"

"You gave me so much pleasure, sir, I thought I'd explode."

The handsome prince gave her the other foot to do. "Simple. The more you release yourself to me, the more pleasure I can give you. The problem is, men instinctively know how to demand total surrender, but a lot don't give anything in exchange. I know the effect that kneeling has on you. Come on now, don't pretend you don't know what I'm talking about. You can't hide anything from me. I see the twitches, the heightened desire, the little quivers, the way you catch your breath. I see all this in your eyes. Meanwhile, it's having exactly the same effects on me. Same thing happens when I make you call me master.

"Listen, I'm not the one who made up those rules, it was Mother Nature. I just know how to apply them. It's a *game*, Sudari. I get to play lord and master, you get to play little harem girl, and we both end up winners. The reason it doesn't work with other men is because they don't make it worth your while. They see a girl on her knees and they love the way it makes them feel, but then they're selfish the way they put that feeling to work. Make sense?"

She nodded.

"I know sometimes you think I'm a control freak. I am, but only in the bedroom. Fortunately or unfortunately, that's the only time you see me, but that's not at all how I run the rest of my life. My wives are almost, almost my equals, and I wouldn't have it any other way. I call Aïssatou my Prime Minister, not my doormat. She's the most amazing woman I know and I'm humbled, and I mean humbled, that she agreed to marry me. An alpha male needs alpha females, not jellyfish."

"My lord, the more I get to know you, the more I respect you on many levels. You really are an amazing person. In fact, I think the word *lord* was invented to describe you."

"Thank you. And you might just be right." He laughed. "Likewise, Sudari. You're interested in everything, you recognize that I know a lot more about life than you do, and you don't let your pride get in the way of your own pleasure. You caught on very fast. You accepted your need to be dominated on a purely sexual level and now you're reaping the rewards, but most women are afraid to. I'm thinking that maybe, just maybe, because you're a slave it was easier for you. A lot of women are even ashamed to even think about it, although it's idiotic, since it's as natural as the need to eat or sleep. Where most people get confused is where the boundaries lie. Women who don't get what they need from their men either turn into bitches or go the other route and let themselves get trampled on, and men who don't have a clue about satisfying women in the bedroom try to get their need to dominate out of their systems by controlling every inch of their women's lives."

Her mind went back to Sheikh Khalid's long-suffering wives. "Better not say that too loud around this part of the world, sir."

She thought he'd laugh, but there was fire in his voice when he spoke. "They're so damned paranoid about fidelity that they've completely lost sight of their wives' sexual needs. The sad part is, men can come to places like this, but women are stuck. They turn into nags, which gets them in trouble. They turn into lesbians, which is an abom-ination. Or they literally go berserk. Do you know that something like ten percent of women here go insane? Their lives are so empty, so pointless."

"Don't act so superior," she said, feigning superiority, "aren't a lot of girls in Africa still given clitoridectomies?" She left off the 'sir' deliberately.

"Indeed," he said, ignoring her breach of the rules, "and it's totally barbaric. My cousin's fighting it, but old traditions die hard."

"The same cousin who roped you into being an ambassador? What exactly does he do?" She was getting away with it. Even he was beginning to accept her as an equal every now and then.

"Yes, the very one. He's...in...politics."

She eyed him slantwise. "And?"

"And, so...he happens to be President."

She shrugged. "Is he as sexy as you?"

234

"Not quite, but he does all right. He's not especially good-looking, but he has a wonderful vitality about him that women find extremely attractive. And, a great sense of humor. When you come home with me you'll immediately notice something. In the U.S. and Europe maybe two out of ten men and one out of ten women are really sexy. In my country, it's more like seven out of ten." His smile now warned, I know what you're up to, you little imp, you. "I cautioned you. Four deliberate, willful violations, and now you must suffer the conse-quences. I'm going to give you that spanking. Just as soon as I catch you."

So, the game button was pushed again. They dashed around the room squealing like children. Her let her duck away from him several times, but finally he caught her in a muscular grip, turned her over his knee, and gave her a few playful spanks. In seconds everything quickly degenerated into giggles, so much so that they both got weak from laughing and she slid off his knee onto the floor.

"Now I get to do what you really wanted me to do." He picked her up without any trouble at all and carried her to the bed. "Let's see," he said. "I love your body from here" – he kissed the top of her head – "all the way to here." He kissed her toes, sending her almost into the ionosphere. "Now if we take an average, it comes out right around here. I wonder if there's any way we could have fun with what's in the middle of you. Hmm, maybe somewhere around here."

Yerima's touch always made her dizzy, but that day, he positively outdid himself. He maintained a single erection for more than four hours – an indoor world record as far as she knew – and her own pleasure fed off itself and multiplied so at the end, when she came to, she could feel her pulse in her gums. She realized she'd been unconscious longer than usual.

Two dark Saharan eyes were peering down at her. "I was starting to get worried. Are you okay?"

235

Her voice was still somewhere on the return trip from Saturn, so she nodded. After a moment she could say, "Can somebody please peel me off the ceiling?"

His laughter washed over her, and he traced the outline of her face with a tender finger. "I really do want to take you home with me. You're something special. I hadn't planned on, uh, liking you, uh, so much. *Mi yidi ma.*" He touched the end of her nose; she grabbed his finger and kissed it. "That's Fulfulde for I want you. I desire you. You know what else it means?" She shook her head. "I love you."

She fought back tears. "My lord. I don't quite know how to say this, but I don't know any more how I could live without you."

"Maybe I'll chain you naked to a bed for the rest of your life. Or put you out in the courtyard and set you to pounding yams." He felt her biceps and shook his head. "Nope, you'd never last an hour." He paused. "I already have four wives, and when I marry it's for life, so I can't even consider marriage. I've been racking my brain trying to come up with a solution, and I know it's not what you're dreaming of, but it's the best I can offer. Maybe you could tutor my children in English, help them with their homework?"

"That sounds wonderful, master."

"I don't want you to think that I hid something. You'd be there as my servant. You'd be restricted to my compound. You'd be under the authority of Aïssatou, my senior wife, who acts as our extremely capable Prime Minister. Oh, and Alizée is the Minister of Cultural Affairs; she's a whiz at entertaining. Amsaou is Minister of Finance, squeezes every franc until it screams. And JoAnn is Minister of Agriculture. Green thumb, amazing what she does with gardens."

"What do your wives call you, master?"

"They call me Yerima. And, let me add, I call each of them Madame. They respect me, and I have a hell of a lot of

236

respect for them. You, of course, would call them Madame Amsaou, or Madame Alizée. I think Aïssatou would like you a lot. You'd live in the ser-vants' quarters. You might go weeks without seeing me. Once a year – say, ahem, on the 11th of Muharram – we'd each decide if we wished to continue with the arrangement. If I didn't want you any more I'd let you go, and if you decided you didn't want to stay, you'd be free to leave. If you're unhappy with something, your first recourse is Madame Aïssatou. I'm the court of appeal. But let me make one thing very, very clear. You will absolutely infuriate me if you just decide to pick up and run away. In fact, when we draw up our agreement I'll add a clause that says if you try to run away and I catch you – which I will, of course – you would forfeit your right to an annual review and I'd get to keep you forever."

"Run away from you, master? Never in a million years."

His offer most assuredly lacked glamor, but it was worth consid-ering. Particularly since it would have one extremely attractive fringe benefit.

As usual, he'd eavesdropped on her thoughts. "Oh, so you're too good to go barefoot and be a nigger's maid? Too proud? You do, of course, have alternatives. You could always remain a whore – excuse the term but that *is* what you are – or you could marry your *nice* man and sleep until noon and spend three hours a day getting dressed, and then attend thrilling tea parties with other insanely bored wives. You'd go bananas in six months."

"But that's not all I'd do, master. I want to write a book about my life."

"Commendable, if your *nice* husband gives you permission, and a computer. Let's say he does, but I wonder if he would. That'll take how long? A year? Two? What'll you do with your mind the other forty or fifty years that you'll be with him? You keep saying how *nice* this man is, but you've never said a word about any encouragement he's given you for your intellectual development, or how much fun you have together, or anything of the sort. I strongly suspect that you fell in love because kindness is in such short supply at this place. He's a possible ticket out, but I frankly don't see much else going for him. You'll be his lonely, ostracized, frustrated, blonde-haired pet that exists only between your neck and your knees. Period. Not his fault, that's how they think of women here, as nice, useful domestic animals."

"That's twenty thousand times better than being a lonely, humiliated, blonde-haired slave in a brothel, master. I know marrying him isn't the ideal solution, but hey, it's a lot better than now."

"Indeed." His high-voltage look emptied her of thoughts, destroyed all attempt at resistance. Damn, she was his, and it was a fact she was going to have to live with. He put his arm around her and drew her close to him. Oh, those arms. Oh, that body.

"Let's talk more about coming home with me. I think you'd fall in love with the children and have the satisfaction of contributing to their development – your Peace Corps mentality would like that. The disadvantage is that your social status would be only slightly higher than it is now, which your pride may not be able to swallow. On the other hand, with your *nice* man you'd be bored for the rest of your life. You'd be more or less respectable, though, until the day people discovered your background."

"Would I ever get to make love with you, master?"

"Every few weeks. That is, unless you're naughty and I have to sell you to some smelly camel-driver."

"Would you beat me, master?"

His look was filled with outrage. "Of *course* not. What do you take me for?" That's when she saw the glint in his eye. "Princes never beat their servants themselves; that's the responsibility of the major-domo." When she shot him the blackest look she could muster he had the nerve to laugh at her. "Actually, I never, ever beat my wives, and have my servant-girls beaten maybe once every five years. When I think they deserve a severe punishment I do something far worse: I deprive them of my attentions. They have actually begged me to beat them instead. Wait. Full disclosure: I did beat Aïssatou once shortly after we were married. She got me straightened out on that score real fast and I haven't laid a hand on her since. We've been married for 18 years."

"But I don't know how you could buy me, my lord. Taymoor has been trying to buy me out of here for almost two years, and my owner refuses to sell. I'm a real money-maker in this place and one of only two nine-rumps in The Office, so I'm worth a bundle."

He shrugged. "So? I'm not too hard up. How much has your *nice* man bid for you?"

"Eight hundred thousand dollars, master."

He coughed. "Well, maybe I'll just ask my cousin to take out a loan from the World Bank. Who's your owner again? I know you've told me, but it's seemed pretty irrelevant before."

"The Prince Macabre, master."

Yerima stiffened. "The one who's mentally unbalanced, and vindictive as hell, and does things with corpses? Not exactly the sort of man I'd like to rub the wrong way. There's no way I could pay what your *nice* man has bid, but maybe we could find some other way."

"You could always set the place on fire, master."

"That could kill somebody. Fire alarm sounds, and you're chained to a bed. The executive and the valet will run for their lives, but you fry. Nice idea, but I'm afraid that's out of the question. Absolutely out of the question. It's the right kind of idea, though. Chaos, confusion, and one sneaky, sneaky ambassador."

Tammy's house was ready. "It's furnished right down to the roses in the vases, ready for you to move in, my sweet," Taymoor told her. Any idea when His Highness gets back from Tahiti? Nigel won't budge; I swear, he won't even take a piss without asking permission."

"Tahiti? I thought he was on the Riviera. And who's Nigel?"

"The idiot who smells like he fell into a vat of perfume. His father's British, didn't you know?"

"Darling, who knows if he's ever coming back? He's been away almost a year now."

"A year? Is that all? It seems like a lifetime. Are we going to have to wait until you retire from this place to be together?"

"Darling," she said, "every day that goes by that I'm not with you is a day wasted from my life."

Whore, said the demons, and they sounded an awful lot like a certain ambassador.

She buried her face in Taymoor's chest so he couldn't see the shame in her eyes.

"Okay, Glute, next assignment is Prince Ibrahim, a member of the Board. An extremely attractive man. An alpha male to the max. He can have a fiery temper, so be very submissive and super-respectful. He's likely to keep you for quite a while and the last thing you need is a ten-hour

Unsatisfactory. Be sweet and very obedient, and he'll love you. Off you go."

Attractive, perhaps, but he'd ordered her to appear at his door naked, which still gave her a major case of the heebie-jeebies. She raced to the Jungle Room and Fernando admitted her.

Her eyes opened wide and her mouth dropped open. There on the sofa was the impossibly handsome man from the garden at Sheikh Khalid's, the silver streak of hair blazing through his thick black hair. Her heart raced. How many times had she thought about him? Fantasized about him? And here she was, only a few feet away.

PART SEVEN
PRINCE IBRAHIM
April 2009 – January 2010
Jumada al-awal 1430 – Safar 1431

Super-submissive, extremely obedient? Mr. Ali's tips about the members were always very helpful. Maybe two or three members a week fit this profile, so she knew to call him master, prostrate, keep her eyes lowered and her head bowed, and to follow every last rule to the T. He absent-mindedly rested his feet on her shoulders while he spoke on the phone.

"Yes, yes, Daood, I agree. But I've been talking with the members, and they want some big changes. They say we're too tame, too boring. They want us to ditch the silly costumes. They think we've been too, um, dainty, in our treatment of staff members. They want collars at the very least, maybe cuffs and leashes. And they want more variety." A pause. "You're absolutely right, we're barely using the atrium. Actually, I have a few ideas about how we can turn it into a serious source of revenue. And we've got to upgrade how we merchandise the girls we're selling off. Members complain that the tits don't jiggle, the asses don't wiggle, and they can't see the pussies at all. We need to make the display interactive. Yes, good idea, maybe something like a marionette. I've got my engineers working on a few ideas and I'll bring a couple prototypes to the next meeting."

He shifted his weight and now both feet rested on her left shoulder. He laughed. "You got that right! More gadgets, more toys. Monthly parties need better shows, more games. Another thing. I positively abhor those isolation hoods. They're bulky, ugly, awkward, like space helmets. We're working on something just as effective, but sleek and classy. And one final thing. An important thing. I was looking over the books the other day and something is way out of whack. We need a special audit." He nodded repeatedly into the

243

phone. "Yes yes. Listen, an exceptionally beautiful slave-girl has just been delivered here, and I would like to avail myself of her services. We'll talk at the next meet-ing. Yes indeed. And hey, again, congratulations on your son's award."

Oh brother, the changes sounded ominous. But what was important: here she was, and he was going to make love to her. She was beside herself with excitement.

"Sorry about that, my dear. I must say, I like the view from here. What are you, nine-three? Nine-four?"

"Nine-four, master."

He sucked in his breath. He placed both feet on her head and held them there. "Do you know what this means?"

This was too easy; Yerima'd taught her well about this little game. "Yes, master. It means that you are my lord and master and that I am your slave."

"Repeat."

"You are my lord and master and I am your slave."

"Which means?"

"You rule me, master. I must comply with anything you command me to do."

"Not exactly. I'm not interested in a compliant slave, I want an obedient one. And I want you to obey me immediately, fully, and willingly."

"Yes, master, I must obey your orders immediately, fully, and willingly." From the smile of anticipation on his face she dared hope that his little game would have the same results as a certain ambassador's.

"Good. You may kiss my feet seven times each. Fernando, warm up some almond oil, will you? Now, my dear, kneel before your master. Massage my tired, tired feet. Would you do that for me?"

"With pleasure, master." She paid special attention to the soles and between the toes, enjoying the visible effect that she was having on him.

He closed his eyes. "Excellent job on that, my dear. I've been away. Our Training Department must be getting a lot better than I thought. Now I'd like for you to massage my back." He stretched out on the bed.

"Ooooh, master, you have such beautiful shoulders, and such a gorgeous back." She swallowed and squeezed her shoulders together with excitement, like a little girl going to meet Cinderella in person. "Oh, goody," she heard herself saying. Happily applying every single technique she'd learned in Training, from Yerima, and a few of her own, she knew she'd given the prince an extremely erotic massage. And in the process, she'd driven herself almost wild.

"Fernando, come check her, please."

"About sixty, seventy percent, Your Highness."

"Okay, a little more prep. How about covering the backs of my legs with kisses, especially the backs of my knees? Now play with His Ecstasy with your fingers. Excellent. Fernando? How are we doing?"

"Ninety percent, Your Highness."

"Good! You have amazingly talented fingers, my dear, but now let me show you what mine can do. Lie on your back and place the soles of your feet together. No, firmly together. Put your hands under your hips and keep them there. This is what I call the position of eager anticipation. It says, Master, I'm yours, whenever you wish to honor me with a visit." He looked between her legs and smiled. "You want me, don't you?" She managed a nod. He lay down beside her, one hand and his lips working her nipples while the other hand busied

245

itself elsewhere. "Do you like that?" She nodded again, panting heavily, squirming with mounting urgency. When she was seconds away from climax he gave her a sideways grin that made her want to swoon. "Get ready, my dear, here comes His Ecstasy."

He was barely inside her when she exploded. She clung to his muscular back, almost weeping with exhilaration. He fed off her and then it was his turn, then hers again, then his. He finally collapsed onto her and lay quiet, sighing with contentment.

The most handsome man she'd ever laid eyes on, and she was in his arms, and he'd surpassed even her wildest fantasy.

At length he rose. "Fernando, come clean her up and get her ready for more. His Ecstasy is already hungry again." He smiled fondly at her. "You're as soft as velvet, so I'm going to name you Mukhmala. Prepare to receive His Ecstasy."

"With great pleasure, master. Only, may I call him His Hardness?"

Prince Ibrahim grinned. "Love it. Yes, you may."

"Master, His Hardness will be my most welcome and honored guest."

This time it was a horizontal tango. He came first, but magic fingers soon had her convulsing with rapture. Even when he moved to her back door, he continued to massage just the right place in just the right way until she thought she'd go into orbit. They came almost simultaneously and lay heaving in each other's arms.

"You just became one of my all-time favorites, Mukhmala. Now I know damned well that it wasn't our Training Department that taught you how to deliver multiple orgasms and that diabolical, satanical foot massage of yours. Were you a prostitute before you came to The Office?"

"No, master."

"You're damned good. Damned good. I'm dying of curiosity." He sat up and checked her file on his laptop. "Hmm, I see you have lots and lots of regular customers but two who show up again and again. Mr. Taymoor, two-and-a-half hours, an hour and forty-five minutes, three hours. Maybe, but I'm not convinced. Oh, and here's Ambassador Abdoulaye. Handsome devil, isn't he, almost as handsome as myself. And from what I hear, an extremely effective ambassador. Four hours. Seven hours, infirmary. Nine and a quarter hours, infirmary." He began to chuckle. "Eleven hours, and back to the infirmary – eleven hours? *Mush maa uul!* Holy Toledo! I think I've found your professor. Am I right?"

"Yes, master."

He was slapping his thigh, howling with delight. "I like a man who takes his responsibilities as a male of the species seriously. Four more trips to the infirmary? Good grief! Please, please, don't tell me he's rough on you."

"Not at all, master, just, um, enthusiastic. And very athletic."

Prince Ibrahim was still laughing, looking so handsome she wanted to cry. "Of those eleven hours, how many was he, uh, actually, uh, teaching you?"

"Probably seven-and-a-half or eight, master."

He threw back his head and roared. "I like this man even more. You're in love with him, aren't you? I can't blame you. Bad idea, though. Those things hardly ever work out. All right, my sweet little Mukhmala, time to show me what else he's taught you. Oh, what a beautiful, beautiful pussy you have, almost as beautiful as your ass. Well proportioned. And so eager to please her master." He chuckled. "His Hardness is hungry again. And he sees a beautiful slave right here that he would dearly love to feast on." He took her in his arms once more. It was more than two hours later when the prince finally col-lapsed in a happy heap.

After a few moments Prince Ibrahim scowled. "Wait a minute. Did you come?"

"I thoroughly enjoyed you, master, but no, not this time. I don't mind a bit; I just love being in your arms."

He gave her a small slap. "Some nerve you have, speaking to me like that."

"I mean no disrespect whatsoever, master. You asked me a question, and I answered truthfully."

He turned her answer over in his mind and decided he liked her frankness. "Well, I suppose that means I need to finish the job." His fingers worked such magic that she had to clutch him to keep from floating away. "Is that better?"

"Thank you, master, that was very kind of you. Not to mention, absolutely amazing."

He looked at his watch. "Yeah, yeah, they all say that. Damn, I have to go." He sat in an easy chair and motioned with his chin for her to prostrate. "Before I dismiss you I want you to kiss my feet seven times each." He rose. "Fernando, give her an Outstanding. Mukhmala, I will send for you often. I love your body, and I love the way you so readily accepted my dominion. You are a very good little slave. You are dismissed."

One of the new arrivals from Belgium was a curvaceous boob/*daya* from the Congo named Nefertitty, or as a Mangbetu noblewoman, Nenzima. She had a series of severe digestive disorders that kept landing her in the infirmary, and since, as Nurse Musa put it, Tammy was a "frequent flyer," they struck up a warm friendship. They furtively called each other by their real names, feeling oh-so-daring. "Zima" had given birth at a free clinic in Brussels, had been told her daughter was stillborn, and soon found herself bound up like a mummy and shipped to The Office. She spoke heatedly of the glib Dr. Hussein who'd double-crossed her; the more she described him, the more Tammy was con-vinced she'd had a run-in or two with the miscreant herself.

Tammy couldn't get over how her friend had taken the double loss of her child and her freedom with such equanimity.

"My grandmother appeared to me in a dream, my sister, and revealed many things to me. She told me my daughter was born alive, but she was black and therefore cost more to raise than they could get by selling her, so Dr. Hussein drowned her and threw her out with the garbage. I know this to be true, because I am my grandmother's name-sake, and she watches over me in a special way. I grieve for my child with a mother's heart, but, my sister, I also know that one day the evil doctor will cross my path again, and I will kill him."

"My late grandmother has twice come to me and warned me about things, too. We were very close. I sure as hell wish I'd paid attention to her when she told me not to go to Marseilles."

Nenzima was so confident of her eventual revenge that she held her head high, had a kind word or cheerful smile for everyone, submitted gracefully to daily humiliations, and sweetly outclassed everybody. Tammy tried to copy Zima's serenity, but it was hard holding back the tears every time she was trundled off to service some other jerk.

Prince Ibrahim summoned her again and again, almost as obsessed with her as she was with him. He always started by making her say an affirmation of submission with his feet on her head, but as soon as that was behind them, he was one of the most amazing lovers – and businessmen – she'd ever encountered. He'd often rest his feet on her as he spent hours on the phone wheeling and dealing; she couldn't help but overhear that he was putting together contracts for hundreds of millions of dollars. Titanium. Tungsten. Copper. Tin. Manganese. Moleb-something. When he'd finally turn his attention to her he was always gener-ous, considerate, and extremely exciting. Not to mention so handsome that she felt shimmers of desire whenever she just looked at him.

But then…well…something would happen. He was unusually strict anyway, but he'd suddenly become intolerant of the slightest breach of the rules. Often it seemed like he'd completely forgotten that she was there; other times, he ordered her to repeat the affirmation of submission four or five times during the same meeting. She still looked forward to their encounters, but lots of unanswered questions lurked in a corner of her brain. She'd seen similar changes in other executives when they'd had way too much liquor or got high, but Ibrahim never touched cocaine and only had a few glasses of Prosecco or chianti. She couldn't figure out why on Monday he'd be funny, charming, and absolutely wonderful, and on Thursday he'd be determined to extinguish even the faintest glimmer of independent thought. Or start out like his incredible self, and two hours later be someone she didn't know at all.

"All right. Today, I want another one of those satanical foot massages of yours, and then I'm just going to lie here, and you're going to make love to me. You may not take His Hardness into your mouth, and you may not use your pussy, but I expect you to make His Hardness very happy. Are you capable of doing that?"

"May I use my tongue, master?"

"Oh, I really like the sound of that. Yes, you may."

Giving a luxurious cat bath was now second nature. She started at his shoulders and his feet and gradually worked toward Grand Central. Then her fingers took over, and they knew just what to do. Deliberate. Languorous. Ever so delicate.

"I can't stand this another damned second," he said raggedly. "Mount me." She slid herself onto him. Very carefully, so as not to disturb the connection, he turned her over and gave himself to prolonged glorious release. "Damn," he said, eyes closed, panting. "Damn. Damn. Damn."

A few minutes later he lay his arm across her. "That was amazing. Amazing. You deserve a special treat. I have only done this twice before to my slave-girls. "Open your legs." Then to her astonishment, Prince Ibrahim went down on her. She closed her eyes half in happy disbelief, half in ecstasy as his tongue worked its magic. Within minutes she was crying out and convulsing with pleasure.

She sobbed quietly.

"What's the matter? I thought you liked it."

"I did, I did, master, it was incredible. Nobody has ever done that for me. Nobody. I can't believe that a royal prince did that for me. An extremely handsome royal prince."

"You're really special, I told you." He sat up. "I took another look at your file. I can't believe that you used to belong to my friend Saud."

She looked up at him in confusion. "I know he had a friend named Prince Fulaan, master, but he never mentioned a Prince Ibrahim."

"Fulaan is one of my names, the one I used when I was a child. He told me about you, how unbelievably insolent you were at first, and then how generous and kind-hearted. I saw him the other day and told him he was nuts to have let you go."

"I was a lot younger then, a lot more naïve, and a lot more rebel-lious, master. That was before my training at The

Office, before the professor, and before a certain extremely sexy Prince Ibrahim." She winked. "He really wasn't missing very much, I'm afraid."

Prince Ibrahim smiled at her. "You mean, you were still a girl, and now you're a woman."

She giggled. "That's a good way of putting it, master. Please send him my warmest respects. I think of him often."

He rose, pulling her to her feet. "Come sit on my lap, my sweet Mukhmala." He kissed her forehead and brushed back a stray tress with tender fingers. "Fernando, a little Giorgio perfume for the pretty girl. Ah. This reminds me so much of when I was a little boy and my nanny Lucia would cradle me in her arms and feed me. Hey, Fernando, please order me a nice osso buco with some risi bisi and tiramisù. With a loaf of hot Italian bread and a bottle of chianti. Every *al-ahad* (Sunday) she'd bake the most wonderful bread and feed it to me while it was still hot. She died twenty-nine years ago on the eleventh of Muharram and I have grieved for her every single day, I miss her so much." He sighed. "My father was always, always, always in meetings, my mother didn't like me because I might get her dress dirty, and my brothers never wanted me tagging along after them, but she hugged me and didn't mind a bit when she'd get Nutella in her hair or strawberry jam all over her dress. She called me her little Prèdiletto, her favorite. One of only two people in my whole life who has truly loved me. Her, and Saud. That's all."

"We all need someone who loves us no matter what, master." Rich, powerful, gorgeous, and only two people in his entire life have really loved him. So sad.

"My wife barely tolerates me and my sons ignore me. This damned title is a curse. I'm forever surrounded by favor-seekers and hangers-on and sycophants. There, you will feed me, please. Oh, what sweet, sweet hands you have. Wait a minute, Fernando, this bread isn't hot. I specifically ordered hot bread. Send it back down and remind them that when I

252

say I want hot bread, I mean it." A fresh loaf of bread soon arrived, steaming and fragrant. It met with his approval.

"Tell me more about your mother, master."

"The most beautiful woman I ever saw in my life. Staggeringly beautiful. But she was cold, arrogant, dismissive, and concerned only about Dior and Versace, New York and Monte Carlo, rubies and emeralds. I was dumped on servants, and none of them loved me. Until the day that Lucia arrived. I fell in love with her." He poured out his heart to her for more than an hour. How his father kept telling him he'd never amount to anything because he was turned down by Harvard. How his older brothers repeatedly bullied and tormented him. How he had private tutors, so he never had any childhood friends. She asked him what he was proud of, and he spoke of his travels around the world to buy the finest girls available, how he'd helped transform The Office from an ordinary men's club into a high-class, extremely profitable, well run business. How he'd become one of the top metals traders in the world. How one of his sons was a successful stockbroker and the other in medical school. "They're polite to me, but we don't have much of a relationship. I don't know how to be a father, I don't know how to be a husband. I try, but I have to admit, I'm a lousy husband and a lousy father."

"How did you and Sheikh Saud become friends, master?"

"Our fathers were friends, and one day Sheikh Ahmed brought Saud with him when he came over. I must have been about eight. We've been best friends ever since. We played checkers. We played Monopoly. We played video games. We told each other secrets. We talked about these strange, strange creatures called girls. Now we go skiing together. He actually skis – he's quite good, by the way – but I like to look at the girls in ski suits and take in the *après-ski* scene." He shook his head fondly. "Years ago, when I was young, I had a serious drinking problem. I'd go through a bottle or two of Johnny Blue a day. Made me do some stupid things. But Saud called me on it. He said, Laani, you've got to fix this, or it will destroy you. I fought him. I thought he was insulting me. For months I didn't even speak to him. Then, well, um, something bad happened, and I realized he was right. I went into therapy, and I'm pleased to say that I've conquered that problem. I have to thank Saud for all of it."

Tammy smiled tenderly at him. "You have really touched my heart, master. I had no idea that a wealthy, gorgeous, sexy, kind and generous prince like you could ever have an unhappy life. I wish so much I could reach out to you, but I'm only a slave. I don't know what I can do." She took his face sweetly in her hands and planted a kiss on his forehead.

"You listened to me like no one has listened to me since Lucia. My other slaves' eyes glaze over. They pretend they love me, they pretend that I satisfy them. Makes me sick. I hate fakes. Continue to take good care of His Hardness; I like what you do with him. And I know for a fact that your body is being honest with me. You can't fake true desire, you can't fake true satisfaction. I like that. On your knees, now, my sweet little Mukhmala. You know what to do next."

Later they lay in each other's arms. "I'm starting to understand your professor. Almost nine hours already and look, His Hardness is waking up again. Listen," he said, not addressing Tammy, "you little glutton, you've had enough to eat. Speaking of eating, Fernando?" His eyes narrowed. "How long have you been on duty?"

"More than twenty-two hours, Your Highness."

"I'm sorry, Fernando, this intoxicating slave made me completely lose track of time. I'm starving again. Can you order me a grilled chicken and asiago *panino* with *panna cotta* and spumoni? When the food gets here, you may leave. Ask Central to send me someone else early tomorrow morning; I'm going to try to get some sleep and won't really need anybody for a while."

The dumbwaiter chimed. Tammy'd been hungry for hours, but now the aroma of food had her stomach growling.

He heard. "How thoughtless of me. Get some food up here for her too. Sit on my lap, now, and feed me. Good night, Fernando, thanks again, my good man!"

The dumbwaiter soon chimed again, but she was busy feeding the prince. He'd consider it insubordination if she dared remind him, so she went hungry and the food in the dumbwaiter remained untouched.

She was still on his lap, feeding him and lifting glass after glass of Chianti to his lips. "I only have Italian chefs and I only eat Italian food, in memory of her. Oh, my phone is ringing. Bring it to me, will you?" He chatted for a few minutes and to her stunned amazement, handed it to her. "It's for you. I know, I know, but I'm on the Board, and I'm personally authorizing you to speak to this person."

She held a phone to her ear for the first time in four-and-a-half years. "Hello?" she said, her voice shaking.

"Hello, Farida? My name is Suraiya. I just wanted to thank you for all the help you gave my husband."

It took her a second to put two and two together. "You mean to say, my lady, that you and Sheikh Saud got married?"

"Three weeks ago. We just got back from our honeymoon in Palm Beach and we wanted you to know."

"I'm so very happy for you! Congratulations congratulations con-gratulations, Sheikha Suraiya!"

Another voice came on the line. "Farida?"

She laughed delightedly. "Hey there, boss. How are you? It's so, so nice to hear your voice!"

Prince Ibrahim's mouth fell open. "I'm so happy for both of you. You've made my week. No, actually, you've made my *year*."

"You gave me my life back," said Sheikh Saud. "Thank you again, from the bottom of my heart."

"God bless you both. And my warmest best wishes for years and years of happiness together." She gave the phone back to Prince Ibra-him, tears of joy filling her eyes.

"Boss? *Boss?*" said Prince Ibrahim. "He was your *master*."

The happy moment was shattered. She shrank back, suddenly afraid. "Yes, my lord, he was. But as time went on, he also became my friend."

Ibrahim shook his head in disapproval. "Shocking. Absolutely shocking. I need to have a word with him. And before you start getting any funny ideas with me, my little Mukhmala, I want you to say the affirmation of submission again." There was something in his voice she didn't much like, but she prostrated herself and repeated the words. "Maybe I rattled on too much about my childhood, maybe I let you ask me too many personal questions. I thought you were different, but now I see right where you're going. I will never be your friend, no matter how cunning you think you are. You think you're the first slave who's tried to curry favor with me? I know all the games, all the tricks. I forbid you to lie to me and tell me that you love me; I know that game inside and out. And I forbid you to ask me any more questions about my private affairs.

"Get one thing clear: I'm not being friendly, I'm just being a nice master. I will not have you forget who I am and who you are. Tonight, I guarantee that you will remember. On your knees, I want you to go over and get that bottle of Prosecco, and bring it to me, still on your knees. And just to make sure you're acutely aware that you are under my rule, tonight you will call me your lord and master, and each time you speak those are the first words I want to hear coming from your mouth."

"My lord and master." She brought him the bottle.

"Do you know how to open it?"

"My lord and master, I do." She picked up a towel and started to work it open.

He slapped her.

"Did I tell you to open it?"

"My lord and master, sort of."

Another slap. "There's no sort of. Either I did, or I didn't."

She gulped. "My lord and master, no."

"Open it." With shaking hands, she obeyed. "Why haven't you served me?" he snarled.

"My lord and master has not yet commanded me to do so."

"Good. You're learning true subservience. On your knees, go get me a flute and serve me. I was going to give you a glass too, to celebrate your former master's marriage, but since you were disrespectful to him, now you will serve me while I celebrate alone."

She crawled over to the cabinet. Oh shit, the glasses were on the top shelf. She assumed the position of petition.

"Yes?"

"My lord and master, may I stand up to reach a glass?"

"Good girl. Yes, you may, then right back on your knees. Now you may serve me." She poured him a glass. He waited. "I said, serve me! Is there something wrong with your ears?"

She trembled as she raised the glass to his lips. "Are you afraid of me?"

"Yes, master."

Oh shit! Her hand flew to her mouth. "My–" She threw herself down and pressed her forehead to the floor. He kicked her. Hard. "For that act of disobedience I will send you to Training tomorrow for a good paddling. Now, serve me again." When the bottle was empty he ordered her to give him a twenty-minute BJ. "To further emphasize my annoyance I will deprive you of your own pleasure tonight. Finally, I am commanding you to do what my slaves tell me is the hardest thing I ever order them to do. You will stay in my bed tonight, with His Hardness in your mouth. You will not change position. You will simply keep him warm. If I move, you must immediately reposition yourself. If I discover that he is out in the cold, I will be very angry and you will pay the consequences. I recommend that you not fall asleep." He pressed a button that put out all the lights, put his leg across her, and was snoring softly in seconds.

Tammy was in an extremely uncomfortable position, she was scared that if she fell asleep she'd accidentally bite His Hardness or he'd fall out of her mouth, and it had been more than 20 hours since she'd had any food. She sighed. Just another fun day at The Office.

She was feeling very sorry for herself, but thought back on her own childhood that was overflowing with happy memories. She remembered the song from Sunday school, "someone far from harbor you may guide across the bar, brighten the corner where you are." Dear God, she prayed as she lay there in the dark, this man is troubled, and grieving, and far from harbor, and I so want to help him, but I have no idea how. The answer was immediate: *try love*. She fought. He's forbidden me to tell him that I love him. *Try love*. But I have no idea what to do, how to go about it. *Try love*.

She spent the rest of the night wondering who this cold and dictatorial stranger was beside her, and how a frightened slave could reach out in love to a complicated, scary, domineering royal prince.

Mr. Suleyman was fired for embezzling more than six million dollars and the file handed over to the public prosecutor. Dr. Kamal replaced him as general manager of The Office; he was stern, con-descending, and helped himself to staff members' services as often as possible.

The member survey, conducted at the same time, showed over-whelming support for a drastic change in policies, and the Office made a sharp turn toward raunchiness. Inactive members returned, and applications for new memberships soared. Members still had to abide by the strict prohibition on violence, but short of that, they could do just about whatever they wanted. No more costumes. A three-inch stainless steel collar was soldered around their necks and they also wore leather cuffs on ankles and wrists. To speed up transit and, not coincidentally, maximize billable time, they were strapped to vehicles resembling hotel baggage carts and delivered by eunuchs.

New rules were posted:

1) Obey orders promptly and cheerfully.
2) No comments, complaining, or crying.
3) You will under no circumstances touch your body.
4) Any infraction will entail 24 hours without food. Two infractions in one week will entail 14 days of probation. Any infraction during probation will result in automatic dismissal.

Central was transformed into a viewing area where executives could watch, through one-way mirrors, every aspect of hygiene, prepar-ation for assignments, and even sleep. The sleeping quarters were likewise "upgraded" to

259

exhibit assets to maximum advantage. Boobs now slept halfway seated with knees splayed wide open; asses were stretched over a hump and secured in place. The display positions were thoroughly uncomfortable, but staff members were so exhausted after seventeen-hour days that most of them immediately fell asleep anyway.

Staff members were horror-stricken, but executives just went wild. Before, maybe one in five would use restraints, but now, with the collar and cuffs begging to be used, it became more like two out of three. Assignments lasted longer, executives were encouraged to order more than one attendant at a time, and The Office became severely short-staffed. The Training Department could scarcely keep up with the influx of new acquisitions, even though the six-week curriculum was compressed to four. They even started giving staff members shots to eliminate the down time caused by female cycles.

The atrium was converted into the Garden of Delight, with a huge phallus-shaped fountain and pleasure stations scattered around. The stations were staffed by asses, boobs, or suckers who were securely attached in user-friendly positions to adjustable service frames that could be rolled into place. When one was used, it would be rolled away and a fresh one would quickly replace it.

Part of the problem with staffing was the newly featured magic capsule, which caused wild, wild gyrations that executives loved to watch. However, it was so potent that it put the staff member out of commission for an entire week, for fear that any residue could have adverse effects on unsuspecting executives. They started out with four shows a day, but they were so popular that they started doing eight, then twelve, then twenty-four a day. Clearly, they had to find another staffing solution. Then someone had a stroke of genius – Jewish whores! Instead of packing them off directly to the New Frontier or the Falcon Club, why not assign them to rotate on capsule duty? No need to pull anyone from assignments, because they'd just use the same ones again and again.

However, before this solution was found, Tammy was once star of the show. Mr. Rasheed explained to the new assistant manager how to set things up. "First, Hussein, you put a shoulder harness on her. Make sure the straps are on tight; it needs to hold her weight and she'll be thrashing around. Put this cloth hood over her head and tie it around her neck. Now you attach these elastic cords to her wrists and ankles. Then comes the good part. You take this perforated stuffer and put it in. Be sure to use rubber gloves. Take one of the capsules – it's basically habanero extract but made safer – put it inside the stuffer, then you turn this knob that opens it up so it can't come out. Then you suspend her from this rod. You set the timer for four minutes while the capsule activates. Then you open the curtain. The show lasts for five or six minutes, then you close the curtain. Got it?"

"I can't wait to see this."

At first she felt nothing, then a delightful warmth. Soon the warmth wasn't delightful at all; it felt like she was on fire. The curtain opened. Everything became a blur. She didn't hear the men howling with delight, she didn't hear her own screams. She could feel her legs being thrown around, could feel herself struggling against the restraints. At length, at long length, the fire diminished and the curtain closed.

"That was amazing," said Hussein as they took her down and put her on a gurney. "Amazing."

"Careful," said Mr. Rasheed, "use gloves. At the Frontier where I used to work, a drop or two of the medicine got onto a cord, and the manager touched it. He thought he was going to die. So we let Central do the extraction." They jumped back when an after-shock rocked her. "At the Frontier they used to pack them with real chopped habanero peppers, and it made for a great show, but the cunts kept dying, so it got really expensive. This is much better."

261

While staff members were reeling under the weight of the new rules, the Garden, and non-stop assignments, management was busy dreaming up even more surprises. There is a famous picture of Marilyn Monroe with her eyes closed and her lips slightly parted. This photo was printed on masks, and along with Marilyn-style platinum blonde wigs, members didn't need to look at real faces any more.

This innovation led to yet another. The same photo was printed onto Spandex isolation hoods that had built-in ear plugs, blindfolds, and optional gags. It could be zipped up the back and clipped to grommets in the collar.

Both the mask and the hood made BJs impossible, so it became fairly standard to order a sucker as well as regular staff member, putting even more pressure on overstretched personnel.

"Hey, Mr. Ali, sir," said Honey Buns, "they made a mistake on our hoods. Look, they left air holes. You mean we're actually still allowed to breathe?"

He cuffed her so hard she landed on the floor. When she staggered back to her feet, holding her jaw, he wordlessly took her ID card from the slot in her collar, placed it on the terminal, and pressed a few keys. No food for 24 hours.

And suddenly there were machines, toys, gadgets, and gizmos everywhere. Frames like the ones in the Garden soon made their way into the meeting rooms, along with specialty creams, sprays, pillows, and a wide variety of mechanical devices. The one Tammy hated the most was the one Mr. Ali nicknamed the Rump-o-Rator, which looked something like a cross between a two-foot-wide hamster exercise wheel and a pasta machine. A rump could be easily attached to it with straps and clips, and then it could be raised or lowered, tipped from side to side, or rotated into the perfect position for attack. By flipping a switch it could be made to vibrate, grind, writhe, jerk, thrust, or buck.

Staff tried not to think of the reasons they suddenly shared service hallways with goats and sheep, glassy-eyed children, and eunuchs intended for enjoyment. Heineken explained to Tammy that there were three kinds. The least disfigured ("floppy dicks") had a perfectly normal appearance, but had severed cords, making them permanently im-potent. Others ("no-balls") had been deprived of their testicles, and, depending on how the operation was done, could sometimes have erections but of course could not procreate. The most extreme ("no-dicks") were full castrates who had lost all of their external sexual equipment. The Office now offered several of each, as well as fully functioning males who'd been devocalized and defanged for homosexual encounters. One had also been hamstrung, and it was rumored that he'd once been a private pilot who refused to sell the Prince Macabre a nine-point-eight.

The Neptune Room was converted to a lounge with live enter-tainers: belly dancers, strippers, and live couples. Disciplinary pad-dlings now became shows members could attend. And a new category of females was offered for rent: *dayat,* or wet-nurses. The three *dayat* originally purchased couldn't begin to satisfy demand, so they were soon joined by five more. Even that couldn't meet the requests, so The Office purchased nursing sleeves, flexible skin-like plastic cones with pouches inside that could be filled with whiskey, gin-tonic, or any other liquid. The sleeves would fit over natural breasts and elastic straps would hold them in place.

The Office also experimented with novelties created by the mad Dr. Rasheed, like the girls whose breasts had been rolled into long ropes resembling sausages, molded into rectangles, or flattened into pancakes. Members thought they were interesting but not really sexy, so they were soon sold. Rumor had it that the man who bought the sausage boobs kept her in the kneehole of his desk with her sausages tied to the crossbar.

"Now there's an exciting life for you," Butter-Butt said wryly.

Yerima attended a conference in Sydney, and while he was in that part of the world took another week to visit his aunt in Auckland, so Tammy went nearly a month without seeing him. The new policies went into effect while he was away.

Orchid wheeled her into his room on the baggage cart, unstrapped her, and handed him the leash. Then he took her ID card from the slot on her collar and gave it to him.

"What the hell am I supposed to do with all this?" Yerima asked, positively dumbstruck.

"Standard issue now, sir." Orchid shrugged. "Do whatever you want. That's the whole idea."

When the door closed Yerima stared at Tammy in disbelief, holding her card in his hand. "Collar? Cuffs? *Leash?* I didn't ask for those stupid decorations. You know me, I'm a purist. No gadgets, no toys, just good old *au naturel*. Take them all off."

"No sir, profound apologies, sir, I can't. The collar is soldered on and only three people have the keys to the padlocks. The leash can come off, but I'm not allowed to touch it; only you or a valet can remove it." She outlined the new policies as he sat in stunned silence. "I think you're supposed to run the card through the service monitor, sir. If you want anything to eat or drink, you can order it right there. Then at the end you run it again when you give me my rating."

"I'm not the least bit comfortable having valets around but I might need to get one in here to explain all this goddam stuff to me." He sighed, then glanced at her card. "Would you believe this? The picture on your ID card isn't your face, it's your *rear*." He shook his head. "If this weren't the only place where I could find you, I'd have given up by now. I think I've figured out how to smuggle you out of here. I'll be going on home leave in Zul-Qedah, and if things go according to plan, you'll leave with me then."

That was four months off. There was a decent shot that she'd be able to program her sanity to last until then. And oh my, such a pity, such a pity, it would be right before her annual review.

He looked at her curiously and knit his brow. Just what, she wondered, had he seen? "How, sir?"

"I'll tell you what to do when the time comes. Speaking of which, I had a very interesting visit the other day. A guy came to my office and said Heineken sent him to discuss a jewel. Now, in my job I have to assume that my phone is tapped and that bugs are planted everywhere, so we took a walk in the embassy garden. He told me that for more than four years he's been working with your father to try to spring you. They actually came pretty close a couple times, but something always happened. He wanted to know how you were doing so he could let your father know. He runs a safe house for fugitives and might be a great resource to help us with our plans. Your code name is Bulbul, and he goes by Chopsticks. Commit this phone number to memory; you never know when you might need it."

"My dad just doesn't give up, bless his heart." Tears welled in her eyes.

He paused. "He told me a little more about Macabre. He said the corpses at Macabre's orgies are always called Lucia, and they're always scented with Giorgio perfume. And yes, he still plays with dead girls. Now, my darling, roll over. I want to eyeball that nine-star butt that will soon belong just to me." He started warming her up, but abruptly stopped. Sat astride her. Looked her over carefully. "Okay, that does it. Just exactly what have you been up to, my dear little Sudari?"

"Assignments just like always, master." Giorgio perfume? And Lucia? Uh...no. And that coincidence about the eleventh of Muharram? They were starting to pile up a little too fast.

"Oh? Just like always, eh? News bulletin: Sudari, you're a very, very bad liar. I hope this will be the last time you will even consider lying to me. Another man took good care of you. Three, maybe four days ago."

She was stunned. This was Thursday; she'd last seen Prince Ibrahim on Monday, and he'd been in rare form. But she'd been to at least 30 assignments in between. How the hell could he *know?* "Okay, there's an executive who made decent love to me and he made sure I wasn't left out of the party."

"I got used to being the only man who took proper care of you, and now I see I have a co-husband. You're so honest, and so completely free of guile, that your face is like a billboard. Today it's saying, there's another man I really like. And your skin and your pussy are saying, He likes me too, well enough to take proper care of me. Three or four days ago. I don't need to ask you if I'm right; I know I'm right. So, tell me about him."

"Are you jealous, my lord?"

"Of course. I'm male. I'd like to have you all to myself."

"Yes, um, master, I've noticed that a time or two myself."

"But I'm realistic. If I have to share you, at least let me be glad that it's someone doing things right. Now stop stalling around, and let me hear about him. Is he as handsome as me?"

"This much more handsome, master." Her index finger and thumb were almost touching.

266

"Oh! So your fantasy man finally appeared, and he didn't disappoint you. I'm relieved; so often we dream of doing something and then it happens and it turns out to be a colossal flop."

"Do you mind my asking, master, how do you know all these things? It's downright spooky."

"Listen, Sudari, I've been a dedicated student of the female body for thirty years. I experiment. What happens if I do this? Or that? To me it's like the most fascinating puzzle ever created. You push this button here" – he drew circles on her nipple – "and look what happens down here." He chuckled when she quivered. "See? How do her womanly parts look just after she's made wonderful love? Or, ahem, three or four days later? What are the tell-tale signs that she's trying to hide something? How do you know if she's holding back, or giving herself to you completely? How do I know if she's holding back because of something I'm doing wrong, or because of a problem she has? What's the difference between 98 percent surrender and 100 percent? How do you control a woman's body without trying to control her soul? I've studied all these things, Sudari. If they awarded degrees, I'd have a post-doctorate. So don't try lying to me, don't try hiding anything from me, it won't work. It simply will not work."

The way he smiled at her made her fall in love with him all over again. "It's unnerving that you know my body better than I do, my lord, totally unnerving. And time after time you know what I'm thinking even before I'm sure of it myself. Drives me nuts, but I'm in awe of you. It gives you incredible power over me. But once I figured out that you were using that power in beautiful ways for both of us and not just for yourself, I just melted. You really do own my body, and to my amazement, I'm not ashamed in the least to say it. In fact, I couldn't be happier."

"You caught on fast. And don't worry, by the time you've finished my course of instruction, you'll know more than probably one woman in five million, maybe ten million.

You already know more than one in half a million, you know. And it seems to me that you don't exactly mind."

"One in half a million? Really? But if anyone would know, it's you, my lord. Even the way you look at me tells me that you're different. Makes me fifty percent nervous because nobody's ever looked at me that way before and fifty percent bursting with anticipation because I know you're gathering information to plan your moves. I've never, ever felt so completely, utterly, naked. You don't just look at a miscellaneous assemblage of body parts like most men; you look into them, through them. It's hard to describe, sort of like you're steam-cleaning every last dust bunny and polishing up places I didn't even know were there. You're right, there's no way I can hide anything from you because you lay every last molecule, even in my brain, completely bare. And then time after time you turn that naked-ness into glory."

He laughed with delight. "Sudari, what you have just said is beautiful, and I will cherish these words the rest of my life. But you're detouring again. Tell me about this man. What you've told me is the truth and nothing but the truth. I'm still waiting to hear the whole truth."

"Like I said, very handsome, my lord. I've been attracted to him ever since I first saw him. It turns out he's a member of the Board here. What am I going to do, refuse to go?"

"It's your job, it's okay, I understand. Did you give yourself to him?"

"He required it, master, but I would have anyway. He was generous, considerate, and he made me happy. He has a lot of games kind of like yours, too; like, he calls me his sweet little slave-girl."

"Did you do some of the things I taught you?"

"Of course, master, he says I've been exquisitely trained. He realized it couldn't possibly have been the Training

Department, so he went into my file to find out who my professor was, and he immediately figured out it was you. He says he likes a man who takes his masculine responsibilities seriously."

His eyes narrowed. "My bet's on Prince Ibrahim. He's definitely your type, nice broad shoulders, muscular legs, and I admit, he's this much better looking than me. And, I'm pretty sure he's on the Board. Right?" She threw up her arms in exasperation. He'd done it again.

"But, my lord, I'm a little bit scared of him. Most of the time he's just wonderful. But sometimes, well, he's downright tyrannical. Once by mistake I called him master instead of lord and master, and it got me forty strokes. He broke all the rules for me and let me speak with Sheikh Saud and his new bride on the telephone, but blew up when he heard me call him boss instead of master and spent the rest of the night giving me lesson after lesson in extreme, extreme subservience. He even kicked me."

"Do you get kicked a lot?"

"Oh, three, four times a day. And I get slapped twenty, thirty times a day, twice that if I'm on Reception duty. Even you've slapped me, remember? It comes with the territory. But I hadn't expected it from him."

"I sure did, didn't I?" He slumped. "I think it's because I knew you were a slave. Does funny things to a man. Sorry about that."

"You apologized right then and there, which surprised me a lot. One of a handful of apologies I've ever gotten here."

"But back to Ibrahim. There must be a trigger, something that tips him over the edge. Does he do drugs? Drink?"

"Never touches drugs as far as I've seen, and he only drinks a little Prosecco and chianti. Master, I've never seen so much alcohol con-sumed as when I got to this so-called alcohol-free country. I've seen members go through two bottles of whisky in a couple of hours. Ibrahim doesn't drink much at all. He told me that years ago he used to be a heavy drinker until Saud told him it was going to destroy his life, so he had therapy and got it under control."

"Recovering alcoholics sometimes react more intensely to even a little bit than most people. Watch him closely. I'm not sure what you'll be able to do, but at least get a handle on what makes him change. Notice and remember everything he does, and we'll talk about it. Okay?" She nodded. "Now I suggest we get back to what we were doing. Only this time, you be the boss. I'll happily do whatever you command me to do."

"Really? Cool! You mean, for once I rule over you absolutely and completely? Okay, you gorgeous hunk, give me one of those cat-baths, and it'd better be a good one, or else." She laughed with glee.

"Je vous obéis avec plaisir, chère madame." I obey you with pleasure, my dear lady.

Several days later Prince Ibrahim and Tammy had made beautiful love, spent an hour in the jacuzzi together, and she'd sat on his lap and happily fed him his saltimbocca. Now she was lying in bed propped up on one elbow, admiring his beautiful body as he stretched out beside her.

"Ready for more, my dear?" She smiled. "Fernando, put her in a control girdle and shackle her to the A-frame."

Shackles? Tammy began to shake.

270

He grew very serious and his voice was stern. "Mukhmala, what did you say a little while ago about obeying my orders immediately, fully, and willingly?"

"Master, please—"

"Stop. One suggestion, and I trust I will not need to make it more than once. When you are petitioning your master, I would strongly advise that you not be lolling in bed but prostrate with your forehead firmly planted on the floor. You have one second to correct this flagrant breach of protocol." There was a steely edge to his voice. "Oh, a very nice touch, I like the way you place your palms facing upward. Shows commendable commitment to be obedient and submissive. Do I have the professor to thank for this refinement?" She nodded, and he chuckled. "He knows his stuff. That man really knows his stuff. Now, what were you saying?"

"I wish to apologize, master. I have tried time after time to overcome this problem. I tell myself, this time I won't shake, and then it happens anyway. I mean absolutely no disrespect or disobedience to you, master, I just can't help it. It's as if a demon has hold of me and shakes me even when I beg him not to."

"Were you brutalized, my dear?"

"Severely, master."

"Listen, my dear, I love chains on my slaves. It makes His Hardness feel powerful, very powerful. I see you lying there, so beautiful, so helpless, obliged to submit to any desire, and His Hardness goes absolutely wild. I won't punish you today because I know you're trying very hard to please me, but you must overcome this. You *will* delight me by being bound; otherwise you diminish the sensations that you are required to deliver. Slave girls who interfere with their master's pleasure don't as a rule have a very long shelf-life. How long have you been at The Office?"

"Nearly two years, master."

"And no one has noticed this problem before?"

"Master, thank you from the bottom of my heart for being the only executive who has ever expressed any concern. Others have noticed, but they think it's because I've taken one look at their dominator and decide that I'm trembling with desire."

He shook his head in exasperation. "I have absolutely no respect for such clueless idiots. Fernando, bring me the phone. I need to arrange for her to have the special Bondage Therapy program. That usually helps. Meanwhile, Mukhmala, lie over here near me on the rug the way I showed you, the position of eager anticipation. Oh, but let's change it a little. Keep your arms to the side and put your palms facing upward. That's a nice little touch. Fernando, read me the inventory code, will you? I need to clear this special program with her owner."

"T-421-AI, Your Highness."

He chuckled. "AI? Well, that works out nicely. That would be me, Amir Ibrahim. Damn, Nigel keeps buying girls for me and I don't even know who they are. Oh, 421, you say? You're a good producer; I see the figures every week on my revenue report. And here you are, my very own."

Tammy's eyes opened wide. Her gasp of stunned horror was not lost on him.

"Look, Mukhmala, I'm getting tired of dealing with your issues here. First you're freaked out at having to submit to shackles, and now you're freaked out about having to submit to *me*. I'm trying to remain calm, and you're lucky, very lucky, that you just put me in such a good mood. First, let's deal with bondage. Your body automatically asso-ciates it with pain, so we've developed a four-day course that associates it with pleasure. It's intense, but it really works. Most of the girls here have been brutalized. The Office isn't trying to make any of you girls miserable; we just want you to be able to do your jobs. Fair enough?"

Fernando handed him the phone. "Board member Ibrahim here. I'm sending you a staff member who needs to be put through the Bondage Therapy course. Bondage Therapy. Bond-age Ther-a-py. Oh, I don't believe it. Where did our geniuses at Personnel find a specimen like you?" He sighed and shook his head. "Go into Courses, then click on Bondage Therapy, and Curriculum, and everything should be right there. Found it? No, we don't use it very often because the student has to already know female pleasure and we don't encourage – yes, believe it or not, females are quite capable of experiencing sexual pleasure. Are you married? And you're still that clueless? Sometimes, I swear, I'm ashamed to be a male of the human species. Forget it, forget it. Forget it, dammit! I just want the girl to start the training tomorrow."

He groaned. "Have you been able to find the registration form? Good. Owner? That would be myself. Amir Ibrahim, you dolt! Do I need to spell my name? I told you, I'm the Prince Ibrahim who's on the Board. You don't need the lease number because I'm sending her to you myself. Yes, I'm her owner. O-w-n-e-r. You got that? Honest, it's not real complicated." He held his head in despair.

"I know this isn't standard practice but I like this girl and I want to make sure she gets at least one bowl of food a day. Have you noted that down?" He sighed in exasperation. "I know. I know. I'm the one who designed the course. Food deprivation is normally part of the bondage experience. But this course is four days long. I'm not trying to starve her, I just don't want her to freak out every time I pull out a pair of handcuffs. All right, I'll send her down first thing in the morning." He handed the phone back to Fernando. "Where on earth does Personnel find these idiots, the toxic waste dump? At least, Fernando, there are still a few really good employees like you. I really appreciate you. In fact, I'm giving you a good raise."

"Thank you very much, Your Highness."

"On second thought, Fernando, I need the phone again. Hello, Kamal? Ibrahim here. Can you please find out what the hell is going on with Personnel? The recent crop of hires has been a disaster. Lots of complaints about valets, and I just nearly fired an idiot in the Training Department. Reminds me of five or six years ago when Ayub was selling jobs to the highest bidder. Worth checking out. Maybe a few undercover test candidates? Thanks. How's your ankle, by the way? Good, glad to hear it. All right, see you around." He turned to Tammy, who was still shaking. "Calm down, calm down, I won't put you in irons today. Now, let's talk about the other issue. May I point out that only a few moments ago you were screaming and I daresay, it wasn't from fear." He leaned back in his chair, his arm draped lazily over the back. He looked absolutely splendid. And now, scary as hell. "What have you heard? Come over here. On your knees. Now, tell me."

Tammy decided not to beat around the bush. "That you like dead girls, master."

"And who the hell told you a crazy thing like that?"

"Dr. Hassan, master."

"So, you've had dealings with him?"

"Yes, master."
"Would you characterize him as a man of, um, great integrity?" She looked up at him, trying to decide how frank she dared be. "Go on."

"He's a ball of shit coated in snot, master."

"Sounds to me like you know him fairly well." He made a face.

"He thinks it's piles and piles of fun to torment me, master. Some day I would dearly love to murder the miscreant."

"Unless I get to him first." He chuckled. "You know, of course, what they do to slaves who commit murder? Especially the Chairman of the Board and someone, shall we say, as um, prominent, as Dr. Hassan? But, more to the point, you still believed him? He's trying to scare you. Torment you, as you say. Years ago, he was my father's private physician, until my father fired him due to his extra-curricular surgery – you must know about the despicable stuff he does. Ever since then, he's been dragging my family through the mud, and me in particular, because when I was young I did some pretty dumb things. Let me ask you. Did he ever tell you something a wee little bit true but overwhelmingly false?"

"Yes, master."

"And he made it sound utterly plausible?"

"Yes, master."

"But, my dear, you still swallowed the lies he told you?"

"I'm embarrassed to say that I did, master. I'm so sorry."

"I can assure you, you have nothing to fear from me, Mukhmala. How many times have I summoned you, eight, ten? And have you ever had any reason to be afraid of me? I think you actually like being my slave, right?" She was relieved he didn't wait for an answer. He paused to admire her collar and cuffs. "Oh, this is such an improvement. Instead of those stupid costumes, this says, I am your very own slave-girl begging to be controlled, begging to be strapped down, begging to offer you pleasure in ways you never imagined. A constant reminder of your station in life without causing physical pain. And I love, love the way it looks. Controlling a slave-girl's body is the easy part; control-ling her mind takes an expert like me. Reminds me. I want you to repeat the affirmation, and I want you to say it as if you mean every last word." She obeyed. "Good. I wanted to see that beautiful cloud of resignation pass over your eyes.

275

Now, back to what we were doing. I'm not going to frighten you, okay? I understand that it's an issue beyond your control and we'll get it straightened out. Look, I won't even hold you down myself. I'll just lie here and you can make love to me any way you wish."

She was so thankful not to be in chains that she used practically every technique she knew, with extraordinary success. When Prince Ibrahim finally regained his senses he said, "You're not going any-where tonight, my little one; His Hardness has decided that you should stay here with him. Fernando, call Central and tell them that I plan to exercise my rights of ownership all night, so they can work around her scheduled assignments. All right. Lie down spread-eagle, as if you were shackled. We'll just pretend this time." He lay fully upon her, arms covering her arms, legs covering her legs. "Turn out the lights, Fernando. I want to get some sleep."

She couldn't move, but instead of feeling suffocated and constrained, his body on hers felt comforting, protecting, reassuring. She wondered if she'd ever sort out her feelings towards this unpre-dictable man.

Giovanni awoke her. "You're late for an appointment at Training. They just called." He set steaming strong tea on a tray next to a yawning Prince Ibrahim.

"For me, Mukhmala, overcome this problem. Whenever you hate what's going on, just remember: my owner, my master, requires this of me. And Mr. Giovanni, sir? Who issues orders to the slave-girl in this room?"

"Your Highness."

"I warned you about this several weeks ago. This is your second warning. You do not speak to her directly. I issue orders to you, and I issue orders to her. Understood?"

"I apologize, Your Highness."

"May I ask you a question, please, master?" Tammy asked.

"Are you petitioning me, or asking me a question?"

"Just a question, master."

"Go ahead."

"Your Italian is so good, master, why don't you use it when you speak to Giovanni?"

He groaned. "You still don't get it, do you? It has nothing to do with communication, but everything to do with *asbiqiyya*, rank. My Italian is far better than his Arabic, like my English is far better than your Arabic. But we speak Arabic because it's one more way that you show me deference. Understood?"

"Yes, master." Zheesh, she thought. Is there one single molecule in this man that isn't focused on control?

Tammy was escorted to a private training room filled with every imaginable type of restraint. Mr. Umaru was extremely tall and thin, officious, and even though the words he used were perfectly polite, his voice was filled with contempt. She took an instant dislike to him.

"The purpose of this course is to educate your body to associate bondage with pleasure instead of brutality. It will last for four days. We will begin with mild restraints such as leashes and tethers and gradually move to straps, harnesses, then chains and finally shackles. We will change your position and your restraint every two hours and fifty-five minutes around the clock. You will have five minutes to rest and have a few sips of water before we move on to the next step. Once a day, at the request of your owner, you will have a bowl of yogurt. We will hook you to a vibrator programmed to give you full female pleasure every forty-five minutes. We will begin."

Four days later a bleary-eyed Tammy was returned to Prince Ibrahim.

He was in a great mood. "Fernando, I can't wait to see if it worked. Strap her down, spread-eagle. Oh, you look so beautiful like that, so helpless, so accommodating. Smile at me, my sweet little slave-girl. Oh, am I a genius or what? It worked! Now you can obey me fully, as your affirmation states. His Hardness is going to have a feast today, and so, my Mukhmala, will you."

When he finally released her, counting the four days of the special course, she received a six-day Outstanding, an Office record.

"How are things with my co-husband?" Yerima asked a few days later.

"Well, my lord, the good news is, the last time I was with him, he was as nice as nice as nice could be. He wanted to put me in shackles–" she appreciated how Yerima closed his eyes "–but he noticed that I was scared to death of them. Instead of just using them anyway, he sent me to a four-day course called Bondage Therapy and now I'm not terrified of restraints any more. The bad news is, and I consider this very bad news: it turns out he's my owner."

His eyes opened wide. "Ibrahim, Macabre? Something isn't adding up right here. Does he know that you know…?"

She nodded. "He says Dr. Hassan wildly exaggerated other stuff to drag his family through the mud, master. His father fired him as his private physician and he was out for revenge."

"Now my bullshit detector just went off the other direction. I don't know what to make of this, Sudari. The more I think things over, the more he's starting to scare the shit out of me. Tell me everything again. I'm trying not to

jump to conclusions, and maybe I've overlooked something."
She went through every single detail. When she finished he
shook his head. "Babe, this fellow is bad news. For one thing,
he's not playing games. You think he is because that's what
you and I do, but he's not. This is *him*. He's way too fond of
the institution of slavery, way too fond of straps and chains,
and way too fond of the absolute power it gives him. And
that's on his good days. He's not pretending that he's your
master and that you're his little slave-girl like we do, he *is*
your master and you *are* his slave-girl."

Tammy wretched and managed just in time to throw up
on the rug instead of on the bed. While she was still heaving
she started to sob.

"Oh boy," said Yerima, cradling her in his arms, "I'm
sorry, I said that a little too bluntly. Let me take care of this."
He pressed a button, and Wilson quickly appeared. "Could
you kindly clean this up? And bring me a cup of hot tea with
lemon?"

"Yes, Your Highness."

"It's not you, master, it's—"

"Don't call me that. I'm in absolutely no mood right
now for any games. In fact, I'm beginning to fear for your
life."

"It's not how you said it. What you said is the plain
truth, and that's what's so scary. I'm getting more and more
frightened of that man."

"When you disobey me, I give you a pretend spanking
and you know how that always turns out. What did he tell you
about slave-girls who don't please him?"

"That they don't have a very long life expectancy. Or a
very long shelf-life."

"Have you thought about what he's actually saying? He's telling you right up front, you'd damn well better please me, or I'll have you put to death, and he's said it *twice*. He likes you because you're a vehicle for multiple orgasms, but you have an off-day, or a deal goes sour and he's in a foul mood, and you're in deep manure. Listen, my father had slaves, but he didn't have to remind them about it every fifteen seconds. It was just a fact of life.

"Oh, shit, Sudari, I just realized something. Here I was, ready to commit grand theft and whisk you off to Africa, but he has access to your records, knows all about us, wonders why I haven't put in a bid for you... how many milliseconds would it take him to figure out what happened and who's to blame? Listen, I know a lot of people, and recently I've been asking a few discreet questions. He used to go by Fulaan, but Prince Fulaan got such a nasty reputation he started going by Ibrahim instead. When he was young, he'd throw orgies and yes, there'd be fresh corpses there wearing Giorgio perfume and he'd call them Lucia. I know he still throws orgies, but I haven't been able to ascertain the full extent of the, uh, entertainment provided. So the allegations of necrophilia are based on fact. And probably still are.

"Okay, vindictiveness? He destroys people as casually as if he were just filing a complaint at customer service. A contractor building Ibrahim's new pool put in the wrong color tile, beige instead of ecru. Personally, I don't even know the difference. I've heard from two dif-ferent sources that he's now in a *cage* receiving hormone treatments and will soon undergo a sex-change operation and be put to work as a *whore*. There's another similar story, but it's so far-fetched I can't begin to believe it, that there's a former baker at his house in the same fix because he burned some Italian bread?"

"The worst punishment imaginable: be turned into a woman," Tammy interjected wryly. Then she remembered Lucia's wonderful bread. "Second story might just be true; he loved the bread that his Italian nanny used to bake for him. And there are two castrated men in cages down at Central growing breasts. They've been devocalized and defanged, too. This is unreal. He's so thoughtful, and generous, and wonderful, and then poof, he's a tyrant."

"That's for a slightly wrong color tile; imagine what he'd try to do to someone who merrily makes off with one of his all-time favorite slaves. He'd destroy me, destroy your father, what's-his-name Marc, everybody associated with you, then send you to the Rodeo. Frankly, Sudari, I don't plan on spending any time at all in a cage, all right? I've decided that Plan A has to be thrown out the window. We need to come up with Plan B — something he couldn't possibly, possibly pin on me. We'll figure something out, but it might not be in time for my home leave."

The tea arrived, and the valet bowed his way out the door. "Madame, for you," Yerima said. "Maybe it'll help settle your stomach."

"Now I remember something else," she said, taking a sip. "Oh! It's hot! But tastes great. Thanks, Yerima. When the Indian girl's owner refused to sell her to him, Nigel said his business would experience 'unexpected reversals.'"

"See? This is no joke." He closed his eyes and kissed her all over her forehead, sighing deeply.

"Meanwhile, though, what do you think I should do, sir? How should I act?"

"So far you seem to be doing all right, but that's a damned good question. We can't afford for you to make a single mistake; I for one would like that you remain in the land of the living. Whatever you do, don't tease him. Do you remember the first day we met and you pretended you couldn't find the little prince? There's almost nothing you can do to infuriate a man more than make insulting remarks about his anatomy. I was so mad I wanted to knock you into the middle of next week, and I don't really think I have any reason to ahem, have an inferiority complex. Then you came back with your comment about the baseball bat, and I realized

281

that you were just messing with me. That's probably the moment I fell in love with you, by the way. But please, don't ever, ever try anything like that with him; you might not live long enough to deliver the punch-line.

"I love it when you act cheeky and then I have to put you back in your place, all part of our games, right? He'd hate that. Don't ever let him think you're being disrespectful or insubordinate or disobedient, even for the tiniest things. Don't blow your nose. Don't scratch. Don't sneeze. And whatever you do, don't fart. I bet he'd interpret any of these as gross insubordination or even downright defiance."

She sighed. "No teasing, no cheekiness, just blind submissiveness. Oh, what fun."

"A little flattery wouldn't hurt either. Go a little overboard about telling him how sexy he is. I bet he'll want you to compare him to me; it won't bother me one bit if you tell him that he's far bigger, stronger, more virile. If you lie, though, keep your eyes modestly downcast, because you're the most incompetent liar I ever met, and he probably hates fakes as much as I do."

"The other members eat it up. You're the only one who ever saw through me."

He moaned, but wagged his finger at her. "Don't underestimate this man. Generally speaking, the sexier a man is, the more observant he is about signals a woman is sending out, even subconsciously. And look, I know it sounds idiotic, but sigh just looking at him, make little whimpering sounds whenever you touch him, smile longingly at him, feed his ego every way you can think of. But make it as genuine, as genuine, as you possibly can."

Three days later she held onto Yerima with particular need. He sensed something wrong. "What's the matter, my sweet Sudari? You seem so far away."

"Last night my grandmother's spirit came to me in a dream and said I was in grave danger. Two other times she's warned me about things, and both times she was right. I'm so scared I don't know what to do."

"You must have been very close. What exactly did she say?"

"You're right. She's even the one who taught me how to twirl. Well, a few years ago, I had a *pied noir* boyfriend named Jean-Paul. She told me to stop seeing him because he was dangerous, and I listened to her. Three or four months later he strangled his new girlfriend. That could've been me! The second time, she warned me not to go to Marseilles, but by that time, I already had my ticket, and besides, what could possibly, possibly go wrong in Marseilles?" She rolled her eyes and made a face. "This time she was with a lady I didn't know. I couldn't see her very well; she kept fading in and out. Grandma said, "Your life is in grave, grave danger. Be honest. Be careful. It will help if you tell Prince Ibrahim that Anna forgave him long ago.""

"Who's Anna?"

"I have absolutely no idea. He's totally obsessed with his childhood nanny, but her name was Lucia, not Anna. His chefs are named Luciano, he has me wear Giorgio because that's what Lucia wore. He only eats Italian food. He gets furious if the bread he orders isn't straight out of the oven because she used to bake him bread and feed it to him hot. He says that Lucia and Saud are the only two people who have really loved him in his whole entire life. She died twenty-nine years ago and he still grieves for her every single day."

Yerima knit his brow. "He has the reputation of being mentally unbalanced, and now I'm beginning to see why." He grinned. "Reminds me. I had a girlfriend once named Anna Lucia. Cute as a button. She–"

"I bet that's it, Yerima! That's it! That must have been Lucia with Grandma, it's the only thing that makes any sense.

But why would she need to forgive him? He loved her as much as she loved him."

"How old was he when she died?"
"Seventeen."

"Did he ever tell you how she died?"

"No. But he told me a couple times that 'something bad' hap-pened, and that he used to do stupid things, and that's when Saud told him he had to get his drinking under control."

Yerima sucked in his breath. "Babe, I just had a horrible thought. I'm speculating here, but I'm trying to figure out what could have triggered this obsession, as well as this general mental instability. What if, at seventeen he got roaring drunk, and accidentally killed the person he most loved in the world? That could mess you up real bad, especially at that young age."

Oh my God! I bet you're right. That would explain so much." She paused. "Wait a minute. Sheikh Fahd had a whole shelf of books about psychological disorders and I read almost all of them, trying to figure *him* out. I'm trying to remember; there was one that talked about a case where a husband accidentally killed his wife, and he felt so guilty he tried to apologize to her by making love to her dead body. Do you think…"

He nodded. "I think we're onto something. Remember what Chopsticks said? Those corpses were always called Lucia. I bet that every time he started feeling guilty again he'd have a girl put to death and pretend it was her."

She began to sob. "Yerima, my love, my lord, this man is my *owner*. What are we going to do?"

He shook his head. "Dr. Hassan really did a number on you when he sold you to Ibrahim. A sick, sick man, rich as all get-out, extremely vindictive, and wielding absolute power over you. I can't imagine a worse combination."

A few days later she was massaging Ibrahim's feet while, as usual, he was on the phone. Fernando gave her a warning look, surreptitiously scratched his cheek with two fingers, and pointed to the two bottles of chianti in the trash can. The prince was hard at work on the third. Ah. The trigger.

He finally finished his call. "I realize I have absolutely no idea what I told that man. How the hell am I supposed to concentrate on business when you're doing that to me? His Hardness is very hungry for some velvety softness. Do you have any ideas, my dear, about how he could possibly be accommodated?"

She smiled. "Oh, just perhaps, master."

"All right. You go lie down, and then you can show me exactly where you have in mind."

Much later, spent but smiling, she snuggled against him and he put one arm around her. "So, my little Mukhmala, who's better in bed, me, or the professor?"

"He is, master," she replied without hesitation. "You're a close second, though."

Prince Ibrahim's mouth fell open. He stared at her. "What?"

"You're the second-most amazing man I've ever known, master. You can check my file; I have no real idea how many I've seen, but six or ten a day, seven days a week, two years, that's quite a few."

He chuckled. "You were supposed to say it was me." He gave her a medium-hard slap.

"I respect you far too much to lie to you, master. That would've been exactly the kind of empty flattery that you've told me many times that you despise. Besides, you're extremely perceptive and you'd have immediately known I was lying, so I thought I'd honor your intelli-gence and answer you truthfully." *Be honest. Be careful.*

"Who has the bigger dominator?"

"It's not the size that matters, master, it's what you do with it. And you certainly know what to do with it."

"In other words, him."

"Yes, master. But your shoulders are nicer. Are you an athlete?"

"I lift weights. Look at me. You really are telling me the truth, aren't you?" She nodded. "How very annoying, and how very refresh-ing. You're the strangest girl I've ever owned. You obey me, but then you go and make up some of your own rules. Be careful how far you take it. That could get you into a lot of trouble. What kinds of restraints does he use on you?"

"None, master."

"What? But–"

"Sometimes he'll order me to stay in a certain position, master, and then I have to obey him, but he doesn't use actual restraints."

"Interesting. Mind control. Very interesting. Fernando, come get her ready for another round." He gathered her into his arms. "Well. I have to uphold my reputation as the second-best lover in The Office. Ready?"

"I beg you, beg you, beg you, master, please don't waste any more time. I need His Hardness sooo bad."

He cuffed her across the face so hard she held her jaw in pain.

"Since when does a slave tell her master what to do? I believe I'm the one who issues the orders here." As quickly as the storm had formed, it cleared up. He looked between her legs. "Just look at your beautiful blossom, so hungry for her master. Honest hunger, which will be fully and honestly satisfied."

Two hours later, after wonderful love-making, she was lying on the floor with his feet resting on her back. "I don't understand. What does he do that I don't do? I mean, I make you scream with pleasure. Scream."

"You make me scream with pleasure, master. He makes me faint. Almost every time."

"Faint? As in, fall unconscious?"

"Yes, master."

His mouth dropped open. "Wow, he really is better than me. Damn! I just acquired a new ambition, and that is to make you faint." He hadn't had a drop the whole time they were in bed, but the first thing he did when he put his robe back on was to get Fernando to pour him a glass of chianti. He made half a dozen phone calls – a copper deal was in peril due to unrest in the Congo, and he was frantically trying to salvage it.

"Come sit on my lap, my little Mukhamala. Fernando, order me some chicken marsala with fettuccine and broccolini. And a nice insalata mista. Time for a break from business. Tell me exactly how he makes you faint."

"He has dozens of games, master, that get me very eager. Then he takes me into his arms and sometimes he lasts for hours and then he makes me faint."

"I gotta talk to this guy. I really need to talk to this guy. Okay, when I was in your file the other day I read a little bit about this Rainbow Harem. It sounds so intriguing; please tell me more."

She described the gardens, the beautiful rooms, the terrace, the gowns and jewels, and how the girls were dyed every two months.

"Dyed? What do you mean, dyed?"

"I was Miss Green, master, and I was dyed green from the neck down. My hair was also dyed green. When Sheikh Fahd would summon us they put colored make-up and glitter on our faces and Sayida would hand us huge colored feathers and we'd line up in rainbow order and do a stupid dance for five minutes and–"

"Dye you? How?"

"They parked us in big glass tubs and told us to sit there for an hour and a half, and then we'd move to a fixing tub, and a setting tub, and then back to the color tub. I really don't know very much about it except that it was a 14-step process, master. I remember that they had trouble with the aniline dyes they used to start with; they had very toxic effects and a lot of girls died. So they switched to vegetable dyes, but there were still a lot of detrimental side effects." She hoped he'd be properly appalled.

"That is sheer genius. Genius! I can just picture how beautiful that must have been. Six of you lined up, right, each wearing a gorgeous gown and dazzling jewels. I love it. Were you pastels or bright colors?"

"Bright colors, master."

"I love it, I absolutely love it. Very nice job, Mukhmala. Pepper-mint oil now. Hello, Central? I want six rumps up here: one purple, one red, one orange, one yellow, one green, and one blue. Yes, just the ass, but with glitter. And make sure each one is stuffed with a wiggle worm. And a barre long enough for six. Oh, not again. Well, do you have a boob who's at least a six or a seven? All right, that should do. Thirty, forty minutes? All right, thank you." Another call. "Amin? Hello, Ibra-him here. Hey, um, who's that guy you know who dyes textiles? You think he could do a special job for me? Okay, I got it. Thanks."

Another call. "Hello, Umar, name is Ibrahim, I'm a friend of Amin's. I have a special project that requires the services of a master dyer and I'd appreciate if you could return my call. Many thanks."

"Fernando, more chianti please." Another call. "Nigel? Me. I've been waiting for your update on the carpet. What's going on? Next week? Well, not ideal, but I suppose I can live with it. Listen, new project. I want you to find me six extremely fair-skinned girls. No particular attributes other than that, but I mean, extremely fair-skinned. Not many freckles or skin blemishes. I'm thinking Icelandic or Norwegian. Special project, I'll fill you in later. How long? Ten days? Can you cut that to a week? All right, do your best. Important thing is to do it right. Ciao."

His phone rang. "Hello, Ibrahim here. Oh, Umar, thanks for returning my call. Tell me a little about your background, the kinds of things you specialize in. Very interesting. I deal in metals, but actually, my background is merchandising. Who are your big clients, and is there some way I could help you with your marketing? Sure, we can talk about that. Now, let me ask you confidentially, do you ever do, um, experimental work? Well, quite honestly, I have something a little more experimental than that in mind, something that would be extremely profitable for you. I'm considering opening a special harem, a rainbow harem, and I'd like for the girls to be different colors. Yes, purple, orange... Hello? Hello? Hello! The bastard had the audacity to hang up on me!"

Another call. "Nigel? Another, ahem, project for you, please sir. This guy named Umar just categorically refused to help me with my special project. Here's his contact information. I want him defanged, devocalized, hamstrung, and brought to me in chains. No, leave his – oh wait, that gives me an idea. We're going to put him on capsule duty. Special shows in the garden. Outrageous, what he did to me, out-rageous."

"What will be your pleasure now, master?" Tammy ventured, trying very hard not to believe what she'd just heard.

"Shut up, you imbecile, can't you see I'm busy?" He pointed to his empty glass; Fernando quickly refilled it.

She shot Fernando a fearful look; he shrugged helplessly.

"Nigel? Me again. In the next thirty minutes I want a list of the top twenty leather tanners in this country with their contact information and major clients. Same thing, Morocco and Turkey. And the top twenty silk exporters in Thailand, same deal. If we can't do this locally, we'll outsource. Thirty minutes, I said! Thirty minutes!"

Fernando admitted the six rumps, backsides brightly colored and glittered.

"Finally! Fernando, set up the barre, bend them all over it, make sure they're in rainbow order and attach their wrists to their ankles. Beautiful. Now, activate the wiggle worms."

Wiggle worms were rubbery fingers that didn't just sit there, they moved. They insistently probed, they relentlessly prodded, they tickled, they made asses wiggle. And wiggle. And wiggle.

"Oh!" said Prince Ibrahim. "This is even better than I imagined. Look, six rumps, all gyrating in unison, all glittery, all different colors. Oh! Blonde slave-girl, bend over, His

Ecstasy needs an asshole so bad! Oh, this is amazing. Amazing."

Tammy gasped as he thrust himself into her, dry, rough, and hard. She whimpered, but he didn't notice. She was nearly in tears when he finally cried out and lay heavily upon her.

The springs ran down, so the rumps stopped wriggling, still bent over the barre.

Prince Ibrahim started to snore.

Nobody could do anything until he gave further orders.

About forty-five minutes later, Prince Ibrahim woke up. "Blue ass, come here." Fernando detached her. He motioned for her to kneel and cupped her shapely breasts in his hands. "You're really beautiful, my dear. What is your name?" He held up his glass. "Fernando? Are you blind?"

"Jiggle-Tits, sir."

"How long have you been at The Office? And where are you from?"

"Almost seven years, sir, and I'm originally from Norway."

"How old are you?"

"I just turned twenty, sir. You're so sexy, sir, please fuck me, sir."

He regarded her sternly. "I liked you very much until you tried to tell me what to do. Fernando, unsatisfactory for the blue ass with a level one warning for insubordination. Send her back to Central at once." He checked her ID. "Oh, how convenient, you happen to belong to me. Well, this is from your owner." The volley of severe slaps had her gasping for breath. He continued routinely. "Let me see which one of these pretty asses I'd like to enjoy. Fernando, unstrap them

291

and line them up. Each of you, turn around, one at a time." The room was filled with nervous giggles as he looked them over. "The orange one stays here."

Just then there was the unmistakable sound of a fart.

"Who farted at me? Who had the unmitigated gall to fart at me?" No one moved. "Fernando, smell them."

As if it were the most routine request in the world, Fernando sniffed the colored behinds. "It's the yellow one, Your Highness."

"Who's her owner?"

"The Office, Your Highness. T-366."

"Get Security up here." Within moments, two armed guards arrived. "Dump the yellow ass into the holding cell pending her transfer to the Ranch."

"Master, I swear, it was an accident. I didn't mean–"

"Take her away. Fernando, get Dr. Kamal on the phone for me. Kamal? Ibrahim here. T-366 just committed a category two offense, gross insolence, and I've sent her to the cell. Please arrange for the Ranch to pick her up tomorrow morning." As soon as he hung up, it rang. "Yes, Nigel? What? You're kidding. I have to admit, the man's an absolute genius. Dyeing instructions, right there in Miss Green's file? Damn. Find me the damn dye-master. Nigel, my man, I've got to give it to you. Any progress on the fair-skinned girls? What? An actual albino? You're amazing." He clapped his hands and guffawed. "This is going to be the best damned harem I've ever created. Oh, yes, uh, Fernando, I want this blonde slave here in the position of Hungry Asshole."

Shortly thereafter she was rump-side-up on the bed with a large wedge pillow under her hips and her knees spread wide.

"How would you like for me to arrange the orange one, Your Highness?"

"Orange one? What orange one? Fernando, you've been acting really strange recently."

Tammy and Fernando exchanged puzzled looks.

"How did a splendid specimen like you ever escape my notice?" Prince Ibrahim asked Tammy. "You're really beautiful. What is your name?"

"Beauteous Gluteus, master."

"How old are you? And how long have you been at The Office?"

"Not quite twenty-two, master, and, a little more than two years."

"Prepare to receive His Ecstasy."

Fernando shrugged helplessly, and Tammy shook her head in disbelief as the handsome stranger took her in his arms.

Heineken had warmed her heart by liberating more chocolates for her for Christmas, for New Year's, for Valentine's Day. "Today's my last day here, dearie. By Easter I'll be in Colorado."

She threw her arms around him and gave him a messy chocolaty kiss. "Oh, Heineken! What good news! I'm so happy for you!"

"That's Peter now," he corrected, wiping his cheek and licking his hand, "got my new passport yesterday. Got more than a quarter million, too. Not near enough to buy you, dearie, but my bones tell me you'll get out of here one day."

"Gisela's coffee grounds said I'll end up with a handsome prince, you know."

"And come to think of it, you have two of them right now. I bet she's right."

She'd intended to be brave and have him remember her smiling. She succeeded, too, for a few seconds.

"Look, I'll be in close touch with Chopsticks. He'll know how to find me. Okay?"

"Okay," she blubbered. "Heineken, I'm going to miss you so much. You've got more balls than any man I've ever known."

He looked at the floor, a bashful blush creeping up his cheeks. "You really think so?"

"I sure do. Good luck, Heineken. God bless you."

"Won't be forgetting you, dearie. Prince Yerima and Mr. Taymoor better take good care of my gal."

Tears streamed down her face as she watched him walk down the hall. When he got to the door at the far end – a door forbidden to staff members – he turned and waved, smiling softly. Tammy watched as her dear friend passed through it, on his way to the real world, on his way to a life of freedom.

Tammy was trembling with anticipation when the delivery cart arrived at the Salle de Versailles. Aïssatou had been visiting her husband and she hadn't seen Yerima in more than three weeks. She automatically dropped to her knees. "What will be your pl– What? Oh my God!"

An elegant table was set for two and a tuxedoed Giovanni hovered nearby. Valet? Was she in the right room?

"Giovanni, you will please uncork the champagne. Where are you from, by the way? Italy?"

"Shall I tell Your Highness alphabetically, or chronologically?"

Yerima laughed. "So, a citizen of the world, huh?"

"My mother is Belgian, my father was a Corsican commodities trader. I grew up in Singapore, Mumbai, London, and Johannesburg."

"Lei parla italiano?" Do you speak Italian?

"Si, Vostra Altezza." Yes, Your Highness.

"Let me guess. Italian girlfriend, sir?" Her dad had always told her, if he's not nice to the waiter, he's not a nice man. And Yerima had been nice to the waiter.

"Swiss, actually. Francesca."

She laughed. "And Anna Lucia. How many languages do you speak, anyway, sir?"

He shrugged. "Ten, twelve, depending on how picky you are. Not hard when you grow up with your mother speaking one language, your father speaking another, your nanny speaking another, the driver yet another, and more than 250 languages spoken nationwide." She sensed something unsaid. "Okay, okay, I can make love in about twenty-five."

She laughed. "This whole set-up tonight is absolutely amazing, sir. How…?"

"Got special permission from Mr. Ali, even though they discourage executives from falling in love with staff members because there've been a couple actual cases of grand theft, can you imagine that?" He winked. "Tonight, no formalities, no rules, no games. Just Yerima and Sudari. A guy and a girl." He clinked her glass. "To us."

"To us."

"Oh oh oh, I almost forgot. Put this on." He reached into a bag and handed her a purple African off-the-shoulder dress with scrolls of silver embroidery. "You look absolutely gorgeous, Madame. I thought you might have fun wearing a bra, too, but I decided your booblets didn't really need one."

"I love love love it, sir."

"Well, I've heard about this fancy French restaurant called the Salle de Versailles. Would you care to accompany me there?"

"Why yes, Yerima, dear sir, what a lovely idea. Thank you."

"I took the liberty of ordering. We're starting with foie gras with truffles, followed by a delightful ragout of turnips and kidneys."

She laughed. He was teasing, right?

"Okay okay, beef bourguignon – they refused to put in the *lardons,* though – artichoke hearts *à la provençale,* and herbed rice. This place has girls and even sheep for rent, supplies enormous quantities of contraband liquor, has illegal recreational drugs right on the menu, but no, using pork is a no-no. Go figure. Then a Roquefort and pear salad, camembert and glazed walnuts, and a Grand Marnier soufflé. Did I do an okay job, Madame?"

"A wonderful job, dear sir."

"Actually it was my chef François who came up with the whole menu. *Giovanni, Madonna ha bisogno di più champagne, per favore. Si può servire il primo corso.* Giovanni, please, madame needs more champagne. And you may serve the first course."

"I'm dying to know all about your children."

He fished out some pictures and described each one, six girls and three boys ranging in age from sixteen to nineteen months, in loving and often hilarious detail. "You promise me that you won't treat them badly because they're not your own children?" He told her about one infamous case where the new French stepmother made her husband's children from his first marriage live in the servants' quarters.

"That's nuts. I love your children already, Yerima, because they're the children of the incredible man I love. And I can't wait to meet them."

"What else do you want to know about me?"

"I'm dying to know how you learned to make love."

"Fair enough. The person who probably had the most influence on me was a girl I met in Paris when I was a grad student. Gisèle. When I think back, I suspect that she'd been a prostitute, because she knew a *lot*. And I mean, a *lot*. But anyway, I played saxophone in a jazz band to make a little extra money, and four nights a week we played at a fancy night club."

"You play jazz saxophone? Who knew!"

"In my book, jazz is just a musical way of making love, you know. We'd play special requests right at the table and, of course, concentrated on the ones with champagne and caviar because they gave the fattest tips. Well, there was this drop-dead gorgeous brunette who was always there with a super-rich businessman at least 40 years her senior. I'd look at her, and she'd look at me, but that guy watched her like a hawk. One night she managed to slip her phone number into my pocket. Next day I couldn't wait – and I mean, couldn't wait – to get to a phone. So I got to her apartment, and there was a guard outside the door. He winked and let me in.

"She showed me boxes of jewels, designer clothes, amazing. I reminded her that I was just a poor African student and I couldn't give her anything even resembling all that. She said that I could give her the one thing she never got – great sex. Her sugar-daddy wasn't just old, he was a closet homosexual and he was using her to hide it. Well, long story short, I learned a helluva lot in those fourteen months. We used to ask each other, whose turn is it to faint?"

"Faint? You?"

"Intermediate course, you'll get there. You think fainting is just your female prerogative?"

Her mouth dropped open. She closed it, and it dropped open again. "So, you've been rescuing starving women for a long time."

"Somebody's got to," he said with a grin. "What else?"

"What's your favorite song to play?"

"Oh, we did a jazz version of *Danny Boy* that always brought down the house."

"Really? I love that song!"

"I'll play it for you sometime."

"So, besides horses and jazz sax, do you have any other hobbies?"

He put his fork down and looked at her. He didn't say a word, just looked at her.

It took her a moment to catch on, but when she did, she laughed until tears ran down her cheeks. "I never thought about it in those terms before." When she finally calmed back down she said, "Please tell me more about your wives."

He smiled so tenderly that she loved him for loving them. "I love them so much, Sudari, it's hard to explain. I feel sorry for men who have to content themselves with just one, because each one of them is so special in her own way and adds so much to my life. Okay, let's start with Aïssatou.

298

Marrying her is the best decision I've ever made. She's a very interesting person. When she was twelve her father forced her into marriage with an eighty-one-year old. Surprise, at age fourteen she was a widow.

"Then he wanted her to marry another sixty-something guy she couldn't stand. So she ran away and went into hiding at an aunt's house. She didn't dare show her face anywhere for fear her father would kidnap her, so she stayed there and read. Her aunt's son was a law student, so there were lots of law books lying around. Now, she only had four years of schooling, but she was hooked. Saw the difference she could make in people's lives. Long story short, she got her *bac*, went to the school of administration and *magistrature,* and now she's a family law judge. This woman is amazing. She runs our com-pound like a general. Everything works, everything operates on schedule. Without her, in two weeks the whole place would collapse."

"I like her already."

"Okay, then there's Alizée. She's a lot more complicated. Our relationship is based about 95 percent on guess what, and the rest of the time we actually don't – well, let's say we try real hard to understand each other. She's really into impressing everybody, and that's not me at all. She also isn't very crazy about living in Africa. One time she actually asked me how a classy guy like me could be from such a hole in the ground. She can't have children, which is a lot more of a problem for her than for me. But she's absolutely spectacular in bed, I mean spectacular, and when I marry, it's for life. I'm the one who took her to Africa and I feel very responsible for her."

"She's the countess, right?"

"She gave up a lot when she married me, and I owe her a lot."

"So, Amsaou?"

299

"Okay. Amsaou." He laughed. "The sweetest lady on Planet Earth. I am so lucky to know her, not even mention being her husband. She sang with a band that I played with, and we were attracted to each other. But she'd had a series of bad experiences with men who abused her, cheated on her, ground her under their foot. Guard was up, artillery deployed, men were bastards. Took me two months to get her into my bed and almost two years to convince her to marry me. She's now the general manager of the second-biggest hotel in the city. She speaks eight languages, and she knows how to make people feel wonderful in all eight. Her employees adore her. Her customers adore her. Her suppliers adore her. The towels hanging in the bathrooms adore her. If she ran for President, she'd probably win. Makes my cousin Antoine nervous."

"He's Christian?"

"Our family is pretty ecumenical; my mother was Christian. He's related to me on her side, sort of her nephew, but if I tried to explain exactly how, we'd be sitting here for forty-five minutes. We don't get all formal about such things. A reasonably close relative is a cousin, a very close one is a brother. If he's older, he's an uncle, or if he's younger, he's a nephew. Anyway, I even have one bi-religious cousin named Peter Ibrahim. He says he's Christian from the waist up so he can eat whatever he likes and Muslim from the waist down so he can have more women."

She smiled. "And the American?"

"I spent two years in New York, you know, with the UN. Loved New York, hated the UN. Great idea, but what a screwed-up institution. Anyway, one day I needed new shoes, so I went to a mall, and there was JoAnn, selling shoes. We connected. We spent one memorable night together, and she dumped her boyfriend of six years. Now she's a botany professor at the agricultural school, but basically, that's just her hobby. There's no other way to explain it, Sudari, she's my extremely devoted and extremely beloved servant. She

300

doesn't want to be like Aïssatou. She doesn't want to be like Amsaou or Alizée. She just wants to dedicate her life to me."

"I can understand that," said Tammy, "I can understand that completely."

"But it makes me feel bad, because a marriage shouldn't be that one-sided. I don't really understand, but she tells me it's not one-sided at all. Damn, I just realized I married my wives in alphabetical order. See how disciplined I am? Do you really think you could fit into a polygamous household like that? Something like fifty, sixty people who live there and you'd be like, fiftieth in rank? Could you really do that?"

"Yerima, how many times do I need to tell you, nothing else matters. I simply cannot, cannot, imagine living without you. I respect and love all of them just the way you describe them. I never, ever, expected that I'd accept being part of such an arrangement, but I don't care. I just want to be with you."

"But I care, Sudari. I love you with all my heart. I want you to be happy. Okay, What else would you like to know?"

"One day you said something about China. Were you actually there?"

"Funny story. Years ago, not long after I'd finished grad school, China offered our government some internships in livestock management, and I was selected. Well, for some reason, when they looked at my file, they somehow got the idea that I liked girls – imagine that! – and I'm black, and they're as racist as racist as can be. I was warned before I left that they'd never let me anywhere near a girl, but can you picture me – me? – going six months without feminine companionship? So I took my precautions. I stopped in Paris on the way and bought myself a life-size inflatable doll equipped with all the necessary orifices and also a wig of long blonde curly hair."

Tammy was already starting to laugh.

"So, I'd been warned that everything I did would be watched, every phone call tapped. So I blow this doll up, put the wig on it, and sit in the window in my tiny apartment and hug and kiss her like, well, you. Without fail, there'd soon be a knock at the door. Quick, I'd deflate the doll and put it back into my briefcase. They'd come in, look all around, and never find anything. This happened five or six times. Finally they called me onto the carpet. Five of them on the other side of a table. We know you have a girl in there. How do you manage to sneak her in? Where do you hide her? I messed with them a while, then I opened my briefcase and took out the doll. Puff puff puff, and there she was. You should've seen the look on their faces! Suddenly, I was just a guy. I just happened to be African, and they just happened to be Chinese, but for a few minutes, we were just guys. And their next question was, Where can we get hold of these things?"

Tammy was almost on the floor, she was laughing so hard.

"When I stopped in Paris on my way back home, I sent them all dolls. China turned out to be one of the most interesting experiences of my life, and actually, one of the reasons that I'm now stuck in the Embassy. The livestock management stuff was a crock, and they were so racist I wanted to scream, but I realized that when I treated them just like regular guys, we suddenly connected.

"Oh, they told me when I got back home, you have such a knack interacting with other cultures. We got such incredible feedback from the Chinese government about you. Look, there's this conference in Johannesburg, or Jakarta, or Milan, and we want you to represent us. Hey, there's this thing going on in Buenos Aires, and we need somebody. Once they sent me to Abidjan, and there were riots in the streets, so the hotel advised us to stay put. We lost electricity, and after a day or so the fuel for the generator ran out and they couldn't get any more, so no TV, no lights, no elevators. I was stuck there for four days eating sandwiches and drinking warm Cokes with nothing to do and nowhere to go.

Fortunately, there was a friendly British girl in the room across the hall, so we entertained ourselves as best we could.

"Another story. A few years ago I arrived in Tokyo for another conference, half-dead from jet lag. I never get much sleep on planes, and I was on airplanes for hours and hours and hours. So anyway, I check into this nice hotel that the conference booked for me, get up to the room, and see that it has a nice view of the pool. I lie down for a nap. A few hours later, I get up to pee, and when I look out the window, all I see is the parking lot. So I'm thinking, shit, I must be more exhausted than I thought. I go to sleep again, and this time when I wake up, I'm looking at the hotel garden. Well, I start absolutely freaking out. Is this what happens after just one of those little dinky airplane bottles of wine? I think I'm going absolutely insane. I was a total wreck. Do you realize how hard it is in Tokyo to find somebody who speaks French at three o'clock in the morning? Finally they locate a Haitian maid, and she explained to me that the whole hotel revolved 360 degrees every twenty-four hours. Nobody had thought to tell me that. All part of the fun of international work."

He winked, and she laughed. "So for years, I've been gallivanting around the world talking about livestock management instead of doing what I really wanted to do, which is have a horse ranch. I have one, sort of, but I'm never there. My brother manages it for me, but it's not really his thing. Anyway, then my cousin was elected President, and you know the rest." He thought about it a moment. "What happened in China is actually just what you did with Saud. You approached him like one actual human being to another, and he was transformed before your eyes."

"That was so weird. We spent a year at each other's throats, and then like, the last couple of weeks, we finally figured it out. I'm scared with Ibrahim, though; he seems to have his own set of rules and his own set of demons, and I really don't know how to get around them."

"Please, Sudari, let's not talk about that now."

"Okay, you're right. How many countries have you been to?"

"Oh, eighty, ninety, a hundred, I'm not really sure. And you know what? There are wonderful people and despicable jerks everywhere. Everywhere. Humans are humans."

"So, tell me about your cousin Antoine."

"He's, like fourteen, fifteen years older than me but we spent a lot of time together growing up. He's more like an older brother to me, actually. His specialty is international finance; he has a doctorate from the Sorbonne. He used to be a bigwig at the International Monetary Fund.

"Great story to show you the kind of guts this guy has. Once he was part of an IMF delegation to South Africa while apartheid was still in full sway. Everybody else in the delegation was white, so for him to be able to stay in the same hotel and go to the same restaurants as his colleagues, the government gave him a special paper that said that he should be treated as an "honorary white person." Well, you can imagine, he was pretty damned *gratiné*. So at the official welcoming ceremony, he wants to make a point, but still be polite. They go around and give everybody a few seconds to say something nice, and when it's his turn, he thanks the government profusely for this generous gesture, and assures them that if they ever come to Cameroon, he'll make sure that they're treated as honorary black people."

Tammy howled with appreciation. "That's guts for darn sure. I like this guy."

"He's hilarious, too. You'll love him."

"Is he a good President?"

"In many ways, yes. Frankly, I'd be doing some things a good bit differently, but he's okay. He closes his eyes to some stuff he shouldn't ignore."

"Do you plan to run yourself some day?"

"Not against Antoine, but if he ever steps down, it's not out of the question. Hey, Sudari, I want us to have some fun. Do you like to dance?"

"As a *raqiisa,* not one bit. But I was a majorette in high school. I love real dancing."

"May I have this dance, Madame? Oh, Giovanni, *grazie, grazie, buona notte."* Thank you, thank you, good night.

"With pleasure, dear sir."

He put on a waltz, held her in his arms, and around they danced. She was badly out of practice, but movements gradually came back to her and soon she was flying around the room oblivious to everything but the music and the muscular arms that held her.

"That was really fun. I mean, really fun. The most fun I've had in four-and-a-half years."

"Now let me show you a couple of our dances." He put on another CD. "You know, I'm from Maroua, way up north, just south of the Sahara. This CD is from a popular group in the south. Better dances than ours, in fact, much better. Here's how you do it."

She stared in wonderment; he was just as magical vertical. "Mind if I try?"

"Very good, but loosen up your shoulders. Roll them. Lots of shoulder movement. Hold your arms out and make more abrupt stops. Kind of like syncopation, only more dramatic."

He danced around her, then she danced around him. The song changed, and he changed style of dance. This one was like a fast-paced hula on steroids, to the rhythm of intoxicating African drums. She tried.

"Well, not bad, but that one takes a lot of practice. The missionaries said this type of dance was obscene."

"That's a hard one, but it's amazing."

"In a lot of African languages to make love and to dance is the same word. Ahem. Speaking of which, Madame, shall we, um, dance?"

Soon she lay cradled in his arms, filled with joy. "Yerima, what a strange strange way to meet somebody. But here we are. God, how I love you. I don't know when I've laughed so hard or enjoyed an even-ing so much. It was beautiful of you to arrange this."

"*Mi yidi ma.* God certainly does work in mysterious ways."

"Amberine and Farook."

"And Yerima and Sudari." He touched the end of her nose; she grabbed his finger and kissed it. There was a long pause while they just enjoyed being in each other's arms. "By the way, I almost forgot. I saw your friend Ibrahim downstairs the other day. He called me Professor and gave me a high five, and invited me for coffee at the snack bar. What an engaging, charming, funny guy. It's hard wrapping my brain around everything else. I called him my co-husband; he laughed, but corrected me, said co-master. Mostly we talked about horses. Are you tired, by the way? Would it be okay if the little prince had another snack?"

"Actually, my love, I was hoping you'd say that."

Prince Ibrahim was resting his legs on Tammy's torso. "What a great body you have, my sweet little slave-girl. You really know how to make a man happy."

306

"What a great body you have, my gorgeous master. You really know how to make a girl happy."

"Maybe one of these days I'll take you home with me. Nigel tells me that we have 14 offers for you ranging from $125,000 to $800,000; only Superboobs has more. Fernando? More chianti, please. That man isn't trying to buy himself a little slave; he's buying himself a wife. Am I correct?"

"Yes, master, he wants to marry me."

"Well, I took a look at our sales figures. You're the fourth-highest revenue generator in The Office now. Let's calculate a fair price for you. Eight hundred thousand dollars is only about ten weeks' gross revenue. Your lease calls for a fifty-fifty split, so call it twenty weeks. Unless a girl has been put up for sale for disciplinary reasons or because she's reached retirement age, standard practice is to buy out the rest of term. How old are you?"

"I'm almost 23, master."

"So, three more years. If we're really being conservative and say you bring in three-and-a-half a year, times three, that comes to ten million. Fifty percent of that is five. Eight hundred thousand sounds like a lot of money, but it doesn't even come close. Besides, I have absolutely no intention of selling you. I love owning you, and I know that you love the fact that I'm your master."

"Being a slave is fine as long as my master is someone like you, my lord, but a lot of times, when I'm with the other masters here, it's no fun at all. In fact, sometimes it's perfectly awful."

He seemed to find this a fascinating but puzzling piece of information. "But if you weren't a slave, you'd never have met me. I'm a member of the royal family. How else would a mere commoner like you meet someone of my rank?"

"Never in twenty thousand years, master," she said with a giggle. "May I tell you a secret?" Time to flatter.

He nodded. "In 1425 I was briefly in the harem of Sheikh Khalid, master, and I saw you from the window. You and Dr. Hassan and the sheikh were in the garden laughing. I was feeling very sorry for myself because I was a brand-new slave, extremely frightened. Anyway, I saw you, and thought you were the most handsome man I'd ever seen. That streak of silver in your hair? Ooooh! Those beautiful shoulders? Ooooh! Ever since then, my lord, I've dreamed of you, fantasized about you. Then you summoned me, and I couldn't believe my good fortune. Even better, the way you made love just blew my mind. You exceeded my wildest, wildest fantasies. I'm very honored to belong to you, master."

"I remember the moment, now that you mention it. So, really? You were fantasizing about me?"

"Yes, master." She smiled guiltily. "I even told the professor about you, that you were even more handsome than him. He was pissed! That was before I knew who you were, before I knew that I was your very own."

He studied her intently. Not quite Yerima, but extremely observant, as he'd warned. "I thought I forbade you to say things like that. You're trying to manipulate me again, flatter me, and I won't hear of it. I'll grant you one thing, though, your body doesn't lie, Mukh-mala. You really do give yourself to me. A little less, I've noticed, since we talked about Dr. Hassan – you're still a little bit afraid of me – nevertheless, I'm quite pleased with you and that's all you need to worry about. "Fernando, bring us some prosecco. Cheers!"

Oh dear. Time to do what she'd decided she simply had to do. She began covering him, literally covering him, with kisses.

"What the hell are you doing?"

"Two things, master. First, I just want you to know how much I admire and respect you. And second, I'm brazenly buttering you up because I need to tell you something and I'm scared to death that you won't like it. I need for you to be in a very good mood." She gave him a huge playful smile.

"Well, I like the buttering-up part, that's for sure. What did you want to tell me?"

"I just want to thank you once again, my lord, for how you helped me. A lot of members here like handcuffs and such, and nobody but you cared that I was deathly afraid of them. The man who first bound and brutalized me left a demon inside me that I couldn't get rid of by myself. Thanks to your kind heart, your generous nature, your genuine concern about a lowly slave-girl, you helped me get rid of that demon. I've tried to thank you by taking good care of His Hardness, but in all humility, I realize it's not enough. I need to do more for you, master. I would also like to express my gratitude and my enormous respect for you by taking good care of the extremely kind and hand-some man to which His Hardness is attached." She swallowed and closed her eyes. "My dear, dear, dear master, please allow me to help you get rid of your own demon. He lives there in the bottom of that bottle."

Fernando gasped. Covered his face with his hands.

Ibrahim leapt to his feet, rage barely under control. "Are you insinuating that I have a drinking problem?"

"No, dear master, I'm not insinuating. I'm telling you."

"Fernando, get Security up here at once. This is so outrageous, you'd better be begging me to spare your life."

Instead of throwing herself to the ground, she stood up. Looked him in the eye. He was dumbstruck. "No, Your Highness, it's not you, not you at all. It's a demon who sometimes gains control of you. Do you remember how I told you that I wanted with all my heart to obey you but I couldn't? That demon had control of me. And you understood, and so generously helped me. I understand that this is not you. I'm not begging you for my life. I'm nothing but a slave, and if I've learned one thing in five years, it's that the life of a slave doesn't count for very much. I don't care at this point what happens to me. But Prince Ibrahim, my sweet Prèdiletto, you are a royal prince, and I genuinely care very much about what happens to you. This demon will destroy you, and as your loyal and loving Mukhmala I cannot remain silent and watch that happen."

The guards arrived. "Take her to the holding cell, disciplinary action yet to be determined."

While they were handcuffing her, she continued with fire in her voice. "It's taken me a while, Your Highness, but I know what hap-pened. The demon held you, and you accidentally killed your beloved Anna Lucia." His mouth fell open and he turned white. "When you realized what had happened you were so overcome with grief and guilt that you wanted to show her that it was all a horrible mistake. So you made love to her body, and that was a little comfort to you. But a few weeks later, you were overcome with grief again, so you had a slave-girl put to death, put Giorgio perfume on her, and made love to her, imagining that once again you were begging forgiveness from Lucia. I know you've been struggling with that particular demon for a long time, and for a while, you almost conquered it.

"But he's trying to come back, and this time, for sure, he will destroy you. I'm telling you the truth, like I always do. You didn't want to believe Saud, and I expect you won't want to believe me. Fernando has witnessed the results of this demon himself. Ask him; he's right here. I care about you very much, Prince Ibrahim. Even with all the power you have over me, you cannot make me stop caring about you. Send me to the Ranch, the Rodeo, but I beg you, please, please, my beloved prince, take care of this demon."

"You have some nerve," he said to Tammy, still so furious he could hardly speak, "talking to me like that. Come here." He motioned her to her knees, her hands still cuffed behind her back. "Look at me." He held out his hand to stay the guards.

She smiled up at him. "I cannot tell you this as a slave to my lord and master. I'm telling you as your precious Mukhmala, one of the two people remaining in the world who sincerely loves you and who tells you the truth."

"I don't believe a damned word of this. What happened? Why are you saying this shit?"

"Please forgive me, my beloved Prince Ibrahim, but I will tell you honestly what the demon did. I'm sure you will be surprised and shocked, because the handsome prince I know is a very kind and considerate person. The demon sent a girl to the Ranch because she accidentally farted. He didn't even recognize his very own Mukhmala and used her so roughly she had to be treated at the Infirmary. He ordered a man destroyed—"

"Fernando? Fernando? Is she telling me the truth?"

The valet gulped. Turned white.

"You mean you don't have the balls to even answer me?"

"That is most precisely the case, Your Highness."

"Sorry. Is this insolent slut telling me the damned truth?"

He looked at the ceiling, looked at the floor. Everywhere except at Prince Ibrahim. "Your Highness."

"So, you're saying yes."

"Your Highness." He covered his face and bowed his head.

311

"Guards, I'm not taking this nonsense another second. Holding cell, until further orders."

Two days later she was brought back before him. He was, as usual, on the phone, this time with his feet resting on Honey Buns. The guards pushed Tammy face down to the floor.

When he hung up he said, "Ah, the prisoner. You will state the affirmation of submission."

Tammy repeated it loud and clear, with two small alterations. "You are my beloved master, and I am your devoted slave. You rule over me completely and absolutely, and I am obliged to obey your commands immediately, fully, and willingly."

His eyes narrowed disapprovingly. "Do you recognize that you committed dozens and dozens of violations, including disrespect, insubordination, failure to address your master in a proper manner? As well as standing up to me when you should have been groveling on the floor, and defiance of my orders? And do you realize that in their aggregate it could mean the penalty of death?"

"My lord and master, I do." Her voice was firm.

"You piled up more infractions in five minutes than most slaves do in ten years. I have tried very hard to be just, because until then you had been a very obedient, very respectful little slave-girl who tried hard to please her master." He remained silent for a moment. "Kneel and prepare to learn your punishment." The guards had to help her to her knees. "Wait a second. How the hell did you know her name was Anna Lucia? I never told you that. Nobody knew that!"

"She appeared to me in a dream, my lord. And she loves you so much, she forgave you for everything long ago."

His eyes narrowed. "In a dream?" He shrugged. "All right. Unfortunately, the lease constrains me considerably. I am ordering you to undergo the maximum, which is forty strokes of the paddle once every week for the remaining duration of the lease – nearly three years. You will be allowed to recover for twelve hours, and then return to work, even if they have to wheel you to your assignments. I'm also giving you a level-three warning and putting you on the strictest, strictest probation for six months. If you fail to live up to all the conditions of your probation, I will rescind the lease and immediately have you devocalized, so you will never again be able to address me disrespectfully, and hamstrung, so you will never again be able to stand up to me. I hope you understand what serious trouble you're in, so that you may take whatever steps are necessary to correct your behavior."

Oh God. Devocalized? Hamstrung? She closed her eyes and bowed her head, a wave of nausea overtaking her. She'd acted out of love; this wasn't how it was supposed to turn out. She knew she'd run a huge risk, but what was done, was done. And now she'd have to live with the consequences.

"Let me make one thing clear. No amount of effrontery or impudence on your part will ever erase the huge gulf that separates our ranks. Saud is opposed to slavery; I am not. It's an institution that's survived thousands of years for one good reason: it works. It satisfies men's needs on multiple levels, and you can pass all the stupid laws you want, or preach all you want, and it will still be around. He let you get away with calling him boss; I never will tolerate such familiarity.

"That you claim to care about me is very touching, but it still doesn't change who I am, or who you are. I am your owner, you are my property, and you are wise to bear that ever in mind. You're like that lamp over there. Fernando, throw it to the floor. See? Broken into a hundred pieces." He paused to let his message sink in. "That was merely an eight-thousand-dollar lamp, but I won't hesitate to do the same thing with you. You still don't seem to understand that you're

313

nothing more than my property. A beautiful piece of property, one of my favorite pieces of property, but only my property. And you will comport yourself in full recognition of this fact.

"Furthermore, we will change your affirmation so that you will express your gratitude for the mercy that I am showing you. In addition, you will henceforth serve your master in complete silence unless I specifically ask you a direct question. And you will not stand up ever again in my presence. Lastly, I sentence you to give your master a full-body cat bath, with other orders to follow, to be carried out immediately."

Tammy knee-walked up to him and kissed his feet. She started to thank him, but sighed and remained silent.

"Guards? You may remove the – no, on second thought, I really like the way they look. Give me the keys, and you are dismissed."

Master and slave were both lost in thought as she went to work. With no hands, it was an awkward project. As usual, she worked from the perimeter inward. When she was nearing Grand Central, he finally spoke. "Don't you ever, ever speak to me so disrespectfully again." He shook his head. "Never in my life has a slave-girl ever had the audacity to address me in those terms. And actually stand up to me. I was so outraged when I saw you on your feet I nearly lost control. Oh, you're so damned good at that. Oh! Why did you act so stupidly? You keep talking about demons, but the demon of foolhardiness really possessed you that day. You may reply."

"I apologize from the bottom of my heart, most merciful lord and master, for breaking twenty thousand rules, but you are twenty thousand times more important to me than they are, and breaking them was the only way I could underscore the importance of what I needed to say. If I'd tried telling you on my knees or prostrate like a good little slave, you would've completely ignored me."

He moaned and twisted. "Why? Why did you put your life at risk to make such wild, unfounded accusations? Did you really mean it when you said you didn't care if I sent you to the Ranch or the Rodeo?"

She remained silent for a few moments, hoping that he'd under-stand her unspoken message. "Yes, master, I did, because I sincerely care about you."

"Anyway, enough of that. My sweet Mukhmala, you've driven me crazy, as always. Now I intend to exercise full rights of ownership and have some fun with one of the most beautiful pieces of property I have ever owned. And I know an excellent way to make you stop talking. On your knees." Even with her hands still cuffed, she gave him a pretty darn good BJ. "Mount me. Now."

A few moments later he lay heaving, covering his face with his hands. "Mukhmala, that's the best damned BJ I ever had in my whole damned life. How the hell did you do that, even with no hands?"

"I just did what I always do, master, but this time there was an extra little something."

Prince Ibrahim studied her face intently and shook his head. "I told you not to talk about that." She looked him in the eye and smiled, the picture of innocence.

"Even when you're following the rules, you're still not following them. There's still this spark in you, somewhere between impertinence and outright rebellion, which I need to extinguish. Why did the damned best-trained girl I've ever owned also turn out to be the most troublesome? Lie down, backside up, so I can see those handcuffs. Oh, you're even more beautiful when you're under my complete control. Raise your ass, and prepare to receive your lord and master." Forty-five minutes later he fell upon her, stretching his body out to completely cover her own. He lay panting with contentment, His Hardness still snuggled warmly inside her.

She felt protected and shielded, but also suffocated, oppressed. Just like the contradictions in the rest of him.

He sighed, shook his head. Suddenly he leapt out of bed. "I don't need you to care about me, dammit! I don't need you to tell me how to run my life! The last thing I need is another damned slave-girl trying to manipulate me, lying through her damned teeth about how much she cares about me!" He slumped into an easy chair, hyperventilating.

Tammy knee-walked over to him and managed with difficulty, with her hands still cuffed, to lay prostrate. Almost without thinking he rested his feet on her. He sat there, not saying a word, far into the night.

A few days later Tammy was cradled in Yerima's arm. She gently rubbed it three times. "You want to ask me something?"

She did what she was supposed to do. "My lord, do you ever use restraints?"

"You're not nearly ready for them," he said, shaking his head firmly. "That's part of advanced training and you're still not quite done with the introductory course."

"So, you do use them, master?"

"Sure, occasionally. It's a huge, huge power rush. Your friend Ibrahim is right. When you see a beautiful girl strapped down so that she absolutely cannot resist you, and is forced to submit to whatever you want to do, testosterone goes nuts. Uh, sorry, no pun intended. It physically changes you. The first time Gisèle let me strap her down, I scared myself. Things clicked in me that I had no idea were there. I'm an extremely disciplined person, as you know, but I almost lost it. I'm glad that you're not afraid of the physical objects any more, but you have every reason to be afraid of the men who use them.

"From the woman's standpoint, it's very close to the ultimate expression of total surrender – the ultimate one, of course, allowing yourself to be killed. It's a game, but the stakes are sky-high. Here I am. I trust that this will be an extremely pleasurable experience. I am placing myself utterly and absolutely in your control, but I know that even if I'm terrified, I'm completely powerless to do anything about it. Takes some guts."

He touched her nose with his finger; she caught it and kissed it. "For a woman too, what makes bondage so complicated and exciting – and terrifying – is that niggling doubt. Okay, I trust you entirely under normal circumstances, but are you going to change a little bit – or a lot – and try something you haven't tried before now that you know you can? It's human nature. If you have power, you use it. If you have absolute power, you use that too. That's why the Rodeo and these other brutal clubs stay in business. Virtually unlimited amounts of money, combined with virtually unlimited power. Literally, with the power of life and death. It creates an extremely lopsided balance that encourages every excess, perversion, and depravity." He winked. "Okay, sermon over. Time for another lesson. You ready?"

"Oh, I suppose so, my lord," she said with a wink, "if you really insist, that is."

"Are you going to do as you're told today?" Ibrahim asked coldly.

"Yes, master."

"Are you going to stand up to me today?"

"No, master."

"Are you going to say anything unless I ask you a direct ques-tion?"

317

"No, master."

"I'm still furious with you. I tried and tried to put you out of my mind altogether, but His Hardness wants that damned, hellified, diabolical cat-bath and foot massage you do. Then you will bathe me and give me a full-body massage. Remember, you will serve me in silence, and you will not rise to your feet."

She bowed her head as submissively as she knew how and set to work. He was furious with her, but loved the great sex she could deliver. She was scared to death of him, but loved the great sex he could deliver. Yerima had just taught her how to draw slow deliberate circles with her tongue instead of simply licking, and within moments, Prince Ibrahim was writhing on his chair and breathing heavily. She'd barely started on the soles of his feet when he said, "Change of orders. BJ. Get ready." Seconds later, he ejaculated all over her face. "Bring him back up, now, gently, gently. Forget about the damn bath, I just want to damn fuck you and fuck you until you beg for mercy. Fernando, hook her wrists together and chain them to the head of the bed so I can turn her over. Oh, look at you. You're so damn beautiful, and so completely under my control. And your ass is still pink from your paddling. Oh!" He swallowed. "Prepare to receive your master."

She'd never seen him in such form. For nearly three hours he made love to her, turning her this way and that. They each only came once, but it was almost simultaneous. Tammy was transported to a place far, far away.

He lay on his side, one arm and one leg across her. "I wish we could get that damned professor of yours to head up our damn Training Department; we'd have men lined up around the damn block. But I was disappointed. Why didn't you scream?"

"I obeyed my master's command and served him in silence."

"But I love it when you scream. You held back because you didn't dare, correct?"

"Yes, master."

"I authorize you to make whatever noise your body insists on making. Just don't say anything or ask me anything."

She nodded.

"And look, after all that, His Hardness still wants more. Fernando, release her. This time, do whatever you like. Just be sure to make me scream."

She worked her magic, and he cried out in pleasure. He lay with a leg across her, eyes closed, chest heaving. She covered him with kisses.

"Buttering me up again?"

She shook her head.

"Why, then?"

She swallowed. Dared look him in the eye. Continued to kiss every square inch of him.

"Listen. What I do with my life is what I choose, not what some insolent slave tells me I need to do. Understood?"

She nodded.

Fernando rubbed his cheek with a zero sign and awarded her a suspicion of a smile.

"You may kiss my feet."

She clasped his feet in her hands, covering them with kisses. Then she knee-walked backwards, smiling lovingly, until the door closed behind her.

319

Yerima and Tammy were blissfully exhausted after another lesson. "What on earth is the intermediate course all about, master, launching spaceships to Mars? NASA does know about you, right?"

He chuckled. "Well, the introductory course, as you know, is all about stimulating the appetite, and teaching you how to surrender and respond to me while I make love to you. In the intermediate course you'll learn how to take more responsibility. You'll never be an entirely equal partner – that's not how God organized things – but you'll learn a lot of ways to make love to me." He lifted her and parked her deftly on the little prince, who was fully awake again. "Well, get busy." She was at a loss. "See? You still have one or two things to learn. I'll also teach you how to resist me and then let me conquer you, in such delicious ways they will blow your mind. How to make won-derful love to yourself, so if I'm away you can still know some pleasure. And a bunch of other fun things.

"Hey, I'm not about to waste this perfectly good erection. Lie on your side and keep your legs tight together. On second thought, I think you're ready. How'd you like to put up something of a struggle? You'll never win, of course, but it does wonders for the libido to try." He outlined the scenario for another game.

Nearly four hours later, when she came to, he was grinning know-ingly. "I thought you'd like that. They could probably hear you scream three blocks away, you know."

"I don't care who hears me, master, all I care about is this unbelievable, unbelievable man called Yerima."

He rested on an elbow. "You seem very pensive today. What's going on?"

"I told Ibrahim that he had a drinking problem, and–"

"You did *what?*"

"I told Ibrahim that his drinking problem would destroy him if he didn't do something about it."

He held his head in his hands. "Holy shit!" he sputtered. "You came right out and told the Prince Macabre, this mental case, this tyrant, this control freak, this psycho, this necrophiliac, this vindictive monster, this murderer, 'Ib, baby? Look, sweetie, you're hitting the sauce a little hard.' I never thought I'd be saying this, but woman, you've got a helluva lot more balls than I do." He shook his head in disbelief. "Holy, holy shit! Holy shit!"

"He blew up, of course, mostly because I literally stood up to him. He called Security on me and I spent two days in jail, and now I'm on a level three warning, and heavy-duty six-month probation, and paddlings for like, the next five hundred years, and a bunch of other things I don't even want to think about." She described their confron-tation. "He had absolutely no idea, and now he can do something about it. Yerima, my love, my lord, I was so scared, I almost chickened out. But I prayed and prayed about it, and no matter how hard I fought it, the answer was always the same, love him."

Tears welled in her eyes. "Some of my molecules are crazy about some of his molecules, but the rest of me is petrified to be anywhere near him. I'm thinking, *love* this guy? Yeah, right. But then I remem-bered how sorry I felt for him, and what a sad life he'd led with nobody to care about him, and realized it was actually love. Not anything at all resembling the love I have for this rascal Yerima here, but it's love. The other day he screamed at me that he didn't need me to care about him, but then he started thinking about what I'd told him. Lucia is dead and Saud has given up trying to help him. So that left me. I just hope it works. When everything else fails…"

"Try love," he finished, nodding his head approvingly.

321

Taymoor and Tammy were in the Romanoff Room. He was in an especially good mood and with unobtrusive coaching from Tammy, had become a fairly respectable lover. In addition, she was genuinely fond of him, and she enjoyed knowing that he was building towards satisfaction.

"Yes," he breathed.

Bells rang. She clung to the dear man, covering his face with kisses as he fell on her panting, eyes closed, his breath warm and beautiful on her shoulder.

Bells were still ringing. Insistent bells. Clanging bells.

"What's that?" he said at length. It hit them both at once. "Fire!"

He grabbed his silk robe. "Let's get out of here." He threw a towel her way and had the presence of mind to hit the Outstanding button before he released the electronically controlled service door. They were driven back into the room by billows of sour-smelling smoke.

"Close that door fast!" he yelled, holding her gently by the shoulders. "Listen. This may be our chance. I'm going to try to help you make a run for it. Hopefully there's so much chaos out there that by the time someone notices, you'll be long gone. Here's my office number." He squeezed his card into her hand. "If we get separated call me, and tell me where to have you picked up."

Her head was whirling. A fire? Yerima's vacation was only three weeks away. Could it be…?

"My sweet? Are you all right?"
"Oh. Oh yes, darling."

"Try to stay with me."

Holding wet towels to their faces, they stepped into the executives' hall, which smelled of smoke but was still passable. Mr. Mohammed was standing in the middle of the corridor trying to calm people down; for his troubles he was pushed aside and cursed. Frantic execu-tives and frightened staff, in various stages of undress, poured down the halls. The smoke stung their eyes and burned their throats. Taymoor and Tammy coughed their way to the stairwell, where it was easier to see, and they hurried down.

On the landing at the second floor Mr. Ali was directing traffic. "Executives and valets will please exit to the right. Staff members will report at once to Central Supply. The halls are still passable if you hurry."

"Sorry," Taymoor said with a sigh as he turned right.

"I'll call you."

Central Supply was in the basement in a part of the building completely unaffected. The only smoke was what they brought in their hair and lungs.

Mr. Fawzi made them each put on a veil and *abaaya* and sat them in the corner on cartons of single malts. Before long there were nine black lumps perched on the boxes. "You will be evacuated only if absolutely necessary and in the strictest security," he told them pompously. Blue sparks from the air conditioning vent diverted his attention. *"Ya Allah!* It's spreading here!" And he went dashing off.

Milky Way sighed, exhausted, and leaned against a storeroom door bar. She practically fell over as it unexpectedly opened. "Hey look," she said in amazement, "the door over there goes outside."

323

PART EIGHT
ESCAPE

January 2010
Safar 1431

They looked at each other and burst out laughing. "We'll have to move fast, before Mr. Fawzi comes back," Tammy said, "we'll never in twenty thousand years have another chance like this."

Cautiously, Jiggle-Tits pushed the door open, revealing another room of shelves stacked with china and crystal. Sure enough, off to the right, a shaft of daylight beckoned under an outside door.

"Wait," Honey Buns cried as they surged forward, trembling with excitement. "Don't you think we ought to split up? Nine women together will be conspicuous as hell."

"We're barefoot," Cute Patoot reminded them. "And we're going to get in trouble, I just know it."

They organized into three groups.

"Shall I?" said Milky Way. With a flourish she opened the door, bowed, and held it open while they trooped through. The security alarm clanged, but nobody paid any attention. There were eight steps next to the loading docks, going up to street level. Giggling like naughty schoolgirls, they climbed into the real world.

All but Cute Patoot. "I'm telling. And I'm going back."

"'Bye," they said, suddenly conscious of the risk they were running.

Tammy scanned the crowd that had collected, looking for Yerima. He said she'd know what to do when the time came. Why hadn't he told her where to go?

A bearded fireman was shouting, "Move back! Move back!" The white-robed men and black-cloaked women paid him little heed, jostling each other for a better view, tripping over fire hoses, pointing, gesturing. When he finally raised his axe in frustration, there was a murmur of reluctant acquiescence.

A familiar face caught her eye. "Oh God, let's get out of here. That's Fuad!"

"Who?"

"Never mind, but we need to get going." Then it occurred to her that he'd never recognize her anyway; one black lump looked like all the others.

Honey Buns, Jiggle-Tits, and Beauteous Gluteus, squinting against the morning sun, walked through the crowd, their quickened pulses and heaving breaths a contradiction to their studiedly casual pace. The other side of the busy street was in the shade, which made walking barefoot on the hot sidewalk a lot more comfortable. They congratulated themselves on how much they looked like three young housewives out to do some routine shopping, snickering at what they wore – or, more precisely, weren't wearing – under their prim *abaayat*.

Everything was under the shadow of a huge skyscraper that reminded Tammy of a particularly elegant handle of a shovel. She hoped Taymoor hadn't been its architect. It had nice lines, but was so gargantuan, it was totally disproportionate to the scale of the city, as if the Empire State Building had gotten lost and wound up in Cedar Rapids.

"It looks like a tall skinny basket," said Honey Buns.

"A Telletubby on steroids," said Tammy.

"A phallic symbol, a tribute to the goddam male ego. But it should be ten times bigger. At least," Jiggle-Tits said.

"We need to put some distance between The Office and us," said Honey Buns.

Still no sign of Yerima.

In her years of confinement, shopping was one of the pleasures that Tammy had missed the most. Her heart brimmed over at the prospects of trying on sweaters, drooling over gowns, choosing fine china for the day she'd be rich.

The three fugitives had no money, of course, but nobody else knew that, and they gave themselves the luxury of window-shopping. "Look at these gorgeous hand-painted silk scarves," Tammy squealed. "Let's go in."

"I just want to feel them," Honey Buns said longingly.

Suddenly, they all felt very silk-scarf deprived indeed, so they started in the door.

A man stood just inside. "Can't you idiots read?" he yelled, and pushed them roughly back out.

They were dumbfounded. It was only then that they noticed the sign by the door. "Women will refrain from entering this establishment."

"How do you like that!" said Jiggle-Tits with a sniff. "I'll just go spend all my money somewhere else."

Thus alerted, they started seeing signs everywhere. "Men Only," "Families Only" – women allowed only if accompanied by an authorized male relative – and "Ladies

Only" – run by women for women. Although there weren't very many of the latter, the trio thought they were a splendid idea, since security men from The Office couldn't come inside. They found one such shop that sold gold and silver filigree jewelry, and tried on everything in sight.

After more than an hour of giddy freedom, Honey Buns said she was hungry. An annoying barb of reality. They were barefoot, still only a few blocks away from The Office, foreigners without any documents, penniless, had nowhere to eat or sleep, and were in totally unfamiliar territory.

"Oh no," said Jiggle Tits. "Here come the religious police. Sometimes they enforce the no-woman-alone rule, and sometimes they don't." Just then they noticed a man with his wife obediently following him two paces back. The three fugitives exchanged glances and fell into single file behind her, heads modestly lowered. The three khaki-uniformed men, whips in hand, ignored them completely.

"Whew, close call," Jiggle Tits said, hand over her heart.

"I want to go to the German Embassy," said Honey Buns. "They ought to be able to do something for me there."

Tammy suddenly felt like a total idiot. Why hadn't she thought of that? Why on earth did she need Yerima or Taymoor or anyone when there was an embassy right in town? Why sentence herself to years and years of boredom or voluntary servitude, even with Yerima, if she had another alternative?

"Good idea. I hope Norway has an Embassy here," Jiggle-Tits said.

They talked things over. Their first decision was to use their real names. Jiggle-Tits seemed totally different when they discovered her name was Toril, and Honey Buns grew before their eyes when she told them she was Monika. Their egos thus reinforced, and having scraped some of the rust off their decision-making skills, they came to some daring conclusions.

First, they'd stick together. It might be easy to brush aside one woman, but not three. Second, the American Embassy was no doubt the biggest and best-equipped to handle situations like theirs, so they decided they'd all go there first. Third, in case anyone asked them, they'd say that they were all three Taymoor's foreign-born wives. They hadn't finished concocting an explanation for why they were barefoot – they were working on a story about some kind of accident – but they kept finding too many holes in it.

"Taymoor actually wants to marry me, and if we can find someone in this city who'll let us use a phone, I can always call him to come pick us up."

Monika was beside herself. "Shit! Why the hell didn't you say so in the first place?"

Tammy sighed. "He's sort of my ultimate last-ditch resort."

"Oh," they said, "one of *them.* "

Cars were hurtling by, dramatically slamming on brakes, cramming themselves into spaces with mere millimeters to spare, careening around corners. They jumped back as one car climbed onto the sidewalk, missing them by millimeters, and then somehow inserted itself back into the swirling maelstrom.

"No women drivers. They all have to prove their virility all the time," said Toril.

Almost all of the passersby were men, but they finally found a lady they could approach.

"Excuse me, madam," Toril said, "would you be so kind as to give us directions to the diplomatic quarter?"

She gave them a disapproving once-over. "Who are you?" she demanded.

It was a good thing they were ready. "We're co-wives of an architect, madam."

"Does he beat you?"

"Yes, madam," Toril and Tammy replied.

"Never, madam," Monika assured her.

"That's because you've always been his favorite," spat Toril.

Tammy wished she could have handed her an Oscar on the spot.

"And you are trying to run away from your responsibilities. Return to your husband. Beg his forgiveness. Ask him to beat you soundly – even you. Promise him obedience from today forward as the Glorious Koran requires of you. Your place is with your husband." She turned on her heel and walked away.

"Well," Tammy began, "you've always been his little favorite. Why don't you just call hubby?"

Monika was not amused. "I'm tired, I'm hungry, I'm stuck with two clowns who don't seem to care what happens, and I'm running out of patience." She began to cry. "This isn't fun anymore. I'm scared."

"I've been trying to ignore it, but I need to go to the bathroom real bad, and I can't wait much longer."

"A women's rest room around here, Toril? Are you kidding?"

They found an alley, sort of, and huddled over her, *abaayat* held out like wings.

Monika panicked. "Hurry up. Do you realize what could happen if the religious police catch us like this?" A call went out over loud-speakers from the muezzin. "Shit. Prayers. No *shershif.* No prayer rug. No place to do ablutions. If these goons..."

"Pray," Tammy said. "Better to do it halfway than not at all."

"I'm praying for everything I'm worth," said Toril under her breath, "but it's not what they think."

They went through the routine of the *salat*, standing, kneeling, pressing their foreheads to the hot sidewalk, trying to look devout.

They inquired directions from a lady with four children; she was polite and apologetic, but had no idea where the diplomatic quarter was. They walked some more, hungry, tired, with grit stinging their eyes and self-pity claiming their hearts. To add to their troubles, Toril cut her foot on a broken bottle.

"Shit, Toril, are you *trying* to get us caught?" demanded Monika.

Toril pulled herself tall. "Yes, how do you like that!" she shot back, "I'd rather be a whore than go back to Bergen and open the seafood restaurant I've dreamed about since I was six. I'd far rather kiss hairy Arab asses than my mother's cheek. If that's what you want to believe–" Her voice broke.

"Sorry," said Monika, "I'm a little tense."

"It's okay," blubbered Toril, "go on without me."

They were still standing on a corner trying to figure out what to do when a small green, red, and yellow flag mounted on an approaching limo caught Tammy's eye. It took her a moment to realize it was the same as the one her favorite ambassador often wore. Yerima's car!

331

The limo stopped at the red light and she dashed over and beat on the driver's window, attracting attention from what suddenly seemed to be thousands of passers-by. "Where's Yerima?" she asked the bewildered driver. "It's an emergency."

"Who the hell are you?"

"I'm a friend of his. Can you take me and my two friends here to the American Embassy? Please?"

The light changed. Horns blared. Curses hurled.

"He's going to kill me."

"Please? You're his cousin Bouba, right? Please, Bouba?" He wasn't nearly as handsome as the ambassador, nor nearly as decisive.

He sighed. "He's going to kill me. The man is going to kill me."

Glaciers formed, melted into oceans. Civilizations rose and fell. She waited.

Bouba finally pressed a button that unlocked the door, and they clambered in, their ears ringing from screaming insults all around.

"We did it!" Toril and Tammy hugged each other in celebration.

"Did *what?*" Monika demanded. "Shit. We got a ride. To where? The Office?"

Bouba pulled over to the side of the road and parked. "I'm not taking you anywhere before I check with His Excellency."

A barrage of furious French in a voice Tammy knew so well blasted Bouba's phone. *"Où diable es tu?"* Where the hell are you?

Bouba coolly explained that there'd been a big fire downtown that had created a monstrous traffic jam, and the package hadn't been ready and he'd had to wait, and oh, by the way, there were three women in the car who wanted a ride to the American Embassy.

They stopped breathing.

"That's impossible!" Yerima roared. "I must say, though, it's the most original excuse you've concocted yet. I'm already late to an important luncheon. Now you get your ass over here before I put it into orbit!"

The driver shrugged routinely and started the engine. Tammy figured that maybe, just maybe, he'd been yelled at before.

"How do you know an ambassador?" Toril wanted to know, then figured it out. "You mean to say this car belongs to an executive?"

"Shit, he's going to take us back to The Office, I just know it," Monika moaned.

"Don't worry, there's no safer place we could be right now than in a diplomatic car."

"He sure does have a temper," Toril said doubtfully, "and I don't like the idea of being at an executive's mercy."

"Don't panic," Tammy reassured them. "Yerima will take care of us."

"I'll believe that when I get off the plane in Munich," said Monika blackly.

They pulled up in front of an ultra-modern office building. Bouba had barely slowed down when Yerima came racing out. Tammy's heart stopped at the sight of him, splendid in a shimmering beige robe rippling in the wind. She'd never seen him with real people before. Just as she'd imagined, he eclipsed everyone around.

"Here he comes," she said, unable to keep the anticipation out of her voice. "Don't you think we'd better let him have the back seat of his own car?"

They sat on the seat opposite, facing the rear.

"He's absolutely magnificent," whispered Toril. "Oh my God."

"He's incredible," Tammy confirmed. "On a scale of one to ten, he's like, a twenty-five."

"I don't trust him," said Monika. "He sure looks like the bossy type to me."

Tammy pretended she didn't hear.

Bouba scooted around and opened the door.

"It's high time you showed up. I'm already more than twenty–" His mouth opened. Closed. Opened.

"What will be your pleasure today, sir?" they said in unison.

He was even more handsome when he laughed, and laugh he did, until tears rolled down his cheeks. Bouba shot him a told-you-so look before shutting the door.

The three fugitives giggled nervously. Their fate was now in those finely shaped hands.

"There was a fire and we got away, sir," Tammy explained. As if he of all people needed an explanation.

"Fire?"

She searched for the telltale impish gleam in his eye. There was none.

"You mean…?" she started to ask. His acid stare burned through her. Uh-oh.

"Should I take them to the U.S. Embassy like they want, Your Excellency?"

They stopped giggling. Breathing. Their blood stopped circulating. This was it.

"You will do nothing of the sort," he said, eyeing Tammy sternly.

Her heart plummeted. Monika turned her face away. Toril wept.

"I'm late for a luncheon. A luncheon I'm co-hosting, and I'm more than twenty minutes late. Bouba, I want all three of these ladies to stay right where they are. When I get back I'll decide what to do."

They sneaked looks out the curtains at people going by, living their lives, unconcerned about three nervous women in the back of an ambassador's limo. They waited. They fidgeted.

"He's going to take us back to The Office, thanks to brilliant Tammy, here," scolded Monika. "I don't want to be sent to the Frontier. I'm really scared."

"When Honeysucker tried to escape, they sent her to the Rodeo," Toril reminded them.

"Yes, but that's because she tried to slit the throat of that two-ton prince," Monika said. "If I ever tried to murder an Arab, believe me, I'd run too."

"I'm still trying to figure out how she got hold of a knife," Tammy said. "I mean, they don't even let us have long fingernails."

Toril knew. "The razor blades he used to cut his cocaine."

Hmm, thought Tammy, filing it away, that's good to know. That's very good to know.

The video of how Honeysucker had been tortured to death had been required watching at The Office. Tammy remembered vividly how a sharpened twelve-inch dildo had been pounded up her ass, then barbed wire hammered into her flesh, then given two hundred lashes, then immersed in red pepper sauce and rolled in coarse salt. And all that was just preliminary. For the main event she was suspended from a trapeze by her wrists and ankles and swung back and forth over a blazing fire. With agonizing deliberacy she was inched lower and lower into a shower of sparks, until one by one the ropes that held her caught fire and burned away. Tammy could see her, after nearly an hour, still hanging by one ankle above the fire, swinging back and forth, closer, ever closer. She could almost smell the acrid smoke when Honey-sucker's long blonde hair went up in flames. She could still hear her horrified screams, as well as the frenzied shouts of the spectators who'd paid to watch her die.

No one could say a word for several minutes.

"Don't worry," Tammy said at last, "none of us is going to end up like Honeysucker. Yerima will take care of us."

"He's gorgeous, absolutely magnificent," agreed Toril. "And he did call us ladies. He makes me nervous, though. His eyes bored right through my *abaaya* and I swear he knows exactly what my pussy looks like."

"What's the first thing you're going to do when you get back to Norway?"

"Go to a fish market and go berserk."

"Shit, I'm going to eat a ton of sauerkraut and a whole West-phalian ham all by myself," said Monika, *"if* I ever get to Germany."

"I can't wait to put on some old blue jeans and a baggy sweatshirt and listen to some good old American music," Tammy said. "Then I'm going to eat two hundred pepperoni pizzas – *pork* pepperoni – drink twenty gallons of Diet Coke, head for the biggest library I can find, and never come out."

"My brother Klaus will be fourteen now," said Monika in wonderment.

"He'll like girls!" Toril offered.

"Klaus?" Monika laughed.

Wellie would be almost eighteen. Dating. Maybe even… Oh brother.

Tammy started wondering what she was going to do. It was hard. After so many years of being shunted around it was scary to think she'd have to take responsibility for herself again. She'd go see her parents, but they'd hardly know her. Their idealistic little girl was gone forever, and she wasn't too sure they'd like how tough and cynical she'd become. Then she'd spend a month or two with Heineken in Colorado, go see Pierre and Clotilde, tell them no hard feelings. France. Now, there was an idea. Maybe she'd start her life all over in Paris. Get a job as a tour guide or something. Go to school. And stay as far away from men – all men – for at least 150 years.

It was nearly two hours later when the grinning ambassador appeared, carrying three carry-out boxes. "Here. I figured you'd be hungry. Hope you ladies like *steack au poivre.*"

Did they ever! And the carrot soufflé. And the lyonnaise potatoes. And the almond mousse. They shamelessly licked the boxes clean.

"I told you he was terrific," Tammy said smugly.

"Excellency?" said Bouba. "May I get something to eat?

"You haven't had lunch?"

"I didn't dare leave the car, sir."

The prince sighed. "All right, but hurry up. There are three ladies here who're eager to get to the American Embassy."

They cheered. They kissed him. They hugged. They wept.

"Enough of that," he said, pushing them away half-heartedly. "Now tell me what happened."

They related their adventure. He listened, amused. "And you want me to be an accomplice in spiriting you out of here."

Oh no, Tammy thought, recognizing the mischievous glint in his eye. No telling what the man was going to do. "You'll be a hero," she said, as if everything were already decided.

"On second thought, it might just set off an international incident. I think I'd better just take you all back to The Office, don't you agree?"

Dead silence. He was kidding. Wasn't he?

"I'm an ambassador. I have to think about such things."

"*Scheisse*, I knew we never should've gotten into an executive's car," said Monika under her breath. "We're goners." She shot Tammy a murderous look.

"Where are you from?" he asked Monika.

"Munich, sir."

"Wouldn't you rather be dropped off at the German Embassy?"

"Of course, sir," she said, stunned, "but we didn't want to be any trouble."

"Trouble?" he sputtered. "Whatever could give you the idea that a foreign ambassador helping fugitives escape from a place like The Office could cause the least amount of trouble?" He shook his head. "I'm nuts, totally nuts." He turned to Toril. "And where do you want to go?"

"I'm Norwegian, sir."

Bouba climbed in, filling the limo with the odor of fried chicken.

"All right. Bouba, first we stop at Norway, then Germany, then we take care of Sudari. You happy now?" he said, smiling.

They covered him with kisses.

"You have more friends?" he said, grinning.

"You're wonderful, sir. I knew we could count on you," Tammy said.

They pulled inside a compound flying the red flag with the blue-and-white cross. Toril's eyes misted over, and she hugged everyone goodbye, sobbing happily. She clutched Yerima's hand and kissed it. "I just don't know how to thank you enough, sir."

"I just might think of a way," he teased. "Here. Here's my card; write me and let me know how things work out for you." And he gave her the equivalent of about $200.

When they were still a short distance from the German Embassy, Monika gasped. "Look," she said, voice trembling, "there's Mr. Fawzi. Right outside the gate!" She began to cry. "He's not going to let me in. He's going to take me back, and beat me, and send me to the Rodeo."

"Nothing of the sort." Yerima pushed the Male Protector button all the way down. He held both of her shaking hands and she calmed down immediately. "I'm here to keep you from harm, and I'll make sure you get safely inside."

Tammy's heart grew sweet. What a man, what a great human being. It was the first time she'd seen him in the real world, doing real things, and he was just as wonderful as she'd imagined.

The gate was opened, guards saluted, and the limo sped through. Mr. Fawzi didn't even glance up.

Monika slumped in relief. Yerima gave her his card and some money. They waited until she gave them the good-luck sign and waved from inside the Embassy, blowing kisses with both hands.

"This is fun," he said, "I feel like Superman."

"You're our hero. You're a prince, sir."

"I know," he said, beaming.

"Where to, Excellency?"

"The U.S. Embassy." He lifted her *abaaya* and discovered that she was costumed the way he liked most. He closed the curtains. "Take that thing off."

"Here, sir? In the car?"

"Why not?"

She was terrified that someone was going to see them, but within moments he made her forget everything. She would miss him so much.

He fell onto her, the look of bliss she loved so much softening his handsome, handsome face. Suddenly he sat bolt upright. "Just a goddam minute here. You say you want to go to the American Embassy, and I'm actually taking you there? I thought we had an agreement. 'Run away from you, master? Never in a million years. I can't imagine life without you.

340

Nothing else matters, I just want to be with you.' Remember that? Am I making any of that up? You deceitful, duplicitous little vixen. You didn't mean a single solitary word of it. Bouba, we're going right back to The Office."

Her world started to cave in. "Yes, but Toril and Monika, sir. The Embassy. You said—"

"I can't believe that you strung me along the way you did and I didn't pick up on it. You just wanted to get out of The Office and thought you could manipulate me into helping you escape. Well, too bad, your little game didn't work, did it?"

"That's not—"

"Shut up! I said again and again that I would not tolerate your running away from me. It was abundantly clear."

Her life was over. The bastard was actually taking her back.

"I'm absolutely furious with you. You really are a whore, aren't you, through and through. Use your body to get what you want and then wad your victim up and throw him in the garbage. Now you're going to get what a whore deserves. Turn over. I said, turn over!"

She was totally numb. This was no game. She started shaking un-controllably. Tammy looked him straight in the face and didn't move.

With a lightning movement he reached out, grabbed her hand, and folded his fingers around it. She tried to pull it away, but he squeezed. "Ow!"

He released his grip, eyeing her expectantly. She sat gasping, holding her hand, checking for broken fingers. Damn the bastard!

"Turn. Over. Now."

"No."

A dizzying slap. "How dare you!" He grabbed her by the arm; she tried to push him away. He hooked his leg over her knees, flipped her back onto the seat, and held her down. The strength that had once been so exciting was now turned against her. Of course he'd get his way, but he'd know exactly what she thought about it. She beat his back with her fists. Strained to push him off.

He caught her wrist, smiling strangely. "Keep fighting."

It wasn't hard obeying. She hit and scratched like a wild animal.

"Oh yes," he moaned, "yes yes yes."

When he finally finished he lay heavily upon her, panting with satisfaction. She was crying as she had rarely cried in her life. "I hate you," she said.

He sat up, got dressed, adjusted the folds of his gandoura, and checked the angle of his hat. "I know you do," he said slowly. His gaze was filled with melancholy. "I will therefore not be taking you to Cameroon, and I will not be requesting your services again. Good luck with your nice man. I…" His voice trailed off.

As the car pulled to a stop at The Office he pressed her hand. *"Adieu,* Sudari. I wish you well."

It was fitting that once again, he should have the final word. A relationship with Yerima couldn't have ended, she thought sadly, any other way.

Tammy was on her hands and knees in the reception room, scrubbing soot and that horrible black goop from the sprinklers off the marble floor. She caught a glimpse of herself in a mirrored wall, smudged and grimy, hair stringy and unkempt, her shapeless work dress splattered and stained. And of course, just when she was feeling her worst, in walked Mr. Ali and the new general manager, Dr. Kamal.

"Have you met Beauteous Gluteus, Kamal? She's a nine-four."

Tammy got to her knees.

"The one the ambassador got way too involved with?"

"The very one. He never even bothered to put in a bid for her. After he fed her foie gras and champagne, we put a theft alert on him. Of course, he benefits from diplomatic immunity, but I'm sure Ibrahim would have found a way to remind him that he shouldn't help himself to other people's property. In any case, he's over her. He's the one who actually brought her back when she tried to make a run for it on the day of the fire, and now he only has eyes for Classy Assie. Just as a precaution, though, we still have the theft alert out on him and we bug her collar whenever she's with him."

"Has an executive ever been able to smuggle a staff member out?"

"We opened in 1978 and since then, there have been nine or ten attempts, but only two have succeeded. One got a girl out in a linen delivery truck, and the other one, we're not sure, but we think she was rolled up in a carpet that was sent out for cleaning. We have since beefed up security in both areas."

"So, little one, you got an ambassador to give you champagne. You must be good at what you do. Excuse me for a few minutes, Ali, I think I'm going to do some quality control here. Don't you look lovely today," he smirked. "Adham, I'm going to appropriate Cinderella here for a few minutes. Is there an office I can use?"

Mr. Adham, always the ass-kisser, rushed over. "Dr. Kamal, sir, you're welcome to use Jibril's; he's off this afternoon. It really isn't equipped for–"

"It'll be fine. Come along, Cinderella." She began crawling after him. "What's the matter with your feet? Oh, of course! Don't worry, they'll be fine in a few more weeks. You really don't need feet in your line of work anyway, since you spend your days on your knees or on your back. And I hope you realize how lucky you are. We're so short-staffed we decided not to give all of you disciplinary transfers. You should have been sent to the Falcon Club."

She eventually made it to Mr. Jibril's office, which was only the third door down but seemed a mile away if you had to crawl there. Dr. Kamal closed the door and undid his trousers for a BJ.

"Very good job. All right, back to work." But meanwhile that had given Mr. Adham the idea, so back she crawled to the office for him. She'd barely picked up her scrub brush when Mr. Mohammed came in. Mr. Adham said, "she's giving BJs in Jibril's office today." Well, he wasn't about ready to miss out, so off she went again. It was going to be a long day.

She tried to be philosophical and remind herself that all in all, she was no worse off than she'd been before. If they'd gone to the embassies on their own they'd have been intercepted – five of the seven girls recovered had been caught that way. And making it safely to an embassy was still no guarantee. She recalled Fritzi's story about the callous official who'd taken an escapee right back to her owner and collected a reward in return, and remembered how Thunder Tits had managed to escape from her captors, but was thrown back out on the street because the heartless bureaucrat who handled her case could find no official record of her arrival.

Nobody made any announcements, of course, but by process of elimination, they concluded that six staff members hadn't come back. The cause of the fire was an untended cigarette that caught bed linens on fire. One of the rookie valets had tried putting it out with a can of nipple spray, which had the opposite effect and acted as an accelerant.

When the club reopened, Dr. Kamal decided that giving the staff members names – such as they were – gave them an overblown sense of self-importance, so he decreed that henceforth they could be referred to only as assholes or cunts or by number. Mr. Ali, deprived of a major part of his job satisfaction, was so offended he quit, and it was rumored that he set up his own off-circuit club specializing in foot, hand, and ear fetishes.

Tammy's annual review took place, and to no one's surprise, her lease was renewed.

"Tamara Lynne, my sweet," said Taymoor sadly. "I must be realistic. I'm afraid I'm going to give up. I'll think of my sweet little American every day for the rest of my life, but it's torture staying like this." He withdrew his bid and stopped coming to The Office alto-gether.

Her three links to sanity – Heineken, Taymoor, and Yerima – were gone, and she rarely got to see Zima. The work schedule was relentless, the weekly paddlings painful and humiliating, the executives demand-ing and short-tempered, and the toys and gadgets disgusting. Cages now appeared in the rooms, along with fish nets, huge assortments of dildos, four types of harnesses, and a wide variety of restraints. She staggered blindly through each day on autopilot, mechanically doing what she was required to do. But the job was so dreadful that she began to contemplate suicide.

"You mustn't think nonsense," Zima scolded her. "You can't kill Dr. Hassan if you've already killed yourself," she said with irrefutable logic. "We will succeed. Picture blood gushing from his throat. Picture the terror in his eyes. You

345

must live to enjoy that. We will pluck that mango from the tree."

There was a new asshole, or more precisely, a booby-dick, to delight the executives: Number 511, heavily made up and perfumed, with his gold-powdered floppy-dick decorated with a little pink satin bow, and heavy gold-powdered breasts. It was whispered that he used to be a dye-master who refused to help Macabre with a special project. He was an instant hit, as was 517, who'd undergone a sex change operation and was now theoretically female, with bulbous breasts, broad hairy shoulders, and a squeaky voice like Donald Duck's. Executives call her Fifi. Rumor had it that he'd refused to sell a nine-rump to the prince.

Prince Ibrahim stopped summoning her. For a while she was relieved, then worried, then panicked. Dear God, she prayed, please help him overcome this demon of his. How can I help him if I never see him?

He's still struggling with what you told him. You did what you could, now just be patient.

Tammy'd just been handed a totally unjust three-hour Unsatis-factory and trudged off to Reception duty, which she hated even on her good days. The rookie valet hadn't known how to set up the RoR, couldn't find the almond oil for the foot massage, attached the light harness wrong, and misplaced the key to the padlock for the leg irons. Then he tripped over the shackles he'd left in the middle of the floor and spilled a $500 bottle of champagne. Dr. Youssef got so mad he told Central to fire the valet and give him his money back because he hadn't been able to use the asshole at all. It wasn't one single bit fair that he'd dumped an Unsatisfactory on her, but that was how things worked.

She was in such a foul mood when she got to Reception that Zima, already there, couldn't even make her crack a smile. At least the swelling in her feet had largely subsided and she could limp short distances instead of having to crawl everywhere. She hated getting down on her damned knees and massaging damned feet while executives made fun of her feet that still showed signs of the beating, made up insulting jokes about her chest, and drove her to distraction making her bend over to pick things up. She knelt before Sheikh Amin, set the basin of warm soapy water next to her, and began to wash his feet. He kicked the basin over. She crawled around to clean up the mess to the tune of loud guffaws, tasteless jokes, and lewd comments. She finally got the water sopped up, but by then she'd forgotten who wanted the glycerin lotion and who ordered the peppermint oil. She guessed wrong, got slapped, and from the scowl on Mr. Mohammed's face at the bar, figured she'd earned herself another paddling.

Then Sheikh Amin kicked the basin over again.

She wanted to sit on the floor and bawl, but this was The Office. Zima took the sponge and started cleaning up the spilled water, but Sheikh Amin said no, he wanted the asshole to do it. Zima rubbed her neck at her, their private sign for Hang in there, we haven't yet had the chance to do you-know-what to you-know-who. Tammy burned with hatred for the miscreant who'd sold her into such a horrid life. Yes, damn it, Zima was right. Life was worth living, just so she could mur-der him. She got the sponge back out.

There was a rustle of activity behind her. A familiar voice.

"Miss Congo, what a pleasure to see you again. And oh, if it isn't my little golden treasure!"

PART NINE
DR. HASSAN
January – October 2010
Safar – Shawwal 1431

Zima and Tammy flicked glances at each other. The object of their worst fears – and their fondest ambitions – was back in town.

"Hello, Central?" he said smoothly, "Why, thank you, yes indeed, I'm back. Look, the two whores on duty at Reception now. When is their shift over? Excellent. Bombay Room in an hour. Oh, hello? With a beef Wellington, duchess potatoes, fresh fennel salad, a bottle of Château-Neuf, a dozen packets of coke, and a fifth of Blue."

Being around him was even worse than Tammy had remembered. He kept her on her knees for more than two hours, giving him an inter-minable BJ while Zima gave him a back massage, foot massage, and intermittently suckled him. He told them again and again how proud he was of them, that they'd become such obedient little whores.

Zima kissed up to him. "Dear master," she told him, "it's such an honor that you request our services. May I please warm some almond oil and give you a full body massage?"

Tammy looked at her in shock; Zima looked back in exasperation. Later, Zima said, "You must, and I mean *must,* learn how to manipulate him, my sister. It's just a game to make him think he's humbled me. Please, please, soften. If he can no longer humiliate us, he no longer controls us."

"But Zi, I *hate* him."

"It's too obvious. Pretend he's Yerima, or Taymoor, or anyone else. But you must disguise this hatred or we'll never be able to do what we want to do."

348

At least once a week he ordered up Zima, Tammy, or usually, both together. He thought up one humiliation after another, gloating as he made Zima crawl with her boobs touching the floor, overstuffing Tammy with a dildo two sizes too big that made her gasp whenever she moved, attaching them to his chair with tit-clamps so they couldn't pull away during BJs...

Tammy couldn't pretend she didn't hate what he did. She couldn't pretend that she didn't hate him. And her billboard face made it all too obvious.

He glowed with satisfaction. "I told you I'd make you miserable. What's nice is, you haven't begun to know what suffering means. Just wait until the prince takes you into his harem."

"You *still* haven't figured him out," Zima told her in annoyance as they put the dirty magazines in order at Reception. It was the middle of the night, so there were occasional lulls between customers. "You keep falling into his traps. Listen, I got an Outstanding from Dr. Hassan last week. A six-hour one, too."

Tammy couldn't believe it. "I had twenty-three hours of Unsatisfactories last month, and eighteen of them were from him. Tell me, what did you *do*?"

"I think of my baby and I can do anything. I smile. I caress him. I kiss his feet. Tell him I need his magnificent body. That I'm happy that he humbled me, washed away my foolish conceit. His pride as a man fogs his vision. He believes me, Tammy. Sometimes he's even careless. It gives me great power."

"You mean, he forgets about his knife?"

"Even that, my sister. Once it fell out of his pocket, and I picked it up and gave it back to him. I want him to think that he has broken me completely. Ten times, twenty times, I will let him see me pass occasions by. He will decide he has nothing to worry about. And then one time..."

"It takes a great actress like you to pull that off, though. I'd never in twenty thousand years make that slimeball think I've forgotten what he did to me."

"But you *must*, Tammy, you *must*. We cannot murder him until you do. Stroke his stupid overblown ego, and you will rule him."

A few days later he summoned Tammy to the Cathedral Room. He was a priest and she was a nun, and the "worship service" lasted more than four hours. He vacuumed up line after line of cocaine. He'd also had a lot to drink. His senses blurred.

His pocket knife lay open on the cushion next to him, the pearls and diamonds on the handle gleaming in the soft candlelight. Tammy's mind flew into high gear.

"Don't even think about it," a stern voice said. "Bring it to me."

"Here it is, master."

"Why didn't you stab me? Isn't that what you wanted to do?"

She swallowed nervously, just like she'd practiced, and cast her eyes down. "I confess that I've considered it, master."

"So?"

"I'm not stupid, master. That knife is too little to do much more than nick you. You're a strong man, I'm just a girl, and there's always a valet or the call button right next to you. I have nowhere to run, nowhere to hide. My chances of succeeding are almost nil and it sure isn't worth getting sent to the Rodeo."

He chuckled. "Ah yes, my golden asshole, the Rodeo. How intelligent of you to remember that. Dozens of people have wanted to kill me. Seven were moronic enough to actually try. I got to select their tortures personally. In one case, we kept the bitch alive almost eight weeks before we finally took pity on her and let an anaconda eat her alive – conscious. I personally fed her my shit. Then, you know, we put her eyes out and fed them to her, then one toe, then another... Then we set her legs on fire and put it out. Brushed her with acid so her skin started falling off. All sorts of interesting experiences."

She trembled, and that part wasn't acting.

"Good. Now, I had the kitchen make a special sauce just for you, my golden treasure. One-half beef kidneys, one-quarter turnips, and one-quarter Office honey. I want you to take this little brush and paint my jewels. Then you will lick it all off. And if you gag or throw up, you will paint my back and lick that off too. You may begin."

Of course she gagged. Of course she threw up. She almost wept in frustration and hatred when he made her do his back too. But she consoled herself by thinking that the mango was starting to ripen.

One afternoon he had both Tammy and Zima in the Romanoff Room. Zima gave him his back and foot massage, as usual, and Tammy gave him his BJ. "We're going to do a little switching around here today; it should be a lot of fun. Giovanni, first let's take care of the ass. Give her some boobs."

"Watermelons or cantaloupes, sir?"

"Oh, definitely, watermelons."

Even Tammy had to laugh at the monstrous falsies. They stuck straight out at least ten inches. She was suddenly *stacked.* Normally deadpan Giovanni couldn't help but chuckle. Dr. Hassan hadn't expected Tammy's good-natured reaction, and he seemed to be wondering whether they were a good idea or not.

In a nano-second Yerima would've known what was going on, but Dr. Hassan was no Yerima. It was amazing how much he'd taught her about men. And Heineken would have reminded her that Dr. Hassan was just a guy. Just a guy.

The laughter soon stopped. "Okay, I want her head in a stanchion, completely immobilized, mouth held wide open with a glass ring. Then put her boob-side up in the inflatable boat and strap her knees down tight. Put a pussy pillow under her ass and inflate it; I want her pussy on full display. Now, Miss Congo, you're going to present us with a delightful performance. Shoulder harness, on a frame, knees raised as high as they will go and secured to the sides. Higher. Higher. Now comes the fun part. Take one of the nursing boobs, fill it with ice chips, and put it in her mouth. Hang it from the top bar so it stays in place. Good, all set. Suck," he ordered. Zima sucked. "Swallow." Zima swallowed. "Keep it full of ice chips, Giovanni. Nefertitty, you keep sucking and swallowing until I tell you to stop. Suck, you stupid bitch!"

In a few minutes Zima started to squirm. "Don't you pee one single drop until I give you permission. Swallow, dammit!"

Soon she was in agony. "Giovanni, roll the frame and position it over the ass. No, move it up farther. A little more. Yes."

Right over Tammy's face.

"All right, you have permission."

A torrential explosion was aimed right where he had intended.

Tammy boiled over with hatred.

352

"There, now wasn't that fun? We'll do that again. No, let her drip a few minutes, then I want her tethered to the hitching post on the bed. She's going to give me a full body massage, then an hour-long BJ. No no, just let the ass luxuriate in the special marinade. It may improve her attitudes."

A few days later he had them back again. "Black whore, you will overpower the white whore and rape her. White whore, you will resist her. You will fight but she will finally subdue you. Black whore, you may use any restraints and any methods of control that you wish. Then you will bring your captive to full screaming pleasure here on the rug in front of me. Go pick out your accessories."

It was shocking, because The Office went to great lengths to ensure that they didn't ever touch themselves or each other. Mr. Ali had once caught Cute Patoot scratching herself after her shower, and she was paddled fifty strokes on the spot. Tammy had no problems with lesbians – it'd been pretty clear since about fifth grade that her good friend Jacqui was one – but deep within her she found the practice off-putting. And here was the Chairman of the Board, ordering them to play an all-out lesbian game.

Zima surprised – no, shocked – Tammy by confidently choosing an electric cow prod, broad elastic bands that could be used as restraints, a control girdle, and heavy leather straps. Her best friend? Ready to use a cow prod on her? Zima responded by giving her a gentle look of warning.

"All right. You may begin."

It was so repulsive to think that she'd be raped by another woman, she really did run, and really did fight. Zima winked at her approvingly. "It's just a stupid game," she whispered. "Play it to the hilt."

"Wilson, get me a sucker up here on the double. This is better than I'd imagined."

At last Zima managed to get Tammy on her stomach and slid the elastic bands around her wrists. Then she strapped them tight. "Turn over, bitch. I said, turn over!" She touched Tammy's thigh with the electric prod.

"Oh please," Tammy begged, "not that. Please, not that."

Zima strapped the girdle around Tammy's hips, pulled the narrow straps tight around her upper thighs, and repeated, "I told you to turn over."

Tammy didn't move. This time the prod touched her nipple, and she screamed. That was no game, and no fake scream.

The sucker arrived, and Dr. Hassan was soon heaving and moaning.

"Surrender!"

"Never."

But now one ankle was strapped to the leg of a table, and the other to the leg of a chair, leaving her wide open.

"Now, you stinking bitch, do you accept my dominion? My control?" She raised the prod and looked at her menacingly. Tammy bowed her head. "Tell me that I am your master and that you are my slave and that you will submit to me." She obeyed. First with her fingers, then her tongue, Zima worked Tammy into a frenzy. She finally cried out, and Zima stood straddling her, raising the cattle prod in victory.

Dr. Hassan's head was thrown back. "Okay, make him come," he said breathlessly. He shrieked. Slumped. Fell asleep.

"I feel really weird about this," Tammy whispered.

"I'm tired of telling you. He's playing games with your mind, and you keep letting him. Play the game right back and

354

he won't be able to humiliate you. You *must* get that figured out."

"I must say, though, you did a great job. I wouldn't have had a clue what to do."

"He's made me do it before, my sister, with Thunder Tits. Who needs a man?" Zima said. "No wonder they don't teach us about that stuff."

"Is she still in the infirmary?"

"I'm pretty sure. Broken jaw, four broken ribs. I didn't realize Mr. Abdullah had such a temper."

"What did she do?"

"Does he need a reason?"

Eventually Dr. Hassan awoke. The sucker still had Dr. Do-Good in her mouth, and Zima was still standing victoriously over her captive. He shook his head. "That was a very good show. A damned good show." He looked at the sucker. "Are you new here?" She nodded. "You did an excellent job. Now, wake Dr. Do-Good up again because we're going to watch another fabulous show.

"Wilson, attach the black whore's left wrist to her right ankle, and her right wrist to her left knee. Excellent. Now, Nefertitty, go fetch me my bottle of Blue and bring it to me between your boobs." She could scarcely move, of course, but she eventually inched her way across the rug. Wilson put the bottle where Dr. Hassan had requested, but it slid out. He taped her breasts together to hold it in, and she inched her way back.

"Here you go, master. That was interesting. What else will be your pleasure this afternoon?"

"I'll deal with you again in a few minutes. Meanwhile, lie here in front of me; I need a nice booby footrest. Asshole, it's your turn to provide some entertainment. Wilson, unstrap

355

her. You know those new stuffers with the screw-in decorations? Stick one up her ass and put the horsetail on it, and cuff her hands behind her back. Oh dear, look what happened, I accidentally spilled this bowlful of rice all over the rug. Rump, you will sweep up every last grain, using just your tail. Brush it onto this metal sheet. And you will spend five minutes on setting four for every grain you miss."

It was hard work, not to mention totally stupid. She tried to apply Zima's advice: forget that it's Dr. Hassan who is making you do it, try to think of it as a game. What if it'd been Yerima who'd ordered her to do it? She would've laughed herself silly. The very thought of him almost undid her, she missed him so desperately. Nevertheless, some-thing suddenly clicked. Everything Heineken and Zima had been telling her finally made complete sense. It was indeed a game, and she'd learned from the very best. She finally understood. The reward wasn't a glorious romp in bed, but an opportunity to wreak sweet, sweet revenge.

She set to work, giggling now and then, making exaggerated wiggles and generally acting like she was having the time of her life. Zima nodded approvingly; Dr. Hassan narrowed his eyes.

"Okay, master, that was really fun. I think I got it all. What would you like for me to do next?"

Wilson found three grains that she'd missed, so out came the spanking machine. While Tammy was being corrected, Dr. Hassan instructed Zima to coat her boobs in date molasses and pick up all the rice and put it into a bowl, using only her boobs. She fell over a few times, laughing. It took a long time, but she finally succeeded. She knelt respectfully before him, looked up at him, and waited to be acknowledged.

"Yes?"

"Master, I've been looking at Dr. Do-Good and he seems to be a little cold. Would you like for me to find a nice warm place for him to snuggle?"

Damn, she's good, thought Tammy.

"Do you like Dr. Do-Good?"

"Well, he's a handsome fellow, and he makes my pussy very happy, master." She smiled adoringly.

Tammy knelt next to her.

"Yes?"

"Would it be okay with you if I sucked your toes, master?"

He looked at her, suspicious. She smiled at him like a child eager to enjoy a favorite toy. "Why yes, you may. You're quite good at that, by the way."

"Oh goody," she said, with carefully calculated spontaneity. She pretended that his toes were the color of dark chocolate. Soon he was moaning. "Nefertitty, give me a lap dance, and Gluteus, you keep doing that." When he gasped with pleasure, Zima winked at Tammy as if to say, see? Now just who is controlling whom? She made a gesture of a mango being plucked from a tree.

"Eight-and-a-half hour Outstanding from Dr. Hassan," Mr. Adham told her. "It's about time. He was really losing patience."

There were limits to their power over him, however. One evening after he'd spent several hours playing with Tammy and Zima as usual, he told Gaston to chain Zima spread-eagle to the bed and chain Tammy with her rear over the back of an easy chair. "Use those steel-reinforced velvet restraints. Not one millimeter of slack, do you hear me, Gaston? Stretch those legs and arms and pull them good and tight. As far as they will go."

357

God, thought Tammy, this isn't just control, this *hurts*. Her shoulders, upper arms, and inner thighs ached like crazy. It really, really hurt.

"All right, excellent. What a lovely view. Now, Gaston, inflate those pussy pillows."

He wouldn't! But he did. Tammy stifled a whimper.

"Come with me, Gaston. You get the rest of the night off. Check on them every eight hours and make sure those cushions remain fully inflated. All right, you two, I'm going out of town, but I'll be back in a couple of days. Don't go anywhere!"

He turned out the light and closed the door.

Forty-two hours and twenty-seven minutes later, Tammy and Zima were wheeled into the infirmary on gurneys. "They just crumpled onto the floor, I couldn't even get them onto the delivery cart," Petunia explained.

"What happened?" Nurse Musa asked the patients. "Just minor restraint marks, nothing to speak of." They were completely incoherent, so he turned to Petunia. "Who was the executive?"

"Dr. Hassan."

The nurse rolled his eyes. "That explains it. Thank you."

Hours later, when they'd recovered enough to speak, Zima said, "and to think the damned devil can do that anytime he damned well wants."

Not entirely true. When Prince Ibrahim reviewed his weekly financial statement, revenues had nosedived. He discovered that one of his top producers had not only been monopolized by the Chairman for more than 45 hours, but had further lost another nine hours in the infirmary. He therefore set a limit of twelve hours a week that any single

Board member could avail himself of one of his leased properties. The Office likewise issued a similar policy. And The Office also decided that if there were no service orders posted for a period of three hours, security would check on the room.

Tammy crawled across the room to where Ibrahim was talking on the phone. He motioned her to lie down and he rested his feet on her shoulders. "Manganese ascorbate. Yes yes, I'm familiar with it, a criti-cal component to reproductive health. I have an excellent source and can supply thousands of kilos with a few weeks' notice. All right, send me your specifications and I'll be glad to give you a quote." He dialed again. "Nigel? What's going on with the greenhouse? I thought everything was supposed to be delivered last Wednesday. You're on it? All right. And I see that most of the landscaping is in for the Rainbow. Nice work. The fountain still doesn't work, though. When? And I've heard there's an incredible stallion at Azzedine's that might be for sale. Check it out?

"And it's been a while since I threw a party. Plan on twenty guests, so we need a hundred girls and forty butlers. I want twenty of the girls to be the ones whose pussies are padlocked shut, you know, a hole on one side and a hole on the other and the padlock closes it? We give every guest a key and whatever pussy it unlocks, they get to take home. And I want you to rent five or six girls with their feet fused together. Yes, yes, they're really not very practical, you know, but they make great decorations. No, no, I'm going to skip the Lucia thing this time. Fly in some Colorado lamb; we'll ask Luciano Maggiore to spit-roast it with white truffles. The ones from Tennessee keep winning taste tests – not sure exactly what the source is, but I'm sure you can track it down.

"Talk to him about what else we can do for the menu. Off the charts. Oh, come to think of it, Jean-Philippe and

Jibril really like the Lucia thing. How many girls are currently in the Arrevederci Ragazza pen? Oh, wow, it really has been a while since I've had a party. All right, we'll need to put two of them down. And it's not nice to have them on death row for months; see if one of the other clubs on the circuit could use a few.

"I'd like twenty of the girls to be covered in different pastel shades of luster dust and disco dust, another twenty to be marinated in various sweet sauces, and I haven't figured out yet how I want the others. Some dancing-girls for sure, maybe a stripper, a male belly dancer, a few lesbian pairs, and I'm still thinking about the rest. I'll send you the guest list. Plan on it for about a month away, but start lining up the personnel and the equipment. And I want my Giardino Posteriore to be all lined up, pearlized, and stuffed with the new electric wiggle worms that you can program to fit music.

"Oh, oh, um, let's do a South Pacific theme. That villa outside Papeete you purchased for me is working out very well. I need a similar set-up in Aruba with a discreet holding facility for two dozen girls. Sometimes I've even had to put them on my yacht, which is absolutely not appropriate. Tropical flowers everywhere, palm trees, we can make an artificial beach... And some of the girls should be Tahitian. Great idea, dancers! Think you can fly some in from Hawaii or Tonga or somewhere? They have to be the best. The best. Oh, come to think of it, not far from my estate on Oahu is a Polynesian Cultural Center. Dance troupes from all over the Pacific; that might be a good place to start.

"Oh, maybe we can change the menu. There's this Hawaiian barbecue that's supposed to be out of this world. They bury the meat in a pit with hot stones and wet moss for hours and hours. Ask Luciano to check it out. Usually pork, but maybe we can do it with lamb or beef. All right, I have a serious disciplinary issue to deal with now. Talk to you later."

360

He motioned Tammy to her knees and studied her for a long moment. "Tell me, my naughty little slave-girl, what category violation is attempted escape?"

"Three, master."

"How many category three violations does your probation allow?"

Oh God. She hadn't even thought of that. "None, master." Oh God. Oh God. She bowed her head.

"I'm not sure why I'm feeling merciful, because I have every right to be as arbitrary as I wish, but I checked the terms of your probation, and it talks about adherence to my rules. I will generously consider your attempted escape a violation of Office rules, not of my own. However, I would like to point out that this extremely serious violation remains on your record and it will now take very little, very little, to push me over the edge.

"By the way, I'm sorry about the professor. Those things never work out, but I know you loved him." She fought back tears. "I'm also sorry about your feet, but they'll be better in a few weeks." She shrugged dolefully. "Speaking of feet, get busy. Fernando, bring over some warm almond oil. And order me some chicken francese, artichoke risotto, green beans with pine nuts and balsamic, and a caprese salad. And a bottle of Pelligrino."

Tammy and Fernando exchanged glances. No prosecco? No chianti?

She knew she was doing an excellent job with the massage, but he was resisting the effects. Wow, she thought, it's been weeks, and he's still really furious with me.

"Not a very good job today. I hope you do better on the BJ."

He resisted her ministrations on that score too. Finally he ejaculated into her mouth. She understood: he was punishing her. Pulling away. Showing he didn't need her.

"Come over here and feed me. Then you will get in bed and give me a full-body cat bath. Make it last at least an hour." He was disappointed in that too. "If you're not going to perform any better than this, I don't need to call you. Fernando, just give her a Satisfactory today. You are dismissed."

Instead of the requisite seven times each, she kissed his feet a hundred times. Fernando nodded discreetly and formed his finger into a zero as Tiger Lily arrived to take her back to Central. Ibrahim'd been cold. He'd been unresponsive. But he'd also been completely sober.

Dr. Hassan couldn't get over the change in Tammy's attitudes, and suspicions lingered. "Just exactly what are you up to?" he asked her one day.

She shrugged. "I'm finally reconciled to being a slave, master. It took five years, but I'm okay with it. It's not exactly what I'd spent my childhood dreaming of doing, but if this is what my life will be, then I might as well find something to enjoy. Master, I tried rebellion; it didn't work. I tried running away, it didn't work. So I've just decided to accept reality and make the best of it. And, also, you, dear master, are an extremely attractive member of the masculine race."

She was counting on his cockiness, his enormous ego, his own set of demons. But, she realized, what she had told him was true. As Heineken had said, it's amazing what you can get used to.

"I've succeeded in turning you into an obedient slave-girl and a fine professional whore, my golden treasure. I'm very proud of you."

"The mango is getting ripe," Zima whispered one afternoon when Dr. Hassan had fallen into a cocaine-induced stupor. "You've finally understood how to make him put his guard down, how to lull him into complacency. We will soon be able to pluck it."

"But there's one big thing I haven't figured out," Tammy told Zima. "What are we going to do about the stupid valet? He'd have security up in a split second."

"Half the valets hate his guts and would probably help us. Like Giovanni, you know, who wiped up the dog food for us. Or Gaston, who came back and deflated those pillows. Or Wilson, who always accidentally puts the spanking machine on three instead of four."

"Those guys just feel sorry for us, it doesn't mean they hate him."

"Let's try to find out which ones really do."

Damn. Where was Heineken when you needed him?

She desperately wanted to kill Dr. Hassan, but to avoid going to the Rodeo she'd have to take her own life. That was the part Tammy didn't like. She wasn't really keen on the idea of committing suicide – she'd come to the realization that you could *die* that way – but Nenzima was right; anything less would be sheer folly.

"Today," Prince Ibrahim said, "I've decided that you are going to show your master remorse. I've been far too nice to you. We're experimenting with new gadgets and it occurred to me that you'd be the perfect girl to try them out. First let's see how you like the new BJ simulator. Fernando, strap her to

363

it and set it for 45 minutes on the highest level. Put the probe up her ass. If you suck hard enough, the green light will stay on. If you take too long a rest or decrease your intensity, a red light will come on. If it's on for more than fifteen seconds, well, you'll see."

She did well for the first ten or fifteen minutes, but it got harder and harder to keep up the pace. The red light flashed on several times. By the thirty-minute mark she was exhausted. The red light came on and a buzzer sounded. Intense pain radiated through her and she was jolted several inches into the air. An electric shock! Damn! The counter was going backwards. Every second she took to recover lengthened the time… Oh no. Damn. She started sucking again but a few minutes later the damn red light came on again. Another shock. And another. And another.

"You will finish, even if it takes you all day. Are you enjoying the experience?" She shook her head. "By the way, the more times the red light comes on, the harder you have to suck to make it go back off."

It took her close to two hours before the simulator finally chimed.

"Come over here and kneel before your master."

Exhausted, she knee-walked to within a few feet of him.

"Did you like that?" She shook her head. Vehemently. "Do you plan to disobey your master again?" She shook her head. "All right, now we're going to try a new disc. Same idea, only it senses circular motion. Fernando, you need to glue it to the bottom of her ass with the cream that comes with it. Put the probe just like before. We're going to make the exercise a bit challenging, what the instructions call advanced technique. Lash the bottoms of her feet together like I showed you the other day and cuff her hands behind her back. Good. You will writhe and grind just like on the RoR, but this time, you do the work. Fernando, set the timer for thirty minutes and bring it to me. You will continue to do this exercise until the final chime."

With her feet lashed together her range of action was very limited, but with only four electric shocks it was finally over.

"Did you like that?" She shook her head. "Do you plan to disobey your master again?" She shook her head. How many more of these torments did he have up his sleeve?

A lot. He had her kneel up, her wrists tied to her ankles with elastic cords. She recognized the stuffer from her screen test. A press of a button, and she was sent reeling. Fernando helped her back into the assigned position. A few moments later, another shock tumbled her over. After fifteen or twenty shocks the prince grew tired. "Did you like that? Do you plan to disobey your master?" She shook her head.

"Okay, now, Fernando, put a silencer on her and cuff her hands. And use that two-hour shit-flavored candy for the pouch." He chained her neck to his ankle, then he walked around while she struggled to worm her way after him. He made her kneel on the marble floor for an hour with burrs under her knees and tit clamps holding her to a chair.

Oh brother, she thought, he was getting just as bad as Dr. Hassan.

"All right. Since you seem so reluctant to prostrate before your lord and master, I'm going to give you some practice. Lie down, forehead pressed down firmly, arms stretched before you, palms upward, all four fingers on each hand in full contact with the floor. To make sure you don't move, we will put a champagne flute of ice water on your back. If it spills, you will be subject to additional corrective measures. And you will remain in that position until I release you."

She smiled to herself; it was just like the start of Yerima's game of contrition, one of her favorites. Oh, how she missed his games. Oh, how she missed the way they'd make her juices flow, the way they'd always wind up in such glorious results.

Prince Ibrahim wasn't playing games at all, but her body didn't know that. Within twenty minutes she was feeling desperate need, but it was nearly an hour before he let her up and told her to kneel.

"Did you like that?" he asked. She wasn't sure how to respond, since she knew he'd meant it as punishment. "Well, did you like it?" She nodded. "What?" She nodded. "Fernando, come take a look at her."

"She's there, Your Highness, I mean, really there."

"Would you please explain this?"

"Master, the professor had what he called the game of contrition. He'd make me lie prostrate, just like you did, to beg forgiveness for all my violations. He had even more rules than you, master."

"So you thought that's what I was doing? Only with me, you discovered that breaking rules is no game at all. And so, where did this little game go?"

"He'd pretend he was going to spank me, and I'd resist him, and finally, he'd conquer me." She closed her eyes and bowed her head, remembering. Oh God.

"He had a lot of games, didn't he?"

"Dozens, master. He called them appetizers. He said the brain is by far the most important sex organ and it has to be in just the right frame of mind before the body can achieve full satisfaction."

"So you thought I was playing this game?"

366

"It's what my body thought, master. He trained me really well. Once you play a game five or six times, your body knows where it's going…"

He chuckled, cocked his head to one side. "You can say that again. I actually like the way this game sounds." A wicked look crossed his face. "Run away from me, you disobedient little slave. Try to escape, because when I catch you, I'm going to teach you the best lesson you ever had in true obedience."

It was just like the old days with Yerima. Of course he caught her. Of course he practically threw her onto the bed. She struggled against him, but muscular arms quickly overpowered her. She kicked. She fought. One arm was pinned behind her back, then the other. She clamped her legs tightly shut. A strong grip forced them apart. Despite all her efforts to keep him away, His Hardness finally found his way into his velvety destination. Oh, such delicious defeat, such luscious craving. She ceased all resistance, then acknowledged his conquest by releasing herself to his mastery. Before she fell over the precipice she enjoyed the look of faraway bliss on Ibrahim's face.

When she came to Nurse Musa, Prince Ibrahim, and Fernando were all peering at her intently.

"You were out a long time," said Musa. "I was just breaking out the smelling salts."

"I did it! I did it! I made you faint! I did it! Who's number one now? Just who's number one?"

"This is the first time in my career I've ever been called because both *monsieur* and *madame* passed out at the same time." Musa went into gales of laughter.

"I was positively scared to death, Your Highness. I mean, both of you–"

"You did the right thing, Fernando. Thank you. Musa, I believe we're all right. You may go."

Musa exited, laughing heartily.

"Now I think I know the professor's secret. Get you to one hundred and twenty percent. Am I right?"

She nodded, smiling.

"Fernando, bring me the phone. Ali? Ibrahim here. Ass 421. Cancel her damned probation. Cancel her damned level three. Cancel all the damned paddlings. And you'd better cancel all the appointments she has for at least the next week, because I don't plan to let this girl out of my sight. Do we have a category better than Outstanding? Some-thing like, Spectacular? Do you know what she just did? She made me faint. In fact, Fernando panicked and called Musa up because both of us passed out at the same time. Ask Musa, I'm not joking. She actually made me faint. Of course, I made her faint too, and she was out a lot longer than I was." He laughed proudly. "So, you've noted the changes? All right, I want to get back, ahem, to what I was doing."

Tammy knelt and began kissing his feet.

"It's all right, my little Mukhmala. I'm restoring your ability to speak and to stand. On condition that you never, ever sass me or stand up to me again."

"I promise, master. Besides, I don't need to any more. Thank you very much, master."

"I made you faint. I actually made you faint." He shook his head in delight. "I need to take another trip to replenish our staff, and I'll be away for several weeks. When I get back I'll need to figure out exactly what I'm going to do with you. You're the only girl I've ever owned who's been really honest with me. Not to mention the only one who's ever made me pass out. I want to cover you with diamonds, keep you in a special harem, give you slaves of your own. One thing for sure, I'm not renewing this idiotic lease. It's a legal document, and I respect my legal obligations, but I'm really tired of being hemmed in every time I turn around.

"Fernando, I want her chained securely to the bed, so she knows exactly where she'll be until I leave for my restocking trip. Put the three-meter chain on; I want her to be able to use a bedpan, kneel beside the bed, and prostrate on the rug. My dear little Mukhmala, you will not eat anything, because I want you to be hungry for your master. And, you will surrender your sight until further orders – Fernando, the padded leather blindfold. I don't want you to know what time of day it is, what day of the week it is, what year it is. I just want you to focus your attention completely on satisfying every last one of His Hardness' desires.

"But first, a bottle of prosecco." Tammy eyed him wordlessly. "No, don't worry. I've appointed Fernando my policeman. He'll let me have one bottle, and that's all. But I think this event deserves some celebration. To fainting! And to one helluva intoxicating little slave-girl."

For eight days, Tammy remained attached to Prince Ibrahim's bed. Every few hours he'd allow her to suck "honey-water" from a bottle with a pacifier top, and every two days he let her suck "honey"-flavored yogurt. Once, after she'd given him a particularly nice BJ, he even let her lick his plate. A couple of times, he briefly had the leg iron taken off, so she could serve as his footrest as he made phone call after phone call, or give him a massage as he reviewed the weekly financials. Almost all of the time, however, she was immobilized in one of four authorized positions: spread-eagle, hungry asshole, total submission, or eager anticipation.

"Fernando, while she has her rear elevated like that, put some sparkle gel on it. Bright pink. Oh, just look at that. That gorgeous ass, and that succulent asshole, belong just to me. All mine! Being rich is really fun sometimes."

369

Life felt so futile, so pointless, so stupid. She thought she'd be-come used to her condition, but those eight days of sheer boredom reopened wounds she thought had long ago scarred over, gave her time to think about the life she should have been leading, her friends who were starting families and launching their careers – careers that didn't involve sparkle gel and wiggle worms. It took all the self-control she could muster to keep from bursting into tears.

One afternoon Tammy was on Reception duty with one of the recently imported Tahitians. She was so beautiful that men drooled over her, and so sweet and smiling – a Tahitian Zima – that they absolutely reveled in her services.

Tammy had just finished giving a foot massage to Gen. Abubakr when in walked Yerima. He took a seat. "Just one moment, please, sir, the water has cooled." She refilled the basin and knelt before him. She'd seen Classy Assie the week before, glowing almost incandescent. She sighed.

If other people – especially the always-nosy Mr. Mohammed – hadn't been present, she would have thrown herself at his feet and begged his forgiveness for being so monumentally stupid. She wanted him to know that she was still his, so she placed her hands palms upward. He gave her half a wink, and she set to work, acutely aware of the effect her hands had on him. And herself.

"How's your nice man?" he asked quietly.

"He finally gave up, sir." She shrugged in resignation.

"Sorry." A long pause. "Oh, um, about what I did to you in the car? I need to tidy up my conscience about that. I've been feeling terrible."

"It's okay, sir. I understood. Not right then, but I understood." She moved close to him and made sure her back was toward Mr. Moham-med. She spoke very softly. "You

370

were very wise to abandon Plan A, sir. After our date they put a theft alert out on you. It's still in force and they've even bugged Classy Assie's collar, sir."

"They're no dummies, and I was way too obvious. Thanks." A few moments later he said, "So, you made your friend Ibrahim faint."

"You heard about that, sir? It was your contrition game that did it. He wishes he could put you in charge of the Training Department."

He gave her a little smile. "Everybody heard about that. Again and again and again. Ironic, how I spent all those months training you and then you turn around and make him faint instead of me."

He's jealous, she thought happily, the man is really jealous.

He shrugged and made a face. "Such is life." Then he added in a whisper, "After we dropped you off, Bouba said he didn't understand why I didn't just take you straight to my house. I was so mad at you for running away I didn't think of it. I really blew that, didn't I?"

She looked him square in the eye. "Yes sir. You sure did, sir."

He eyed her right back. "May I point out, madame," he said, "as gently as possible, that you were so mad at me, you didn't think of it either."

Mr. Mohammed bowed. "Prince Yerima, Your Highness? Your room is ready, Your Highness."

Tammy stared after him until he was completely out of sight, struggling not to lose her composure. He didn't smile at her, didn't turn around to wink at her.

The Tahitian smiled. "The way sparks were flying, I thought you two were going to set fire to the building."

371

"Yes," Tammy said, fighting back tears. "We used to be in love."

"Used to be?"

Tammy waited and waited, hoping that he'd send for her again. He didn't.

The Nursery became such a popular room that The Office outfitted a second room like the first. Many of the executives were spoiled brats anyway, so it was perfectly in character for them to mess in their diapers and throw tantrums like 18-month-olds.

One day, Tammy arrived in the Nursery to replace a *raqqisa* who'd danced to exhaustion and found Zima nearly in tears. Dr. Hassan had gnawed on her nipples until they were bleeding, and forbade her to use ointment because he didn't like the way it tasted. "I've already been here for almost five hours. I was supposed to go off-duty nearly two hours ago, but my sister, from the amount of cocaine he's laid in, it looks like we'll be here for hours and hours more."

He lounged on the floor by the high chair surrounded by his toys – a baby bottle filled with Blue and Perrier, a good ten packets of cocaine, a teddy bear with huge boobs, a pull-toy of a baby whipping a naked woman.

"Do the one where the whore gets whipped," he told Tammy, "and keep doing it until I say stop."

She absolutely, positively hated that dance. It was set to an odd sort of Arab cabaret music, punctuated at intervals by the sound of a cracking whip. Whenever the whip cracked she was supposed to stop dancing, throw herself to the floor, writhe in agony, then pick herself up and dance again until it cracked another time. So, to the tune of slurping, spitting, snorting, and burping, she danced. Nenzima spooned salmon

372

mousse into his mouth with one hand and nursed him intermittently, all the while giving Dr. Do-Good a massage inside the diaper.

Tammy danced.

The valet was one of the new recruits. Rats, thought Tammy, he hasn't been around long enough to know what a skunk Dr. Hassan is.

"Mikhail, I told you to bring me another bottle of Blue. Where is it? And the molten lava cake that I ordered more than thirty minutes ago."

"Yes sir. Coming right up, sir."

"Stop the music. I want the *raqqisa* to be stuffed."

"Stuffed, sir?"

"Stuffed! Haven't you learned anything, you idiot? Stuffings are over there in the drawer. Show him, ass. The one you can screw stuff onto. I want the big feathered tail."

Tammy obediently showed Mikhail the selection of dildos, and pointed to the one requested. She even had to show him how to insert it. Dr. Hassan was shaking his head.

"Where's the tail, sir?"

Dr. Hassan groaned. "In the cabinet, you incompetent fool! How long have you been working here?"

"My fourth day, sir."

"And you haven't stuffed an asshole? Screw the damned tail in. And dammit, Where … is … my … Blue?"

"Let me check the dumbwaiter, sir." It was there, along with the lava cake that had grown cold.

373

"Send the damned cake back. I'm losing patience with you very fast. Have you ever hooked up an ass to the Rump-o-Rator?"

"The Rump-o- what, sir?" He started to laugh.

"Unbelievable. And Central assigned you to work for me? Chair-man of the Board, and they sent me an idiot like you? Nefertitty, show this nincompoop how to do it. Then turn it onto buck. I want to see that ass flying, those feathers waving like mad. Then come back over here, change my diaper, and give me my bottle."

Mikhail was spellbound. "Craziest and coolest thing I ever saw," he said to no one in particular.

"Mikhail, warm up some almond oil. I want the black whore to give me a rubdown."

"What on earth do the women think of these things, sir?"

"For your information, you idiot, they aren't women. They're whores. Women live in harems; whores live in clubs. They are highly trained, very expensive, carefully controlled specialty livestock. Period. Whores do not express opinions, but I expect that they love them, because it used to be that they had to actually do some work, and now the machine does it for them. Second of all, I asked you to warm some almond oil and you totally ignored me because you were too busy watching the flying ass. That show is for me, not you. And third, you're *fired*. Black whore, bring me my phone. Hassan here. I have just fired Mikhail for total ineptitude. Send me a valet who at least knows how to stuff an asshole and hook up an RoR, and get him up here on the double. What? Oh, shit. I thought we had fifteen or sixteen in training. Oh, shit."

He looked up. "What the hell are you still doing here? Clear out of here before I turn you into a booby-dick. I repeat, you're *fired!*"

374

"What on earth's a booby-dick?" Mikhail asked Zima.

"Out!" The baby bottle went flying and nearly hit the ex-valet's head.

Zima wordlessly started warming the oil and knelt before him.

"Yes?"

"Where would you like for me to start, master?"

"Help me up. Start with my feet, work your way up, then with my shoulders and work your way down. Finally you will give Dr. Do-Good one of your beautiful massages."

He was far more drunk than he sounded. He staggered to the bed and flopped down heavily. Zima started to work on his feet, humming softly. Within a couple minutes he was snoring.

She stopped massaging. Waited.

No reaction.

Stood.

No reaction.

Turned off the machine.

Unstrapped Tammy.

Made a motion of picking something off a tree.

Tammy and Zima exchanged excited, almost disbelieving glances.

Leather straps were still in place on the bed from where Zima had been restrained earlier, but of course the Chairman of the Board wasn't wearing cuffs that could be rapidly hooked in place. Tammy remem-bered the supply drawer, and came back with the same steel-reinforced velvet cuffs he'd used so many times on them, stopping on the way to change the DVD to nursery lullabies and with a flourish flushing his cell phone down the toilet. Slowly, tenderly, they slipped the cuffs around his wrists.

A cough. A murmur. They froze. Zima cooed at him, suckled him. "Hmm," he said. The snoring resumed.

Slowly, tenderly, the cuffs went onto his ankles. The straps were hooked to the cuffs, then pulled tighter, shorter. Millimeter by milli-meter they pulled until they were snug. Millimeter by millimeter, until his wrists and ankles were completely immobilized.

"Better double them, just in case. He's a strong man, and we can't afford to screw this up." But now it was easy to add the shackles.

He was theirs!

Zima and Tammy hugged, shaking with excitement. Zima crossed herself. Gripped the knife tightly. Jabbed him a couple of times to get his attention.

His eyes opened half way. "Gmpf," he said, and they closed again.

She jabbed him again. This time he didn't even stir.

"Let's just do it," Tammy said.

"I want him to know that it's Zima and Tammy. I want to see the fear in his eyes."

Tammy said, "Just a second." She came back with a pitcher of ice water and dumped its contents into his diaper. That worked. His eyes opened and stayed open, filled with confusion. He tugged at his bonds. They held. He began to understand.

"You wouldn't dare," he said.

"Try us," Tammy said, twisting herself mockingly, raising his chin with her finger as he'd so often done to her. "And, you will address us as master." She turned to Zima. "You want to go first?" She hadn't realized that murder could be so much fun.

"No, that's all right. Here." Zima handed her the knife and started taking off his diaper.

It became obvious what they intended to do. He thrashed in panic; the bonds held tight. "My golden treasure, you know what awaits you if you continue this act of stupidity."

She slapped him hard, enjoying the look of shocked disbelief in his eyes. "I told you to address us as master. It's worth it, shitball. I don't care what they do to me. I've waited five years, two months, and eleven days for this moment, but there again, who's counting?" Her hands shook as she threw the diaper aside and took into her hand the part of him that had given them so much trouble.

"Please," he said. "Don't do this. For heaven's sake, Miss Congo, warn her to stop this foolishness."

Tammy slapped him again. "We are now your masters, and you will address us as such."

"Oh," said Zima, "Tammy, did you hear something? Is the doctor begging? The fearless master is begging two lowly whores? But he hasn't assumed the position of petition, so we just ignore him. He taught us so much about restraints. He taught us so much about humility. We know he is very proud of us."

"Maybe we can negotiate." Tammy toyed with Dr. Do-Good, again and again stretching him much farther than he was really willing to go. She reveled in the way perspiration beaded on Dr. Hassan's forehead. "Although, since you arranged for me to become royal property, there's not much you can do."

377

His lips were dry and white. "Don't. Please."

"He's begging again, Zima. But he still obstinately refuses to call us master, and he's not on his knees, waiting for us to acknowledge him. Hey, he looks sort of hungry. Zi, do you need to shit, by any chance?"

"Not really, my sister, but wait – there's his dirty diaper over there." She cooed at him and spooned some of his own shit into his mouth. "Come on, now, lick it clean. Doesn't that taste nice?" To their enormous delight, he gagged and spluttered. "Now I think it's time for him to howl in pain."

"Give me just a second here, and you'll get your wish." Tammy picked out her place and began to saw. He screamed. He fought. Tammy sawed.

"Thoughtful of them to soundproof these rooms so well, isn't it?" Tammy commented.

It was more difficult than she'd imagined, especially with the way he was writhing around, but after a few minutes it came off in her hand. It was small and soft, like a blood-covered mouse. She showed it to him and smiled triumphantly.

Mouth agape, eyes fixed in horror, he made strangulated sounds. "You – you'll die for this," he gasped.

"Do you think he'd like to give himself a BJ?" Tammy asked Zima. Nenzima grinned, so she put it in his mouth. He gagged and spluttered some more. Threw up.

"Hmm, now you know how we feel. Hey, let's put some tit-clamps on him too."

"Ow! Take these damned things off. Right now." His commanding voice had a few cracks in it.

This time it was Zima who slapped him. "We're the ones giving orders here. Don't they feel nice? Make you feel controlled, shitball? Submissive? Obedient?"

She went and fetched a silencer. They put Dr. Do-Good and a select piece of his own diaper in the pouch, put the silencer in his mouth, and fastened it tight. "You taught these two little whores so well. See? You can't make a squeak. Aren't you proud of yourself?"

Tammy handed Zima the sticky knife. She studied his neck.

"Gmmpf!" he said. Apparently he thought that unmanning him was all they intended to do.

"Tammy, poor baby, what's left of teeny tiny Dr. Done-For is bleeding all over the bed. Hand me the diaper again, will you?"

She folded it neatly under the bloody stump. "Oh, I know," she said gleefully. She put a pussy pillow under his hips and inflated it. "Now we can see better what's not there anymore."

"Maybe we should just let him bleed to death like that," Tammy suggested.

"No, it would take too long. Besides, I have dreamed many dreams of this moment. We've been trained to be very thorough, dear doctor, and to make sensations last as long as possible. I'm sure you will enjoy this experience just as much as we enjoyed serving you."

"Oh, wait. That pussy pillow gave me an idea." Tammy brought back a wiggle worm, stuck it in, and wound it up. The results were so hilarious that the two assassins held onto each other laughing. Zima laughed so hard she fell over. "Oh, just look at that cute little ass, wig-gling like crazy. Trying so to please his masters."

Nenzima got back to her feet and to the main event, feeling his neck with possessive fingers, picking out her spot.

They were frightened by the intensity of the struggle he put up. He was amazingly strong, but the shackles were stronger.

"I'm glad we doubled those restraints," said Tammy. "Whew."

Nenzima slashed. Gurgles. Gushing blood. They looked at each other, splattered with blood, and it began to sink in that they were really committing murder.

After a few minutes the writhing diminished, but the wiggle worm was still in full swing.

"Just look, he's still entertaining us," said Tammy. They laughed until they cried.

Nenzima looked full into his disbelieving eyes. "You murdered my baby," she said softly.

"Maybe God will forgive you for all the suffering you've caused, but we sure as hell won't," said Tammy. "We've made reservations for you at the ultimate Rodeo, where you'll be roasting for eternity. Shitball, the gates of hell await you."

There was a shudder, a strangled gasp, then nothing. The spring ran down and a few moments later, even the wiggling stopped.

They stared at the gory scene with detachment, as if it were a TV movie and they could flip the channel. He didn't move. It was incredibly satisfying, that look of frozen terror in his eyes.

They stepped back and gaped, like they halfway expected him to tell them what to do.

"He's really dead, isn't he?" Tammy said at length.

"He's dead, my sister, because we killed him. We killed Dr. Hassan!"

They fell into each other's bloodied arms laughing and weeping like drunken fools. "We did it! We did it!" Tammy put the cabaret music back on – loud – and they danced wildly around the room, ignoring the cracks of the whip, ignoring everything but their unbridled glee.

After a few minutes, though, the bloody mess put a damper on the party. They sopped up most of the blood with diapers, put a fresh one on him, washed off the blood from his throat and chest and from themselves.

Nenzima was remarkably serene. "Before we kill ourselves we might as well have some fun," she said, "and just think, our party will go on his bill." Zima stuck his membership card into the service terminal and ordered Mediterranean style Chilean sea bass, chateau-briand, a Norwegian omelet for herself and a chocolate tart for Tammy, as well as a magnum of Dom Perignon.

"Better order more hits of cocaine too to give us more time," said Tammy.

The dumbwaiter soon chimed, and they sat in the playpen and feasted. They polished off the champagne, then started working on the Blue, not caring that they were soon roaring drunk. They told silly stories. They wept. They hugged. Cried. Then it was time to do what they had to do.

Tammy didn't want to die. But give Dr. Hassan the satisfaction of knowing she was being tortured? Never! Suicide was less horrible, but it made her sacrifices seem so futile. She started to cry.

"Don't weep, my sister. We have both realized a dream. We have saved other lives, other babies. Now we must die. Most people die without making even a little bit of difference in this world. We have. And I leave this earth with a heart filled with satisfaction, knowing, like you told him, that he already burns in hell. Would you like for me to help you?"

"No, that's okay, I'll do it, it's just that…"

"Give me the knife. I must be dead when they find us, and so must you. Let me show you what to do." She traced with her finger the places Tammy should cut her wrists. "Like this," she said, crossing herself, then cutting her own cleanly and deeply. "Oh," she gasped. "It stings, but not too much. Oh. Oh. Here. Your turn, my sister."

Blood streamed from both wrists. Nenzima lay on the rug. "Please, my sister, lie beside me."

Tammy cradled her head in her arms, sobbing miserably. "Zima, Zima, you're the only friend I have left in this world. I don't want you to die."

"Don't be afraid. I go to the embrace of Blessed Jesus. My grandmother and my baby daughter are calling me. I do not regret. Don't be afraid, my sister."

"Sure," she said, turning the knife over and over in her hand.

Nenzima's breaths became short and ragged. "Oh yes!" she called out, "oh yes! Mama is coming, mama is coming!" She gave a small shudder. A blissful smile lit her face.

Tammy kissed her friend goodbye, bawling like a baby.

After a while she pulled herself together enough to close Zima's eyes, lost in love and admiration for her cool courage, her quiet serenity, envious of her smooth dark body as it grew cold beside her.

Rrrrrring. Rrrrrring. The phone! Security! Oh no! If she didn't answer, they'd come right up. Maybe, she thought with sudden panic, they might come anyway.

"Nursery Room, Ass 421 speaking. What will be your pleasure today, sir? Yes sir. I understand, sir. I shouldn't be, but I'm the only one who can right now. No sir. No sir. Sort of, sir." She realized that she was slurring. "Dr. Hassan got really mad at him, fired him, and Central didn't have anybody

382

else. No sir. Dr. Hassan and his good friend Johnny Walker spent a lot of time together today and it doesn't look like he's going to wake up anytime soon. Also, snorted line after line. Yes sir, she's here, yes sir, completely immobilized. Yes sir, you're quite correct, sir. I didn't have very much but it sure doesn't take a lot when you're never allowed to have any. He ordered us to. We know sir, but he's Chairman of the Board and he says he makes 'his own goddam rules.' Understood, sir. Thank you, sir."

Whew!

She'd thought about death. She'd wished for it. Reconciled herself to it. She knew it was her only choice. And yet, now that it was time to take her life, she couldn't do it. She'd spent all those years thinking that she'd survived to kill Dr. Hassan, but now, she discovered that she'd lived for herself.

Nearly an hour passed while she went through it all again. She drank another shot of Blue, but now it burned and tasted horrible. She said silent goodbyes to her mom and dad and brother. Cleo. Marc. Elaine. Saud. Amberine. Fritzi. Taymoor. Yerima. Heineken. She tried to think of a screaming Dr. Hassan, on his knees begging mercy from cackling demons as the flames of hell engulfed him. It was time.

The knife felt cold. Imagining she was slicing through his evil throat, she cut, deep and true. Just like slicing meat for stew, she thought. The sight of her blood soaking into the carpet reassured her that she'd done it right.

She was tired, very tired. Just wanted to close her eyes and go to sleep. It was good to know that her final escape was so much easier than the life she'd led. She was at peace with herself. Everything became a blur. She grew heavy, then deliciously light.

Savitsky helped himself to another lotus root dumpling and smiled fondly across the table. "Simmons, in this business, you can never stop trying. Oh, try one of these. Outstanding. Absolutely outstanding."

"Who says I've stopped trying? Only thing is, it's been more than five years."

"She's still alive, right?"

"Yes. That's all that keeps me going."

"And she's still your Tammy-girl, right?"

"Always."

A bite of pot-sticker disappeared into Savitsky's mouth. "Sim-mons, I was on the phone with Abubakr last week. Don't give any indication that I told you, but he's got a new chap working for him now. This guy's amazing. He managed to spring four girls from another club on the circuit using an experimental new technique. He's very optimistic."

John looked up sharply. "I'm on the phone with him every week, but he hasn't said a word."

Savitsky grinned. "I think he wants it to be a surprise."

Heaven, thought Tammy muddily, was a strange place. The lights were way too bright and it sure was noisy. She blinked. The fuzzy noise distilled into familiar sounds. Words. There was a shout. Arabic? When everybody knew angels spoke English? The light hurt her eyes. Her head pounded. Her tongue was wearing a fur coat. Heaven was not at all what she expected.

"Ya Allah! She's coming to."

Damn.

She was shackled to a hospital bed, transfusion running into one ankle, IV running into the other, wrists bandaged, mouth taped shut. She couldn't move a millimeter.

Damn.

"All right, she'll be okay. Call the Rodeo and tell them they have a pick-up."

Damn.

"How long do you think it'll be before we can reopen?"

"Not sure. Rumors flying. Why did it have to happen on my shift? Why does shit like this always happen on my shift?"

"Sir? Article 16 of the lease says we need to notify her owner, and he has to give written confirmation. Then they'll send the truck."

"So, what are you waiting for?"

"He's in Aruba. I've sent him an email."

Damn.

"She's ready for the butcher-shop. Still no word from Aruba? It's been almost three days."

"Just got a reply. The truck's on its way over. Hey, meat, have a message for you. 'Dear Mukhmala, congratulations on your achievement. Unfortunately, article 16 of the lease is very explicit, so I am releasing you for execution. Always, your darling Prèdiletto.'"

The lease, of course, was more important than anything else. She was just his property. And she would die, she realized despondently, with a stainless steel collar around her neck.

PART TEN

THE RODEO

October – November 2010
Zul-Qeda 1431

She was blindfolded and suspended by a shoulder harness from a meat hook, her feet resting on a roll of barbed wire, hands bound tightly with barbed wire behind her back. She was already dead; she was just waiting for it to be official.

"Now here's a new arrival, a nice juicy piece of meat. She murdered her owner, can you believe? I'd suggest roasting her on a spit, or perhaps boil her in oil."

"No thanks, I'm looking for something with a lot better tits."

An hour, a day, or perhaps a week later, another potential customer considered her. "Let me turn her around. Can't you just picture this ass roasting on a spit? Or being torn apart by hyenas? She murdered her owner, so she deserves whatever she gets."

"No, I don't think so, too skinny, no boobs at all."

"Here's a criminal for you. Murdered her master. Hasn't been devocalized, so you can count on some robust screams. I'd suggest roasting this ass on a spit, what a sight that would be." There was a slight pause. "Yes yes, we can arrange that. Do you know what you'd like to do?" Another pause while she strained to hear. "Yes indeed, the package includes the glass pot and lid, a sturdy propane burner, a body bag, and even a bag of spices in case you'd like to sample the meat. We deliver and get everything set up for you, and when you're ready you call us and we come pick up the equipment and the corpse; we dispose of it for you."

Boiled to death. And possibly cannibalized. At least, now she knew.

"Tomorrow? Yes, we can deliver say, mid-day? Do you want her already in the pot? All right, in the pot. Head in or out? Okay, out it is. Now, we suggest, for safety reasons, that we set up outside on a patio…"

The voices trailed off, the formalities finalized.

And so it was done. Lowered into a pot like at the Rainbow, two-piece lid fit around her head and bolted down, into a truck. Maybe a twenty-minute ride.

"Where would you like the delivery from the Rodeo?"

Offloaded, set in place. She thought about all the people she'd been nice to, all the people she'd been mean to, all the things she'd wished had been different. She hoped God wouldn't judge her too harshly. Time to shut her brain down and revert into a second state. She no longer wanted to hear anything, feel anything, know anything.

"You guys act like you never saw a girl in a pot before. Now, help me get her out of this stupid thing and into the gr – no, make that the rose bedroom."

Bolts came off. Strong arms lifted her. They removed her hood. She lay crumpled on the patio stones, practically lifeless.

"Bouba, call Dr. Suleyman and ask him to get here as soon as he possibly can. And tell Jeanne-Rose to find her a nightgown."

Yerima tucked a sheet around her, kissed her on the forehead, and sat on the bed next to her. "I'm here, Sudari,

389

you're at my house now. You're not at the Rodeo. You're going to be all right. Do you understand that?"

Nothing.

"A doctor will be here in a few minutes. Do you want something to eat? Drink?"

Nothing.

"I'll be right here with you, babe. François, bring some tea with lemon, maybe we can get a little of it down her."

Nothing.

"Very dehydrated, Excellency. I'll give her an IV and a sedative so she can get some sleep. Sweetheart, did you try to commit suicide?"

Her eyelids flickered.

He pulled the sheet back. "Slave-girl, Excellency?"

"Long story, doctor. I got her from the Rodeo, where she was supposed to be executed for murdering Dr. Hassan."

"That was you, sweetheart? I heard about that. The black slave was dead, right?" She started to sob. "A long list of people wanted to do the same thing. I do believe congratulations are in order. Physically, Excellency, she'll be fine in a few days. Psychologically, well, I expect she's extremely traumatized. I could recommend a therapist."

"She's an amazingly strong person, doctor. I told her once that she has more balls than I do, and I meant it. I'll see how she's doing in a couple of weeks."

Something seemed to click, and she opened her eyes. Swallowed. Looked around in total confusion. Began to shake and sob hysterically. Gripped Yerima's arm with both hands. He tried to stand to accompany the doctor to the door, but Tammy would not let go. He stayed with her, holding her, kissing her, reassuring her, until the sedative took effect and she fell asleep.

Late next morning she was still crying and shaking uncontrollably, but she accepted the pills that Yerima gave her. "You're going to be all right. No more Office. No more Dr. Hassan. You're here with me now, in my house, and I'm going to take care of you. Is it starting to sink in, babe?" She nodded. "I tracked down your father in Istanbul. He was so relieved and happy he wept. He tried so hard, so many ways, to get you out, but nothing worked. He's flying in tonight and says he'll stay right here with you until you're okay again." She began to bawl. "Have a little sip of broth, Sudari, just a little sip, please?" She didn't move. "All right. Time to break out the major artillery. This is your lord and master speaking. I hereby order you to drink at least a cup of this broth. Right now." Still sobbing, she bowed her head. Sighed. And obeyed.

He sat next to her, holding her hand. She dozed off, she awoke, she dozed off again.

"Yes, Bouba? He's here? Great, bring him right in."

"Tammy-Girl!" They hugged and wept, wept and hugged.

"Oh, Daddy," she blubbered, "oh, Daddy."

Yerima smiled.

Over snifters of Courvoisier, Yerima related the story. Tammy had a faraway look in her eyes, as if it had nothing to do with her. "We had a big fight. I tried for months to live without her, I really did. So when I found out what they were going to do, I realized that they were going to take her away from me forever. Forever. I couldn't let this woman be put to death at all, much less in such an unthinkable way."

"Excellency, I don't know how you pulled it off, but you did, and here she is, and here we are, and there simply aren't words to thank you. May I ask you for one small favor, though, please? Can you find a scarf or something to put around her neck? I'm having a really hard time…"

"Of course, sir. I apologize; I should have thought of that." He arranged a tartan muffler around her neck.

She spent the better part of the next three days asleep, but whenever the medication would wear off she'd lie in bed and shake. The fits of sobbing became less frequent, and occasionally she'd eat a little yogurt or chicken broth. Yerima and her father took turns sitting beside her bed.

"How's Mom?" she asked.

"Not doing too well, honey. Do you want something? Need anything?"

"Shampoo?"

"I'm sure that can be arranged." John and Yerima exchanged looks of relief.

That evening she managed to eat a whole bowl of vegetable soup. Her dad caught her up with the news. "Wellie's studying criminal justice at Maryland, wants to be an FBI detective specializing in human trafficking. He wants everybody to call him Caldwell now. Elaine got her nursing degree and just married an Australian and moved to Melbourne. Marc got his naval commission and is stationed in Jacksonville. Let's see…"

"Mom?"

"Honey, I'm sorry to say that she went into a deep depression and hasn't been able to shake it. She's attempted suicide three times and has been hospitalized for more than eight months now. François, you're a talented man. This *coq au vin* is outstanding."

"And Cleo?"

"Honey, once again, I'm sorry, she died about a year ago. She was sixteen, you know, and had a kidney problem. We buried her in the back yard."

This news upset her even more than the word about her mother. She cried and cried and cried.

The chef bowed and served the fennel and green apple salad.

"So, John, what were you doing in Istanbul?"

"Leather. I have a fraternity brother there from my days at Duke. Esat's now the leather–"

"Daddy," Tammy said, oblivious to anything else, "Zima and I murdered a man. Murdered him! And it was the most fun I had in five years. Except for that night, Yerima, when you were showing me your dances. Daddy, I didn't know murder could be so much fun." Yerima took her hand and clasped it tight. She began to sob again.

Next day she was on the floor, kissing Yerima's feet. "You know when I got jealous?" he asked. "It was when I found out you'd made Ibrahim faint. I thought holy shit, that should've been me. And I was thinking about sending for you again. Then, the stuff happened with Dr. Hassan."

A week after his first visit, Dr. Suleyman came back to check on her and said she was doing better than expected. It was also time to remove her decorations. The surgical saw made quick work of the cuffs and ankle bracelet, but the collar was stainless steel and fit snugly, so it presented quite a challenge. It finally came off.

"You want me to flush these horrible things down the toilet?" asked Yerima.

"No sir, Yerima, please. I want to save them. Nobody will believe me otherwise. I might not even believe it myself."

"Yerima?" John said, "I used to know another Fulani prince, but they called him Yaraam."

"Farther west," he explained, "and they call the king *lamdo* instead of *lamido*. Slightly different dialect, same language. The Fulani people stretch all the way from Sudan to Senegal, so there's quite a bit of room for variation."

She made steady progress, walking around, sitting up, even catching Oprah. Her first words had been for her father, but her first smile was for Yerima. She lay at his feet, kissing them and kissing them and kissing them, sobbing with relief. "I can still scarcely believe that I'm here, my lord. Alive. Kissing my beloved Yerima. I'd completely given up hope. When you took me out of the, uh … when you took me out…" Her voice broke. "I was so numb I thought it was all over, that I was dead. Then I started hearing your voice, and I thought no, this can't be possibly be heaven."

Yerima howled. "You're going to pay for that one, Sudari, and I mean, you'll pay for that one dearly."

"It didn't come out quite the way I meant, sir." Yerima was doubled over laughing so hard that she caught the bug and started laughing too.

John opened the door and found his daughter on the floor clasping Yerima's feet, both of them weak with laughter. "I'm sorry, I seem to have stumbled onto a private moment."

"No, come right on in, John."

"It does my heart good to see you laughing like that, honey."

"John, she won't stop kissing my feet. I do have plans to let her express her appreciation in a horizontal position, but this isn't exactly what I have in mind. Anyway, have a seat. We were talking about when I went to the Rodeo to get her."

John sat down. "You two have the most unconventional relation-ship I've ever seen. I suppose extraordinary circumstances require extraordinary measures, and, I might add, an extraordinary man. Yerima, what would we have done without you?"

"Daddy, I haven't exactly had a conventional life, you know. A couple of years ago he turned me into a full-fledged woman and I've been in love with him ever since. Then he saved me from being tortured to death. He's given me my life twice over. Plus, you kind of, sort of know the life I've led for the past five years; but he's one of a handful of people who really appreciates what I've been through and he loves me anyway. What's so hard to understand?"

"You're right, honey. And if it works for you, God bless you both."

"So, when I found out what was going on, I realized I had to do something. I wasn't about ready to let them do that to her. Not my sweet Sudari. I almost came apart at the very idea of putting you into a pot, but I had to make them think that the sentence would be carried out. Of course, that made you think so too. François cooked a lamb in it, so when they came to pick up their equipment it was obvious that it'd been used." He shook his head. "And oh, by the way, when I found out how much it cost to become a member of the Rodeo, I nearly passed out. And when they told me what the tab would be to have an off-site party, I nearly passed out again. You know who gave me the money? Your friend Sheikh Saud. He said you gave his life back to him, so it was the least he could do for you."

She looked up at him in surprise. "That is unbelievably nice of him, unbelievably nice." And she broke down again. "Sir? How long was I at the Rodeo?"

"Four days. So, counting the time you were in the infirmary, you're looking at five years, two months, and eighteen days. But that's over now, Sudari. All that's behind you."

"Thanks to you, my lord." She clutched at his feet as if he were an anchor to the Planet Earth. She did some arithmetic. "One thousand, nine hundred, and four days of hell."

François brought them some roast chicken and cucumber-and-yogurt salad.

"You've got your smile back, your appetite back. I'm so relieved, honey. Yerima, would it be all right if I borrow Bouba for a little while? I need to run a few errands."

"No problem at all. Keep him all afternoon if you like." As soon as she'd finished eating Tammy went right back on the floor, holding Yerima's ankles and kissing his feet.

"When you feel ready for the little prince again, you come to my room, all right? It's the second door down on the left. No rush. And, again, no rush, but when you think your brain is in working order again you'll need to decide whether you're going back to Washington with your dad or coming home with me."

"I want to be with you, sir."

"Are you absolutely sure?"

"I've never been so sure of anything in my entire life, sir."

"Even the way we talked about?"

"Even like that. Yes, sir." She put her arms around his ankles and held tight, voice breaking. "For one thing, sir, you bought me. It's the first time I've ever been really glad to be somebody's property. But since you're giving me a choice, I still choose you. My beloved lord, you owned my body from the first time you touched me and now I owe you my very soul. How can I not give my life to you?"

396

"The thing is, I didn't buy you for myself, but for you. I don't want a slave. I want a woman who truly wants to be with me. Never-theless, twelve hours a day pounding yams and scrubbing pots can make gratitude wear pretty thin, you know."

"I'm not agreeing to this arrangement out of gratitude to you, sir, but out of an obligation to myself. I held a referendum of my cells and they voted overwhelmingly for me not to screw it up this time. They never forgave me for being so monumentally stupid. If you're still willing, sir, I can only imagine my life if it includes you."

"You've just escaped servitude. Are you really sure?"

"I'm used to it, sir. I caught a few minutes of a sit-com a few weeks ago and nobody was on their knees, nobody was calling anybody master, and I thought, how very weird. Then I realized how much I've been brainwashed. Five years is a long time. I'm not qualified for any job except giving BJs, and that's not exactly something to brag about on a resume. You understand what I've been through and I know you'll help me readapt. Who else could possibly do that, sir? Sort of like a halfway house. Maybe it'll take two or three years, maybe I'll never be normal again. But as long as a gorgeous guy named Yerima is my master, I don't mind a bit."

"Sudari, you did what you needed to do to survive, and you did a helluva good job of it. Don't be embarrassed one bit. In fact, be proud of yourself. You're a brave, brave woman and I can't begin to tell you how much I admire the way you're coming out of this. All right. I'll draw up a brief services agreement so there's no misunderstanding." He helped her to her feet and gave her a long reassuring hug.

Two days later John came into the dining room where Tammy and Yerima were feeding each other croissants and François' own strawberry jam. "Oh, honey, you look so much more relaxed this mo – ah. Of course."

397

Tammy was looking adoringly at Yerima, and Yerima was staring at the ceiling.

Later that day he handed her the draft agreement. "Let's make sure we have everything clear. You would become not my slave, but my servant. Slaves are on duty twenty-four hours a day; you would have a set schedule. You would also have the option to terminate the agree-ment if you're not happy, and a slave would have no such option. I don't think there'll be any surprises here because we've talked about almost all of it. If it's agreeable to you, then I'll take you with me when I go home next month. If it's not, no problem, you go home with your dad."

Everything was there, down to calling his wives Madame and him Master, being confined to the compound, 12-hour workdays under the supervision of Madame Aïssatou, annual optional renewal unless she tried to run away, in which case the agreement would automatically become permanent, providing "miscellaneous" services to him...

"Miscellaneous, sir?" she said with a giggle.

"Never know what that could involve."

There were two provisions they had not discussed: first, that if either one ever decided to terminate the agreement, Yerima would give her a lump-sum payment of $10,000 for the first year, $11,000 for the second year, $12,000 for the third year, and so forth. And second, that he would give her a physical reminder of her commitment, such as a bracelet or anklet, which she would not be allowed to take off as long as the agreement was in force.

"Exactly what would that physical reminder be, sir?" She'd just gotten rid of her decorations and wasn't wild about starting a new collection.

"That's for me to decide."

"And that's nice of you about the money, sir. Hey, I didn't realize you wore glasses."

"Lots of things you don't know about me, and lots of things I don't know about you, but we're going to have a helluva good time finding out. I figured your resume may not make you immediately employable in polite society, so it seemed only fair. You're ready to sign? Are you accepting this of your own free will? That I'm not forcing this down your throat? Write that down and sign your name. Then we'll both sign the agreement. I'll give you a copy you can keep, and I'll keep one in your file. Are you absolutely, positively sure that you want to do this?"

"My lord, I'd live in a doghouse if I could be with you."

"Now you tell me! I have two perfectly good doghouses and I can still amend the agreement, you know." They both laughed. "Please. I want to make extra-sure that this is what you want. Tell me why you're resigned to doing this instead of going home with your dad and getting a job somewhere."

"Not resigned at all, sir, I want to do it. I've thought about this a lot. I've spent five years in the worst possible kind of servitude. This is still a form of servitude, but it's the best form. I love and trust my master, my master loves me, and I know that instead of grinding me under your foot like the late Dr. Hassan, you'll find ways to lift me up. I'm not afraid of work; doing something productive instead of spending my life on my knees or on my back appeals to me a lot. And most important of all, my lord, I simply cannot imagine a life without you."

"You're a very sweet girl, Sudari. So, shall we do this?"

He gave her the agreement, and she signed. It felt very strange; she hadn't signed anything in more than five years. Then he signed with the practiced hand of someone who signed dozens of documents every day.

"Now we make it official. Prostrate yourself. Kiss each of my feet seven times. Then, since this is entirely voluntary, with your own hands take my feet and place them on your head. You will hold them there for seven seconds. Good. Now I will give you the physical reminder and draw your attention to the fact that you will not be allowed to remove it. Sudari, stand up." He pulled a small box from the pocket of his gandoura and got down on one knee. "May I have the pleasure of placing this ring on your finger as my future bride?"

"W-w-what? But I thought, I mean…"

"It's all quite recent. Alizée went back to Grenoble, met someone, and decided she no longer wanted to be part of a polygamous household. The divorce was finalized just a few weeks ago."

"She's nuts!"

He shrugged. "She's *French.*"

"You bastard! You sneaky, calculating, good-for-nothing bastard! You really had me going!"

"This, my dear lady, was a test, and you aced it. Look, what I'm doing right now is very un-African, and this sneaky, calculating, good-for-nothing bastard doesn't plan on staying in this position very long. May I have an answer please? And by the way, we have your father's blessing."

"Of course I'll marry you, you ninny."

"You ninny *sir,*" he corrected, giving her a long and delicious kiss. "I've got some champagne chilling. Oh, but first, another formality here." He ripped the agreement into confetti, grinning from ear to ear. "I declare you fully emancipated. Now, let's go have a glass, madame, and then we'll figure out some, um, miscellaneous way to celebrate."

"There's one thing that worries me, sir," Tammy told Yerima after lunch the next day. "I know that you're a public figure and some day you may run for office. You know how mean people can be, especially journalists. How are you going to explain about me?"

"If someone asks me anything, I'll just say that I was doing quality control inspections in cat-houses all over the Middle East and I concluded that the quality of your services was exceptional. Most people will think that I'm joking, and it's close enough to the truth to sidetrack the ones who know that I'm not. Or, we can say that we were introduced by a member of the royal family, which is also the truth. Right?"

She thought a moment. "You know, sir, you said I shouldn't be ashamed of anything because I did what I had to do to survive. And you were right. I'm going to refuse to be ashamed. What would you think if I went on a speaking tour and told people exactly what happened to me? And showed them the decorations I wore? Would that be an embarrassment to you?"

"Embarrassment, madame? Sudari, once again you've proven that you've got more balls than I do. I'd be so proud of you I'd explode."

"And the fact that you rescued me, sir, isn't going to make you look too bad, you know."

A few days later Yerima adjusted his brimless hat. "John and I are going to sign some papers and when we come back, you'll officially be my Mrs."

"But–"

"Nope, you don't even have to be there. Basically, John is signing you over to me."

She groaned. "I'm twenty-three years old, for heaven's sake! But I want Daddy to walk me down the aisle, sir. I want to stand up in front of people and tell them how much I love you."

"Sure, madame, we'll do anything you want. But first, let me make it all legal."

Three days later, Yerima looked resplendent in a white damask gandoura embroidered in gold. He stood at the far end of the state dining room as John slowly walked his bride toward him. Sheikh Saud and Heineken served as groomsmen, and Amberine and Suraiya as matrons of honor. Sheikh Farook officiated. Prince Ibrahim was still in Aruba, but sent a bouquet so large they could scarcely get it through the door, tied with a huge rose-colored velvet bow. The whole embassy staff was assembled, as well as a few friends.

The bride wore a two-piece African dress and head tie that matched the bridegroom's gandoura and carried a bouquet of burgundy roses in honor of Sheikh Saud, tied with a mango-colored satin ribbon in loving memory of Nenzima.

Marie-Claire, Yerima's secretary, had a beautiful singing voice and sang Tammy's favorite song from *Carousel*.

> When you walk through a storm, hold your chin up high
> And don't be afraid of the dark.
> At the end of the storm is a golden sky
> And the sweet silver song of a lark.
> Walk on through the rain, walk on through the wind,
> Though your dreams be tossed and blown,
> Walk on, walk on, with hope in your heart,
> And you'll never walk alone;
> You'll never walk alone.

Then Saoudou, the Political Affairs Officer, sang Yerima's selection, *Bridge Over Troubled Water*.

> When evening falls so hard,
> I will comfort you.
> I'll take your part when darkness comes,

And pain is all around,
Like a bridge over troubled water, I will lay
me down;
Like a bridge over troubled water, I will lay
me down.

Her voice broke and her eyes filled with happy tears as they clasped hands and she read her vows. "My beloved Abdoulaye, I will love you, honor you, respect you, and care for you with all my heart from this day forward. I promise to be respectful to my co-wives, love their children as much as the ones we will have together..." She bit her quivering lip. "...and always conduct myself in such a way as to bring honor to you." She gazed up at him. "With the help of Almighty God, today I am putting behind me whatever I have endured so I can devote myself to you. Against all odds, this strange and sometimes tortuous journey called life has somehow contrived to bring me here to you. I faced a horrible death, and by a miracle, you saved my life. I now offer that life willingly, lovingly, and completely to you."

The guests applauded.

"My beloved Sudari Tamara Lynne," he began, slipping a wedding ring onto her finger, I will love you, honor you, respect you, pro-tect you, and care for you with all my heart from this day forward. I will encourage you in whatever endeavor you wish to pursue, and take pride in your achievements. Whenever you are sad, or frightened, or when ghosts of the past grip you tight, I will put my arms around you and comfort you. I accept with great humility the beautiful gift you are bestowing upon me and promise that you will never regret placing your life in my hands." He couldn't help ad-libbing. "Sometimes, you know, I plan to put my arms around you for other reasons, too. And oh, by the way, in my capacity as president of the household, I hereby appoint you Minister of Education."

Applause mixed with chuckles.

Sheikh Farook said, "You may kiss your bride."

He pulled her into his arms, bent her backwards, and planted his lips on hers. The kiss lasted so long that the guests began to laugh. Still it continued.

"Look, you two," Sheikh Farook finally said, "may I please remind you that John has a flight out tomorrow afternoon?"

"To be continued," Yerima said, finally pulling away. He touched her on her nose, and she caught his finger and kissed it to the sound of prolonged applause.

Toasts were offered all round, and the guests were treated to a sumptuous feast. François had pulled out all the stops and everyone was exclaiming over his spit-roasted lamb *méchoui* with parsley and garlic, his own special duck pâté, and Taj Mahal chicken. Heineken found his way over to Tammy while she was enjoying a slice of wedding cake and blushed. "Dearie, I can't give you rubies like Sheikh Saud and emeralds like Sheikh Farouk, or a stallion and diamonds like Prince Ibrahim, but I brought you something I hope you'll like. He handed her a basket and she opened the lid. Two black-and-white tuxedo kittens! She gave him a messy kiss, and he blushed bright red. "See, um, I used to wear a tuxedo, and they're black and white like the bride and groom. They're both girls. I hope you'll think of me sometimes?"

"Think of you? Are you kidding? Dozens of times a day! I'll name them Nefertiti and Cleopatra. They're wonderful! Thank you!" She picked them up and covered them with kisses. One snuggled content-edly against her, and she almost melted with love.

"Madame, do you realize that you got ten times more excited about two kittens than you did about three-hundred-thousand-dollar necklaces?" Yerima asked.

"Three hundred thousand dollars, sir? Are you *kidding?* A *neck-lace?* They're beautiful, they're wonderful, but what on earth am I going to do with them? These kittens, I can love them, and they can love me, that's all."

"Those stones are the size of aircraft carriers. You probably have a million dollars' worth of jewelry here. One of the 25,000 reasons that I love you, madame, my darling Sudari."

"You know? I was wondering how I could finance my foundation. I'd never wear all this, but just think how far that money could go to educate people about what really goes on."

"I know a few people who could help, principally, my cousin Maïmouna. She's a *commissaire de police* and probably the best detective on the continent. She'd jump at the chance. And, if you're planning to give up your jewelry for this, let me also contribute a certain stal-lion."

"But Yerima, he's your dream Arabian!"

"This is more important, madame, much much more important. Deal?"

"Deal. Very sweet of you, sir."

Sheikh Farook quieted the guests. "The bridegroom would like to say a few words."

"Thank you, all of you, for coming today and sharing in this moment of happiness. Many of you don't know that Sudari was a victim of human trafficking and spent five years in servitude. Various things happened and she was sentenced to death by torture. Thanks to Sheikh Saud, here, who provided the very substantial amount of money for the rescue, she's still with us today. She carried burgundy roses in his honor. Please give him a heartfelt round of applause." Sheikh Saud blushed as the guests cheered. "Her bouquet was wrapped in mango-colored ribbon, in loving memory of her best friend Nenzima, who, like most victims of this horrible crime, did not survive. May peace and blessing be upon her."

He paused until the murmuring subsided. "You have all meant so much to us, and we thank you from the bottom of our hearts for how you've helped us reach this joyful milestone in our lives. As you know, my sentence as ambassador is coming to an end and I'll soon be going back home, with this brave and beautiful lady by my side."

Everyone applauded and Tammy started to sob quietly again, overcome by emotion.

"What will you do now, Tammy?" Sheikh Saud inquired.

Her response was met with loud applause. "First, I just want to be a wife to my amazing husband. I'd really like to continue my education, and eventually, I plan to set up a foundation that will combat human trafficking and educate people about how horrible it is."

Didier, the Deputy Chief of Mission, said he had a special announcement. "We have just received the following message from His Excellency the President of the Republic. 'I wish to extend my warmest congratulations to His Excellency Ambassador Abdoulaye and my condolences to the new Madame Abdoulaye. Yerima, you've done it again, capturing a beautiful woman and carrying her off to Africa. Madame Sudari, our crazy but loving family welcomes you with open arms, and your country-in-law is eager to embrace you. Yerima says that you are a very brave lady. You certainly must be, if you had the guts to marry him. I look forward to welcoming you in person at the earliest possible occasion. And let me take this opportunity to make another announcement. Yerima's sentence as Ambassador is finally coming to an end, but service to his country is not. I have just named him our new Minister of Foreign Affairs. He is eminently well qualified because he's had more of them than anyone I know.'"

There was sustained applause midst gales of laughter.

Sheikh Farook said, "All right, now we have a special treat. I understand that His Excellency wields a mean saxophone, and he would like to play *Danny Boy* for his bride. Elizabeth, the Cultural Affairs Officer, will accompany him on the piano."

Yerima grinned. "Please, people, spare my feelings and don't stampede for the exits." He licked his lips, Elizabeth played a few introductory phrases, and Yerima began, looking at Tammy in just the same way he always looked at her just before they made love. Never taking his eyes off her, he ran his hands up and down her length with long mellow swoops of sound, planted passionate kisses on her shoulders with swirls of music, guided her to ecstasy with crescendo building upon crescendo, then gently brought her back to earth with soft plaintive notes overflowing with love. She was almost embar-rassed, in front of everybody, it was so obvious what he was doing.

Standing ovation.

"You *really* can play. That was absolutely amazing."

"I told you I could." Then he whispered wickedly, "How many times did you come?"

The bride and groom shared their first dance to Billie Holiday's *Come Rain or Come Shine*; then, weeping unashamedly, Tammy danced with her father to Celine Dion's *Because You Loved Me*. "Yerima's quite a guy," he told her as he led her off the dance floor. "He loves you to pieces. I can't wait to get home and tell your mother how you practically glow in the dark when you're around him. I never imagined that you'd be okay with this polygamy thing, but it doesn't seem to bother you. Tammy-Girl, I can't imagine anybody better for you."

"Daddy, I knew you were looking for me and trying to get me out. It meant so much, and really helped me have the strength to get through this nightmare. Knowing that I wasn't abandoned was a crutch I needed so badly and used so often.

407

Praise God, it's over now. Tell Mom that she probably saved my life because whenever I faced a difficult crossroads I applied her favorite maxim, when everything else fails..."

"...try love," John said. "That news may just be the spark she needs to climb back out of the dark place she's been in, Tammy. That, and knowing that you've just married the Minister of Foreign Affairs. Wow. Considering where you were a month ago, I'd call that a meteoric rise."

"Hey! Don't forget that now I'm Minister of Education! And Daddy, he might just be President one day."

"The dance floor is open," announced Sheikh Farook.

The room burst into life with the throbbing of African drums, African music. Tammy's mouth fell open. These people didn't just enjoy dancing, they were positively transported. In a room of 80 people, maybe 50 of them were exceptionally competent dancers. At least ten rushed over to show her the moves. She felt so welcomed, so accepted, so loved, that she could scarcely take it all in.

"Now *that's* dancing," said Sheikh Farook, shaking his head in awe.

Sheikh Saud gave the couple big hugs. "Farida, I mean Tammy, Suraiya and I would like to endow that foundation of yours."

"Thank you. Thank you. There are no words..." She paused. "I was wondering. I mean, that necklace is so amazing, but I have no idea where I'd wear it. Would it bother you, boss, if I used it to help finance the foundation?"

He gave her a mischievous smile. "It's your property," he said, "and you can do anything with it you damn well please."

Their guests eventually went their separate ways and husband and wife were alone at last.

"Yerima, my love, who really knows for sure what the future holds for you and me, but all I can say is, I'm just so happy, so happy, that my future is with you."

"I know exactly what your future will be, madame," he said, eyebrows dancing, "at least for the next few hours. Turn over. I believe that you wanted to express some gratitude?"

EPILOGUE

Maybe you've figured out by now that my real name isn't Tammy. But indeed, this is my story.

Writing this book has been one of the hardest things I've ever done, because you can't describe the life of a sex slave without saying certain things out loud, even intensely personal details that I'd rather not talk about at all. And sometimes, going through all the ugly stuff again was so painful, I'd just sit and shake for minutes on end. But people need to know what really happens to girls who disappear, and I'm one of the rare ones who got out alive, so it was something I absolutely had to do.

I've been married now for a year and a half, happier than I ever dreamed possible. Being part of Yerima's life is a non-stop adventure. The better I get to know him, the more I stand in awe of him. His personal magnetism, integrity, generous heart, and profound sense of justice – not to mention his great sense of humor – somehow make everyone around him a better person. I wasn't the least bit surprised to discover that he's one of the most beloved people in the country, and it's not only an honor but just plain fun being his wife.

This said, I confess that I'm still adjusting to polygamy. I'm jealous of my co-wives, but not in the ways I'd expected. I knew they'd share his bed, and I really have no problem with that. But Aïssatou is the one who always accompanies him on state occasions, and I thought I was okay with the idea. I didn't realize how much I'd feel left out, though, time after time, month after month. And when he had to have surgery on his knee, he asked JoAnn to take care of him. That hurt. A lot. Who'd ever have guessed, by the way, that it'd be the other American who'd drive me nuts? The two of us got off on the wrong foot big-time. She hogged the car that we were supposed to share, and was always pulling rank on me, and we went round and round; it got to the point that Aïssatou had to step in and lay down the law. JoAnn and I still aren't

411

buddies, but at least now we're not squabbling all the time. I have a lot of respect for Aïssatou, who's strict, but also loving and supportive, and I've become best friends with Amsaou, who's classy and smart and loads of fun.

Aïssatou cut me a good bit of slack for nearly a year because of my circumstances, but now I'm subject to restriction when I screw up, and of course, I sometimes do. After all the crap I lived through, *obey* has become a dirty word to me, but I'm the wife of a Fulani prince, and I'm expected to submit unquestioningly to his authority. He's neither a tyrant nor a control freak; in fact, his requests are eminently reasonable. Nevertheless, I've repeatedly rebelled. Aïssatou – a remarkable student of human nature – says I'm still just proving to myself that I'm no longer in bondage, and that I'll get over it soon enough. She helped me realize it wasn't all that complicated when she asked, Doesn't your husband, whom you love, deserve better from you than your master, whom you feared?

I thought I'd like, push a button and be myself again, but readjusting to the real world has been a lot harder than I'd expected. Managing money has been especially challenging. When you live for five years surrounded by staggering wealth – yachts and Lamborghinis and huge estates and private 747s – you lose perspective, and what's worse, you don't even realize that you've lost perspective. I went over budget for supplies for the children again and again, not because I was trying to flaunt the rules, but because I thought, this is so trivial, we can certainly afford this. And for weeks I was afraid to leave home without Yerima or Aïssatou or Amsi going with me; the real world was too big, too confusing, too intimidating. And, gloriously African. Fun, but it still takes some getting used to. I'm pretty okay now, but there are occasions when something will snap, and for a terrifying moment I'm back on my knees at The Office, or watching Marisa or Zima die, or hanging from the blankety-blank meat hook at the Rodeo.

Our leisurely love-making, uninterrupted by urgent telephone calls and pressing appointments, is pretty much history. Even when Yerima's not on one of his many overseas trips, or when our appointments aren't pre-empted by other official responsibilities, our time together is limited. We use it well, however. I've succeeded in making him faint several times, "the Ibrahim thing," as he calls it, still a touch jealous. And it's a wonderful, wonderful treat to wake up and realize that we've spent the entire night clasped in each other's arms, something we could never do at The Office.

I've suffered two miscarriages, which have been very hard on me. I want so badly to give Yerima children, concrete symbols of my total commitment to him. I'm only twenty-five and otherwise healthy, so I keep hope alive. Our first son will be named Saoudou, the local version of Saud (for some reason, most Muslim names in Cameroon are in the nominative case of Arabic), and our first daughter will be named Suraiya, after his wife.

I positively adore the children, from the meltingly beautiful but insecure seventeen-year-old Samira – like a little sister to me – to three-year-old Michael, hands-down the cutest kid on the planet. We get together after school in the family dining room where I help them with their homework and find books for them to get excited about. We go on pretend trips all over the world and talk about everything from different cultures and languages, to active volcanoes like Mt. Cameroon, to the phases of the moon, to the Presidential elections here and in the U.S. (Antoine was handily reelected last year, and the children enthu-siastically support Obama, which is a fairly common local name.)

I have my own spacious apartment upstairs in the women's house – three bedrooms, two bathrooms, a small kitchen, a living room/dining room, and balcony. I usually take my meals in the common dining room, where I cracked up when I saw that the hand-woven tablecloth was embroidered with spiders. (They admire them here for their ability to make something out of nothing.)

413

I'm not used to living with such a large extended family, so when I get overwhelmed I just go to my apartment and study, or get out my laptop and write. Or play with my wonderful kitties, who purr at me and help keep my priorities in line. And when I need company, there's always someone friendly nearby to help me practice my Fulfulde. I have a special place in my heart for the emancipated slaves, who now live in comfortable retirement. I've tried to hear their stories, but they won't talk to me; they just smile and bow, smile and bow.

Antoine thrilled me to pieces by asking me to serve on his newly created Presidential Task Force on Human Trafficking. As such, I've been helping Commissaire Maïmouna, who heads up a police department specialized in crimes against girls and women, and it's extremely gratifying. She's arranged for me to tell my story to a number of human rights groups, and I've discovered that I really enjoy public speaking. I start out with lots of butterflies, but my passion soon takes over and I forget everything else. I show them my decorations, and say see? This really happened to me. And the response has been incredible. Mind you, I'm not looking for pity; I just want people to fight this crime. But I need to get the foundation up and running to be able to focus on action.

I'm still trying; it's about twenty thousand times more complicated than I'd imagined. Yerima just grins and tells me not to get bent out of shape, that *everything* here is complicated. Sheikh Saud has generously offered five million, two hundred and eighteen thousand dollars as an endowment (representing the five years, two months, and eighteen days I spent in slavery), and the jewelry and stallion brought in close to another two million, but even with Yerima's amazing contacts, we're still struggling to make it all official.

Meanwhile, I've poured my whole heart into my long-postponed studies in the Faculty of Law and Economics. Big fat books! Intel-lectual challenges! Sheer joy! My heart swelled with pride when the other students eventually figured out who my husband was. I try not to flaunt it, but most students come to the university by motorbike, not in a chauffeured Mercedes. Aïssatou says I need to be the best student, but also the most self-deprecating. I sure as hell know how to do that; I used to be a slave.

Mom, Daddy, and Caldwell came to visit us last summer. Yerima pulled out all the stops, putting them up in the guest house and personally squiring them around town. I was so proud; people would rush over to present their respects just because they were with him. He even arranged for us to take a week-long waterfall tour, so we could all get a glimpse of this stunningly beautiful country. Mom still hasn't started back to work, but she's doing a good bit better. She saw for herself that I'm not only free, but that I have a wonderful, comfortable, exciting life with a man like few in the world.

Other updates. Sadly, Amberine has just broken the news that she has Stage III breast cancer. She's facing this challenge with great courage and grace, but the chemo and radiation aren't doing very much, and it's not good news for Sheikh Farook or for their two small sons. Suraiya recently presented Saud with a beautiful baby daughter whom they insisted on naming, much to my embarrassed delight, Farida. Heineken sends me hilarious emails about his three-legged raccoon Tripod, a one-eyed bobcat named Robert, his German Shepherds Alpha and Omega, and all the fun he has with Angela, a devocalized blonde who used to work at the Candlelight Lounge. He's managed to locate Fritzi, who's in New York working as an assistant to a psychiatrist, and we exchange regular emails.

Saud says that Ibrahim is in a deep depression, and he's drinking heavily again. As if that news weren't bad enough, Taymoor scared the daylights out of us by warning us that Ibrahim has commissioned him to design a private harem for *me,* and that it's under construction. I'm *married* now, Ibrahim, wise up, for heaven's sake!

It's been quite a ride. Never in my life did I imagine I'd be a slave – and never did I imagine that I'd become the wife of an African prince, much less, Minister of Foreign Affairs. Except for the occa-sional screaming nightmare, the worst is behind me now. When I wake up to the screeching of wild parrots, it takes me a moment to remember that I don't have to start another depressing day at The Office. In fact, nobody makes me get out of bed at all. But I want to. Because there's an extremely handsome prince who just happens to be my husband, and every single miraculous day that I'm alive I need to find new ways to show him how grateful I am that he saved my life, and how much, how very much, I will always love him.

-Yaounde, April 2012

Made in the USA
Lexington, KY
12 March 2014